Scottish engineering c

Gareth Parry
and
Scott Johnston

Thomas Telford

Also available from Thomas Telford Books
Adjudication under the NEC, Richard N.M. Anderson ISBN: 0 7277 2997 7
The New Engineering Contract: A Legal Commentary, Arthur T. McInnis ISBN: 0 7277 2961 6
NEC and Partnering, John Bennett and Andrew Baird ISBN: 0 7277 2955 1

Published by Thomas Telford Publishing, Thomas Telford Ltd, 1 Heron Quay, London E14 4JD
URL: http://www.thomastelford.com

Distributors for Thomas Telford books are:
USA: ASCE Press, 1801 Alexander Bell Drive, Reston, VA 20191–4400, USA
Japan: Maruzen Co. Ltd, Book Department, 3–10 Nihonbashi 2-chome, Chu-ku, Tokyo 103
Australia: DA Books and Journals, 648 Whitehorse Road, Mitcham 3132, Victoria

First published 2003

A catalogue record for this book is available from the British Library

ISBN: 0 7277 2999 3

Typeset by Apek Digital Imaging, Bristol
Printed in Great Britain at the University Press, Cambridge

Contents

Preface

Little has been written on engineering law in Scotland in contrast to the many works on construction law. Yet the two are very separate and distinct areas of expertise both in terms of the industries they relate to and in the law that applies to them. The purpose of this book is to provide the professional engineer with a basic understanding of the principles of Scots law relating to engineering contracts. It follows that this should not be used as an alternative to reading and researching particular areas using the primary sources outlined in Chapter 1 and in the list of publications and further reading. Footnotes are also provided as reference sources should readers need or wish to further explore a particular topic.

Whilst this book covers the areas that one would normally expect to find in a book covering engineering law it does also cover an area in which other books are surprisingly deficient. Environmental law is one of the fastest growing areas of law both in terms of its level of importance and in the volume of legislation, case law and commentaries generated around it. A rudimentary knowledge of environmental law is particularly important in the engineering sector where the interface between the environment and engineering works is often acute.

The book considers not only general principles of law and contractual practice, but also reviews how these are reflected in a number of standard form engineering contracts. We have focused in particular on the ICE Conditions of Contract 7ᵗʰ edition and CECA Form of Sub-contract, July 1998 edition (as amended April 2001) as we believe most readers would benefit from such an emphasis. Although the New Engineering Contract is becoming increasingly popular as the basis for main contract conditions for civil engineering projects, use of the ICE conditions (and the connected CECA Sub-contract conditions) remains very common. The book does not aim to provide a 'clause by clause' analysis of these conditions of contract, but instead highlights the clauses most frequently relied on in day-to-day practice. Particular emphasis is placed on payment provisions. Where it aids understanding of the issues being discussed, clauses are reproduced in their entirety. We did, however, not wish to clutter the chapters with contract clauses unnecessarily and have therefore in many instances assumed that the reader will have a copy of the relevant conditions of contract to hand. Finally, please note that in this book the word 'he' is to be taken to mean 'he or she'.

We have received valued assistance from members of the Construction and Engineering Team at McGrigor Donald. In addition to those named in the Editors' acknowledgement, we must thank our secretaries Jayne Russell, Kirstie Fraser, Lisa Jones, Emma MacDonald and Suzanne Geraghty for their valued assistance in preparing the manuscript and turning often illegible script into tidy prose, and also the tireless (and often, to our shame, thankless) work undertaken by our trainees past and present, particularly Rosalie MacKay, Russell Kostulin, Mhairi Weir, Helena Anderson, Alison Rennie and Angela Kerr. We are also grateful to our indispensable Information Services colleagues, in particular to Louise Laidlaw and Maria Gunn. Finally, we would like to thank Jeremy Brinton at Thomas Telford for his unfailing encouragement and good humour, which was tested to breaking point on many occasions during the preparation of the book.

The book aims to state the law as at August 2002. It should go without saying that any errors are entirely the responsibility of the editors.

Gareth Parry
Scott Johnston

McGrigor Donald
Pacific House
70 Wellington Street
Glasgow G2 6SB

August 2002

Editors' acknowledgement

Lawyers in the Construction and Engineering Team and the Environmental Team at McGrigor Donald wrote this book. Without their dedication and thoroughness production of this book would not have been possible. The editors would therefore like to take this opportunity to express their gratitude to Brandon Nolan, Colin Fraser, David Scott, Michael Allan, Gavin Paton, Simona Williamson, Alastair Collin, Gillian Petrie, Iain MacPhail, Louisa Walls, Gavin Brown and Gavin Walker.

About the authors

Gareth Parry is a Partner and the UK head of Construction and Engineering Procurement at McGrigor Donald.

Gareth specialises in advising on risk allocation and project procurement for construction and engineering projects in both the public and private sectors. He has been involved in some of Scotland's largest infrastructure projects in the health, roads, ports, education and energy sectors and his clients include government agencies and departments as well as constructors, developers, and financiers. In addition he regularly advises on both pre-contract tender risk assessment and post-contract on site matters.

He is the co-author of a guide to the Construction (Design and Management) Regulations (Sweet & Maxwell) as well as being both a regular conference speaker and a regular contributor to the construction press.

Scott Johnston is a Director in McGrigor Donald's Construction and Engineering Disputes team.

Scott specialises in dispute avoidance and resolution in the construction and engineering industry. He is regularly instructed to represent clients in adjudications, arbitration and court proceedings and has extensive advocacy experience in all forums. Scott is also involved in the drafting and negotiation of multi-layered dispute resolution procedures in PFI and PPP projects, and has acted as legal adviser to arbiters and adjudicators.

Scott is author of *Debts and Interest in the Construction Industry – The Late Payment of Commercial Debts (Interest) Act 1998* (Thomas Telford, 1999).

Abbreviations

AC	Law Reports, Appeal Cases
All ER	All England Law Reports
App Case	Law Reports, Appeal Cases
B&S	Best & Smith's Queen's Bench Reports (121-2 ER) 1861–5
BCLC	Butterworth's Company Law Cases
BLR	Building Law Reports
CA	Court of Appeal
Ch App	Chancery Appeal Cases
CILL	Construction Industry Law Letter
CLC	Commercial Law Cases
CLR	Commonwealth Law Reports
Con LR	Construction Law Reports
Const LJ	Construction Law Journal
COPA	Control of Pollution Act 1974
D	Dunlop's Session Cases 1938–62
DLR	Dominion Law Reports
EGCS	Estates Gazette Case Summaries
EWCA	England and Wales Court of Appeal
EWHC	England and Wales High Court
Ex	Exchequer Reports
F	Fraser's Session Cases 1889–1906
FIDIC	International Federation of Consulting Engineers
GWD	Greens Weekly Digest
H&N	Hurlstone & Norman
HL	House of Lords
Hudsons BC	Hudsons Building Contracts
KB	Law Reports, King's Bench
Lloyd's Rep.	Lloyd's Law Reports
M	Macpherson's Session Cases 1862–73
NSWLR	New South Wales Law Reports
NZLR	New Zealand Law Reports
PD	Law Reports, Probate Division
QB	Law Reports, Queens Bench
R	Rettie's Session Cases
S	Shaw's Session Cases 1821–38
SBCC	Scottish Building Contract Committee
SC	Session Cases 1907–
SCLR	Scottish Civil Law Reports
Sh. Crt Rep	Sheriff Court Reports
SI	Statutory Instrument

SLR   Scottish Law Reporter
SLT   Scots Law Times
TCLR   Technology and Construction Law Reports
WLR   Weekly Law Reports
WN (NSW)   Weekly Notes, New South Wales

Glossary

For ease of reference, a number of standard forms of contract, statutory sources and titles of industry organisations have been abbreviated. The following list sets out definitions of the terms used in the book.

ACE – Association of Consulting Engineers
CECA – The Civil Engineering Contractors Association
FIDIC – International Federation of Consulting Engineers
IChem E – Institute of Chemical Engineers
ICE – Institute of Civil Engineers

the Act – The Housing Grants, Construction and Regeneration Act 1996
the English Scheme – The Schedule to the Scheme for Construction Contract (England and Wales) Regulations 1998
the Scottish Scheme – The Schedule to the Scheme for Construction Contracts (Scotland) Regulations 1998

CECA Design and Construct Sub-contract – CECA Form of Sub-contract, November 1998 edition (amended April 2001) (For use with the ICE Conditions of Contract, Design and Construct)
CECA Sub-contract – CECA Form of Sub-contract, July 1998 edition (amended April 2001) (For use with the ICE Conditions of Contract, 6th edition)
ECC – Engineering and Construction Contract
ICE 7th Conditions – ICE Conditions of Contract 7th edition, Measurement edition (as amended April 2001)
ICE Design and Construct Conditions – ICE Conditions of Contract Design and Construct (2nd edition)
ICE Minor Works – ICE Conditions of Contract for Minor Works, 3rd edition
MF/1 or MF/2, as applicable – Model Form
NEC – New Engineering Contract

1. Introduction to engineering contracts

Introduction

This chapter takes a general overview of engineering contracts. It looks at the key players who are involved in the contract, the form of procurement route and the standard forms used in the profession. Tendering procedure is looked at very briefly, as is partnering, but detailed coverage of these topics falls outside the scope of this book. The chapter concludes with a brief look at the sources of law, and this is clearly something that each engineer will need to monitor closely.

Persons involved in engineering contracts

Many other parties may be involved in an engineering project in addition to the Employer and the Contractor. The parties may include the following:

(a) **Engineer** – the engineer's role is more fully discussed in Chapter 3, but broadly, his role is to produce plans and specifications and monitor the execution of the works on the employer's behalf and ensure that they are completed in accordance with the contract. His relationship with the employer is as the agent of the employer. He owes the employer a contractual duty of care:[1] a legal responsibility to carry out his obligations with due skill and care to the standard that would normally be expected of an engineer. Good practice dictates that the employer and the engineer will enter into a Professional Services Contract to ensure that the roles and obligations of each party are clear and unambiguous.

(b) **Quantity surveyor** – engaged by the employer to compile the bills of quantities, the quantity surveyor therefore undertakes the task of specifying estimates of all the quantities required for carrying out the works. The engineer may also require him to carry out measurements and valuation as required, or the engineer may carry out this function himself.

(c) **Consultants** – in large engineering projects, there is likely to be a number of specialist consultants in addition to the engineer and the quantity surveyor. These may include, for example, structural, mechanical and electrical engineers, a hydrological expert and an acoustics consultant. Professional Service Contracts should be entered into for each of the consultants to clarify their duties and responsibilities (see Chapter 13).

(d)   **Project manager** – in some large projects, the employer may engage a project manager in addition to the engineer to organise all the various parties involved in the project. Particulars of his relationship with the other parties will vary from one contract to another. It is worth bearing in mind that contractors occasionally employ a person whom they also call the project manager.

(e)   **Clerk of works** – a clerk of works may be engaged by the employer in a large project to oversee the works and guard the employer's interests on the site. The clerk's role has been described as 'the eyes and ears of the employer'.[2]

(f)   **Sub-contractors** – the contractor often sub-contracts a large portion of the work to sub-contractors. The sub-contractor can be 'domestic', meaning that he has been appointed by the contractor, or he may be 'nominated', which means that he has been chosen by the employer and nominated under the terms of the contract (see Chapter 12).

(g)   **Suppliers** – the suppliers are responsible for providing the necessary goods and materials under the contract.

(h)   **Sureties** – sureties are persons who give various guarantees (sometimes referred to as performance bonds) in relation to the project. They may guarantee the carrying out of the works by the contractor or payment by the employer, or occasionally the good faith of the engineer or other persons who have control of finances (see Chapter 11).

(i)   **Funder** – in the case of commercial development, the employer is likely to be financed either entirely or partly by a funder whose interests will have to be protected (along with the interests of prospective purchasers and/or tenants).

Types of engineering contracts

Procurement routes

The traditional engineering contract procedure in Scotland is for the employer to engage an engineer directly. The engineer will then produce a detailed plan in accordance with the employer's requirements. Once the amount of materials and amount of manpower necessary to carry out the works has been calculated, the employer will put the contract out to tender and then enter into a contract with the successful contractor. It is for the contractor then to delegate as appropriate to sub-contractors. The employer may enter directly into Professional Service Contracts with specialist consultants. In this traditional procedure, the design work is carried out by the employer and the engineer only. Recently, different permutations of contractual arrangement have become possible. The different types and a brief description of each are listed below, while diagrams showing the main procurement routes are set out in Appendix 4.

(a)   **Design and build** – the employer engages a contractor to carry out both the design and construction works (also called 'a package deal').

(b)   **Novated design and build** – the design element will be prepared for the employer at the outset in conjunction with his appointment of the engineer. This completed design will constitute the employer's requirements. Following appointment of the contractor the design team, originally employed by the employer, will then be novated to the contractor (so that the design team is effectively employed by the contractor), and the team will work with the contractor until the works are completed.

(c)   **Design, manage, construct** – as (a) above except that the contractor is also engaged to carry out management obligations.

(d)   **Turnkey contract** – this is a derivative of design and build contracts. Under this route the contractor undertakes to provide works fully ready for use. 'Turnkey' itself has no specific legal meaning.

(e)   **Fast-tracking** – the construction works for a completed design stage are commenced before the design stage is fully completed. The aim is to achieve earlier completion.

(f)   **Management contracts** – similar to traditional procedure noted above except that the employer will employ a management contractor to coordinate the parties carrying out the works.

(g)   **Construction management** – the employer enters into direct contracts with trade contractors and appoints a construction manager whose job it is to ensure that the employer gets the best possible terms from the trade contractors. This type of contract is often used on complicated fast-track projects where design will evolve over the duration of the project and early completion is required.

(h)   **Build, operate and transfer** – a contract structure used for private investment in public infrastructure projects (known as the Private Finance Initiative (PFI) and/or the Public Private Partnership (PPP)), in which the contractor will normally be a private consortium and will delegate to appropriate sub-contractors the responsibility for carrying out the works and maintaining the completed works to standards set by the public sector authority awarding the contract. In return for providing the services (building and operating), the public sector authority will pay the consortium a monthly service charge for the term of the contract (usually around 25 years). On expiry of the contract, the consortium will transfer the facility to the public sector authority.

(i)   **Prime contracting** – Prime contracting is an initiative introduced by the Ministry of Defence (MOD). It is essentially concentrated around partnering at the supply chain level. The initiative aims to provide best value to the customer by fostering a more cooperative and less adversarial relationship between customer and contractor.

Standard form contracts

Engineering contracts in Scotland are usually entered into on the basis of standard form contracts. The following are the main types frequently employed in engineering projects:

(a)   **ICE Conditions of Contract 7th edition September 1999** – the standard form of engineering contract was issued under the auspices of the Institution of Civil Engineers (ICE), the Association of Consulting Engineers (ACE) and the Civil Engineering Contractors Association (CECA). It is used extensively in all types of civil engineering work by both the private and the public sectors. The most recent edition was produced by the Conditions of Contract Standing Joint Committee (CCSJC) and was published in September 1999. For ease, the numbering used in previous editions has been retained and the 7th edition also includes an index and table of contents. The Conditions are published together with a Form of Tender, Appendix, Form of Agreement and Form of Default Bond with Schedule. Separate, unnumbered, Contract Price Fluctuation Clauses are also included.

The form creates a 'measure and value' or 're-measurement' contract under which the employer is obliged to pay for the actual works executed, primarily at the rates quoted. However, the rates fluctuate depending on the type or volume of work completed. Additionally, there are numerous other provisions which set out how further payments and adjusted payments can become due. Wide-ranging discretionary powers are placed on the engineer and it is important to think about whether and in what circumstances the engineer should be bound to exercise his powers. Most of the changes brought about by the 7th edition are largely minor or cosmetic changes to the drafting. However, there are also a number of more significant amendments for clarification.

(b)   **ICE Conditions of Contract for Minor Works 2nd edition 1994** – traditionally, the ICE Conditions of Contract were only published in one version. However, the ICE has begun to produce different types of contract tailored towards specific projects. In 1988, a set of conditions for minor works was introduced and was approved by the ACE and the CECA. The standard form for minor works is accompanied by guidance notes which advise that the minor works standard form should be used for simple and straightforward contracts: that is, those limited to 6 months duration and having a value of £100 000. The form has proved a popular choice for smaller scale projects and has been used for contracts outside these limits. A second edition was issued in 1994.

(c)   **New Engineering Contract (NEC)** – this contract signalled a radical new approach in the construction industry. It was first produced as a consultative document in 1991 and further editions were issued in 1993 and 1995. It is intended for use in all different types of contract including conventionally-priced contracts with or without bills of quantities, target cost contracts, costs reimbursable contracts and management contracts. Although there was initial uncertainty as to the style of drafting, the NEC has attracted significant interest from the Government and was endorsed in the Latham Report[3] as a standard form contract for engineering and construction work. The current version of this form is known as the **ECC** – the Engineering and

Construction Contract. A dedicated form of sub-contract is also included.

(d) **ICE – the Conditions of Contract for Design and Construction Works 1992** – these are produced by the ICE, ACE and CECA. This form follows the same structure and layout as the ICE main form, in particular its clause numbering. The same bodies are considering producing a form relating to maintenance works on the basis of the minor works. The ICE has not produced a form of sub-contract (other than that issued by CECA) that reflects the restricted use of nomination in civil engineering projects.

(e) **Sub-contract** – this is published by CECA and although an entirely separate document, it is intended to complement the ICE main forms of contract.

(f) **FIDIC** – these forms of contract are published by the Federation Internationale d'Ingenieurs Conseils (International Federation of Consulting Engineers). International contracts often adopt the FIDIC conditions of contract. The Conditions of Contract for Works of Civil Engineering Construction 4th edition 1987 contain general conditions in part I and are linked to conditions of particular application which are referred to as part II. FIDIC also produce Conditions of Contract for Design Build and Turnkey, known as the Orange Book (1995) and Electrical and Mechanical Works, known as the Yellow Book, 4th edition 1987. More recently they have also published four new forms of contract.[4]

(g) **MF/1** – the model form of General Conditions of Contract for the Supply of Electrical, Electronic or Mechanical Plant with erection. Revision 4 was published in 2000 jointly by the Institutions of Mechanical Engineers and Electrical Engineers (the third revision was in 1988, and was reprinted in 1995 with amendments). It is intended for use in connection with home or overseas contracts for the supply of electrical, electronic or mechanical plant with erection.

(h) **IChemE** – the Institution of Chemical Engineers publishes various forms relating to process plant. The most up to date version of the Conditions of Contract for Process Plant suitable for lump sum contracts in the UK (otherwise known as the Red Book, first published in 1968) was published in 1995. The Green Book (Model Form of Conditions of Contract for Process Plant suitable for reimbursable contracts) was first published in 1976 and its second edition followed in 1992. The increasing use by the industry of these model forms led to the publication of the Yellow Book in 1992, back-to-back sub-contracts for use with the Red and Green books. A second edition of the Yellow Book was published in 1997. The first edition of the Orange Book (which relates to Minor Works) was published in 1998. Guidance to the Model Forms (the Purple Book) was published in its third edition in 1999. Guidance on Arbitration (the Pink Book) and Adjudication procedure were published in 1997 and 1998, respectively. The sub-contract for Civil Engineering Works (the Brown Book) was published in 1999 in response to numerous requests by sub-contractors undertaking main contracts under the Red or Green books, and wishing to award sub-contracts for civil engineering works. The Yellow Book is not appropriate in this instance, as it was drafted on the assumption that the sub-contract plant will itself be an item of process, mechanical or electrical plant.

Categories of law

Fundamentally, engineering law is the specific application of contract law as it applies to engineering projects. However, elements of other types of law are also encompassed, such as the law of delict (known as tort in England), property law and employment law. Increasingly, the influence of health and safety law and also environmental law (see Chapter 14) is being felt in the engineering industry. The impact of increased European influence in this field has also been significant.

Sources of law

Scots law is derived from Roman law and, like continental legal systems, recognises a distinction between public and private law. Broadly, public law regulates the rights and obligations of persons in their dealings with the state, whereas private law (of which contract law forms part) regulates dealings between persons themselves. It is therefore private law rights and obligations with which we are concerned when we talk about the employer's or the engineer's rights and obligations under an engineering contract. The law of Scotland is derived from a number of sources, as follows:

(a) **Common law** – a body of established principles having their foundations in ancient customs, standards and practices. It is essentially Judge-made law. It is developed according to its application in specific cases. Principles or common law rules derived from judgments are frequently referred to as precedents. A Judge in a lower court is obliged to follow a precedent of a higher court.

(b) **Institutional writers** – legal writers have varying degrees of authority and are always seen as less authoritative on the letter of the law than statute and common law. However, certain writers, called institutional writers, have a high level of authority accorded to their writings and are often quoted both by practitioners and academics alike. Many of these writings date back to the seventeenth and eighteenth centuries and are works consisting of commentaries on the entire law of Scotland, or a large portion of it. The institutional writers on civil matters are Craig,[5] Stair,[6] Bankton.[7] Erskine[8] and Bell[9] and on criminal matters, Mackenzie,[10] Hume[11] and Alison.[12]

(c) **Statute law** – law also comes from the legislative arm of the state (the Legislature), in the form of legislation (known as Acts of Parliament) and delegated legislation (known as statutory instruments). This type of law begins life as a bill, put forward either by a select committee appointed by the Government or a Member of Parliament (a bill in the latter case is known as a Private Member's Bill). It is then debated in

Parliament, first in the House of Commons and then in the House of Lords, usually resulting in a number of amendments and modifications along the way. If it has a safe passage through both houses of parliament, it then goes on to become law by receiving the signature of the monarch, known as the Royal Assent.

In 1998, the **Scotland Act** was passed giving Scotland its own devolved parliament. Accordingly, Scottish legislation is now comprised both of legislation passed by Westminster which is applicable in Scotland[13] and legislation passed by the Scottish Parliament within its legislative competence. As for Westminster, the Scottish Parliament's legislation must be compatible with European law and the European Convention on Human Rights (ECHR) (see below). The Scottish Parliament may not modify certain acts of parliament; the Scotland Act itself is such an example. In addition, some areas are reserved to the legislative control of the Westminster Parliament such as home affairs, defence and health and safety.[14]

European law

European Community law is having an increasing impact in the UK in all areas of law, but of particular relevance to construction law is its influence in procurement (see above), employment and environment matters.

The treaties forming the basis of the European communities[15] were incorporated into UK Law by the European Communities Act 1972 and accordingly have force of law in the UK. The treaties also established the community bodies – the Council of Ministers, the European Commission and the European Parliament. It is the Council and the Commission who are primarily responsible for law-making; the Commission is the instigator of policy and makes proposals in consultation with Member States to the Council. The Commission cannot legislate itself, although it can be empowered by a regulation issued by the council to enact delegated legislation. The Council is made up of one minister from every member state and the Presidency is held on rotation, for 6 months at a time. The council votes on commission proposals usually by qualified majority[16] (which means the votes are weighted by reference to the population size of the Member State) and sometimes by simple majority. In the case of very important matters, unanimity is required.

The Single European Act 1986, incorporated into UK law by the European Communities (Amendment) Act 1986, made changes to the way the communities operate. The treaty on the European Union 1992, commonly referred to as the Maastricht treaty, was incorporated into UK law by the European Communities (Amendment) Act 1993. This treaty established the European Union, increased the powers of the parliament, sought to create a common foreign and security policy and made provision for a move to the single currency with the creation of a European Central Bank having financial and legal powers.

The impact of joining the European Union was a significant one, as UK law must be consistent with European law and, in the event of inconsistencies with UK law, community law prevails. Some commentators attacked this as being a surrender of the Crown's sovereignty, as the primacy of EC law is such that the European Court of Justice could strike down an Act of Parliament if it was considered contrary to EC law. In addition, some legislation made by EC institutions has direct effect, which means they are directly applicable to Member States without the need to be incorporated into national law. It is necessary to distinguish *prospective* application (forward looking only) from *retrospective* application (which applies to the past, as well as to the present and future). Normally, community legislation is prospective, and is retrospective only if there is clear provision within the legislation to that effect.

The different types of legislation produced by the EC institutions are as follows:

(a) **Regulations** – the Council and the Commission are both empowered to make regulations, which have general application, are directly applicable to Member States and have immediate force of law in the respective territories on the date specified in them. If no date is specified they come into force on the twentieth day following their publication.

(b) **Directives** – the Council and the Commission can also issue directives, which are not immediately applicable and require to be ratified by Member States. The directives state the ultimate result to be achieved by the legislation, but the Member States are given leeway as to how they achieve the result. In the UK, the result is usually achieved by amendment to relevant legislation.

(c) **Decisions** – these are issued by the Council and the Commission and are binding only on the Member State, corporation or individual within the Member State to whom they are addressed. They are, however, binding in their entirety and give no leeway as to how they are carried out.

Both directives and decisions require to be notified to those to whom they are addressed and then come into force on such notification being given.

(d) **Recommendations** – if a recommendation is made under the ECSC treaty it binds the Member State in question, however any other recommendation issued by Community Institutions is not binding.

(e) **Opinions** – these are not binding.

Accordingly, both recommendations not made under the ECSC treaty and all opinions do not have the force of law to bind Member States. They merely serve as a guideline of what the EC institutions consider the EC position to be in relation to specific matters, on the basis of their interpretation of the treaties.

The *Official Journal of the European Communities*, known as the 'OJ', contains legislation (the 'L' publication) and general information, notices and proceedings of the parliament (the 'C' publication). The OJ is published by the Office for Official Publications of the EC and HMSO (Her Majesty's Stationery Office).

The **European Convention on Human Rights** ('ECHR') recently became part of UK law by virtue of the coming into force of the Human Rights Act 1998. The impact of this piece of legislation will be separately examined. Importantly, the ECHR is not a product of the European Union, but is produced by the European Commission on Human Rights. The Court of Human Rights sits at Strasbourg and enforces the Convention as required. It has no links to the community institutions in Brussels. In May 1997 the UK signed up to the **European Social Chapter** which was devised to complement the ECHR and guarantees a number of economic and social rights, particularly in relation to employment (including the minimum wage).[17]

Researching the law

Reference has been made above to a number of different sources of law. This section aims to provide the beginner with assistance on how to locate the sources and how to keep on top of developments in construction law. Reference should also be made to Appendix 3. Dealing with each of these sources in turn:

(a) **Statute law** – Acts of Parliament and Statutory Instruments are available from HMSO. Before a bill becomes law it is printed on blue paper and can also be purchased from HMSO. Once a bill has received the Royal Assent, it is printed on white paper. Acts of Parliament are given a chapter number for the year in which they were passed and are eventually bound in hardback volumes along with other enactments as Public General Statutes of that year. These volumes can be found in law libraries/university libraries. Current Statutes and Halisburys Statutes (Westminster legislation only) are also commonly available (see also 'IT' below).

(b) **Case law** – case decisions are published in legal journals which are usually issued monthly. Construction case decisions can be found in the following journals: *Scots Law Times*, *Scottish Civil Law Reports*, *Construction Law Reports*, *Building Law Reports* and *Construction Law Digest*. Cases are cited, for example, as follows: [1999] 2 SLT 48. '1999' is the year, '2' means Volume 2 of the case reports, 'SLT' stands for *Scots Law Times* and '48' is the page number of that volume.

(c) **European law** – as we mentioned above, the OJ publishes all new regulations, directives, decisions and European Court of Justice case decisions. Regulations are cited by their classification, number and year, with the number, date and page reference of the *Official Journal*, e.g. Reg. 1234/99 (OJ L 123, 9.4.99, page 13), or by the letters OJ with the year, series letter, number and page (e.g. OJ 1999, L 123/13). Directives and decisions are cited by the year and number (e.g. OJ 99/678). Community law is also available in textbooks, such as the *Encyclopaedia of EC Law*[18] which consists of three series: A, UK sources; B, EC treaties; and C, Community secondary legislation.

(d) **Periodicals and textbooks** – the standard reference textbooks are Keating, *Building Contracts* and Hudson, *Building and Engineering Contracts*. Also useful is Marshall Levine, *Construction and Engineering Precedents*[19] which is in the form of a looseleaf folder. These textbooks should be used with care as they are written with English law in mind. In addition, the following periodicals are available: *Building Law Monthly*, *Construction Law Journal*, *Construction Industry Law Letter*, *Construction Law Yearbook* and *International Construction Law Review*.

(e) **IT** – there is access to the wide variety of research material on the Internet. Many of the more useful website addresses are set out in Appendix 3.

Application of the Housing Grants, Construction and Regeneration Act 1996

The Act is set out in full at Appendix 1.

Part II of the Act applies only to 'construction contracts' entered into after the commencement of Part II (1 May 1998) and which relate to the carrying out of construction operations in England, Wales or Scotland.[20] It applies whatever the governing law of the contract.[21]

For the purposes of the Act 'construction contract' means 'an agreement' for the carrying out of 'construction operations'; arranging for the carrying out of such operations by others (whether under sub-contract or otherwise); and providing labour for the carrying out of such operations.[22] The definition includes contracts for 'architectural, design or surveying work' and for the provision of 'advice on building, engineering, interior or exterior decoration or on the laying-out of landscape' in relation to construction operations.[23] It is generally considered, therefore, that the Act will apply to professional appointments.

A full definition of the word 'agreement', for the purposes of the Act, is contained in Section 107. Essentially, the agreement must be 'in writing'; either originally in writing; made orally but by reference to terms which are in writing; or otherwise evidenced in writing (for example, originally made orally, but thereafter recorded or confirmed in writing).

A decision of the Court of Appeal in England in March 2002 has held that all the material terms of an agreement have to be evidenced in writing in order for the contract to come within the terms of the Act. It is not sufficient that simply the existence of the contract should be evidenced in writing.[24] Ideally, and in order to avoid possible confusion as to whether the Act applies, parties should strive to embody their agreement in one single document or, at least, a complete and consistent exchange of correspondence. Uncertainty over contract terms is one of the major causes of disputes and can make the management of such disputes very costly.

Care should be taken, if the existence of a written contract is denied, to clearly to plead such denial in adjudication proceedings. If this is not done the pleadings themselves may amount to evidence in writing of the agreement.[25]

The term 'construction operations' is defined in Section 105 of the Act and is very wide in its ambit. Care should, however, be taken to ensure that there are no specific exclusions applicable to the contract in question. Section 105(2), for example, excludes certain contracts relating to the drilling for or extraction of oil or natural gas; the extraction of minerals; nuclear processing; power generation; or water or effluent treatment. Additions or amendments to the provisions of the Act defining or excluding from the definitions of 'construction contract' can be made from time to time by Statutory Instrument.

Further important exclusions from the definition are contained in The Construction Contracts (Scotland) Exclusion Order 1998,[26] and in its equivalent in England and Wales. The Exclusion Order, for example, excludes contracts entered into under the private finance initiative which fulfil a number of conditions set out in the Exclusion Order. Essentially, the exclusion applies to the umbrella Project Agreement between the Special Purpose Vehicle and the public body commissioning the works. It does not apply to construction and engineering contracts operating under that umbrella. Facilities management contracts will often provide for construction operations such as the repair and maintenance of buildings, cleaning during repairs or painting of buildings. The Act will apply to such contracts insofar as they relate to construction operations (see s 104 (5)). The Exclusion Order also excludes 'finance agreements' and 'development agreements', as defined in the Order.

Finally, section 106 of the Act excludes from the operation of Part II any construction contract with a 'residential occupier' (one who occupies or intends to occupy, as his residence, the dwelling subject to the construction works). A contract to construct domestic dwelling houses between a developer and a contractor will not be excluded.

Once it is established that the Act applies to the contract under review, the substantive provisions contained in section 108 (Adjudication Provisions) and sections 109 to 113 (Payment Provisions) can be accepted as applicable to the contract in question.

Summary – does the Act apply?

There will sometimes be no substitution but to work through the relevant provisions of the Act to determine if a contract is a construction contract affected by Part II of the Act. The following represents a brief 'check-list'.

- Is the contract a 'construction contract' (as defined by the Act—s 104)?
  - is it an agreement in writing (as defined by the Act—s 107)?
  - does it relate to construction operations (as defined by the Act—s 105)?
- Is the contract excluded from the ambit of Part II of the Act:
  - by provisions in the Act itself (see, e.g., s 106)?
  - by the Exclusion Order?
  - by any other Statutory Instrument?
- Was the contract entered into after 1 May 1998?
- Does the contract relate to construction operations carried out in England, Wales or Scotland?

Notes

[1] He may also owe his employer a duty of care in delict.
[2] See Keating para 1–09.
[3] Sir Michael Latham, *Constructing the Team – Final Report of the Government/Industry Review of Procurement and Contractual Arrangements in the UK Construction Industry* (HMSO, 1994).
[4] Conditions of Contract for Construction, for Plant and Design Build, for EPC Turnkey projects and a Short Form of Contract.
[5] *Jus feudale* 1655.

[6] *The Institutions of the Law of Scotland*, 1681.

[7] *An Institute of the Laws of Scotland*, 3 volumes, 1751–1753.

[8] *An Institute of the Law of Scotland*, 2 volumes, 1773.

[9] *Commentaries on the Law of Scotland and the Principles of Mercantile Jurisprudence*, 1804, and *Principles of the Law of Scotland*, 1829.

[10] *The Laws and Customs of Scotland in Matters Criminal*, 1678.

[11] *Commentaries on the Law of Scotland Respecting Crimes*, 2 volumes, 1797.

[12] *Practice of the Criminal Law of Scotland*, 1833.

[13] Acts passed by the UK parliament apply to Scotland unless they state expressly that they do not. Occasionally, Westminster will enact legislation that is to apply to Scotland only; in this event, the act will have '(Scotland)' included in its name.

[14] The list of reserved matters is included in Schedule 5. Part 1 relates to General reservations and Part 2 sets out specific reservations. A purpose test has also been included in section 29(3) which provides that 'the question of whether a provision relates to a reserved matter is to be determined, subject to subsection (4), by reference to the purpose of that provision'. Section 29(4) provides that: 'A provision which (a) would not otherwise refer to reserved matters, but (b) makes modifications of Scots private law, or Scots criminal law, as it applies to reserved matters, is to be treated as relating to reserved matters unless the purpose of that provision is to make the law in question apply consistently to reserved matters and otherwise'.

[15] The communities are the European Coal & Steel Community, European Economic Community and European Atomic Energy Community.

[16] The European Summit in Nice took place in December 2000 and led to the signing of the Treaty of Nice, to be ratified by end 2002. Among the issues discussed at the Summit was proposed changes to the qualified majority voting system. The main points are: (i) changes to the voting system giving more power to Member States who wield the greatest economic influence, e.g. Germany, Britain, France, Italy and Spain; and (ii) Britain's veto in the decision-making process lifted in 39 areas, including rules of the European Court, external border check procedure, and maintained in relation to areas such as tax, social security and foreign trade in culture.

[17] At the time of writing the minimum wage is £4.20 for employees over 21 and £3.60 for employees under 21, or over 21 but in the first six months of a new job with a new employer and receiving accredited training.

[18] Edited by K R Simmonds, published by Sweet & Maxwell Limited.

[19] Fourth edition, July 2000, published by Sweet & Maxwell Limited.

[20] Section 104(6).

[21] Section 104(7).

[22] Section 104(1).

[23] Section 104(2).

[24] *R J T Consulting Engineers Limited* v. *D M Engineering (NI) Limited* (2002) BLR 217. Readers should also note the further commentary on this case in Chapter 10.

[25] Section 107(5); *Grovedeck* v. *Capital Demolition Limited* (2000) BLR 181.

[26] 1998 No. 686 (s.33).

2. Forming the engineering contract

Essential elements of a contract

There is no short legal definition of the word 'contract', but the question 'What is a contract?' can, in lay terms, perhaps best be answered as 'an enforceable agreement'. In other words, whilst parties may have come to agreement on various matters, it does not necessarily follow that a contract which is enforceable at law has been established, The essential, or supposed, essential elements under Scots law of an (enforceable) contract are as follows (see also Figure 2.1):

(a) there is agreement on all the essential items of the particular contract required by law for that type of contract
(b) the agreement is sufficiently certain
(c) the parties entered the agreement with the intention of creating legal relations between them
(d) the parties do not remain in dispute on a material matter affecting the contract
(e) notwithstanding satisfaction of all of the above, the contract is not otherwise unenforceable.

Each essential element is dealt with, briefly, in turn below.

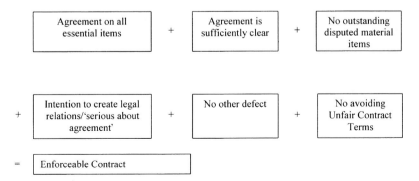

Figure 2.1.   Essential contract elements under Scots law.

Agreement on essential items

An engineering contract comprises an agreement to perform services. The elements of a contract on which a court will likely hold it to be essential that the parties have reached agreement are:

- scope of work
- time for performance
- price or a mechanism to establish what payments should be made.

There is nothing to prevent the parties agreeing that any such issue is not, in fact, essential to the conclusion of the agreement between them, or for such issue to be determined at a later date. That aside, if agreement on the essential elements of a contract is missing, the court will hold that no contract exists. 'As a matter of general law of contract, all the essentials have to be settled. What are the essentials may vary according to the particular contract under consideration.'[1] It was said by the court in the case of *R&J Dempster* v. *Motherwell Bridge Engineering Co.*[2] that 'The matter for decision must always be whether parties have not got beyond the stage of negotiations or whether there is a concluded bargain'.

'Agreement' for these purposes does not necessarily mean 'determination'. Thus, for example, in relation to price, it may be agreed that the actual price be determined by a particular mechanism.[3] Such agreement will be sufficient as long as it is not dependent on any further agreement being reached between the parties. An 'agreement to agree' is not enforceable at law.[4]

If it can be demonstrated that no agreement was reached on an element of the contract other than those listed above which the parties believed to be essential, it may be that in the absence of agreement on *that* element no contract will be held to have been formed.[5]

Certainty

Where the terms of a contract are not sufficiently clear, the contract, as it stands, will be unenforceable. There is a debate as to whether or not an insufficiently clear contract ever in fact existed (i.e. is void *'ab initio'*), but that debate is beyond the scope of this book.[6] There are various reasons why an agreement might be unclear; for example, certain words or expressions used may be too vague or imprecise to bear any recognisable and enforceable meaning; or a particular expression used may be imprecise. Alternatively, there may be contradictions in the terms of the contract, rendering any definitive interpretation impossible.

A court is always reluctant to 'make a contract for the parties'; and in such circumstances is likely simply to decline from interpreting the unclear contract rather than attempting to determine what meaning the parties might have intended.

Generally speaking, extrinsic evidence is not permissible to assist the court in its interpretation of a contract. Such evidence may, however, be allowed to cure an ambiguity in a contract. The extent of what may be permissible by way of extrinsic evidence is beyond the scope of this book. Suffice it to say, however, that the courts are increasingly looking for ways to interpret contracts such that the interpretation makes commercial and business sense, and to that extent they will look at the 'factual matrix' in which the contract was formed; and indeed, in a dispute, the factual matrix surrounding the piece of litigation.[7] Evidence will not, however, be admissible of what the parties say they really meant.

Where a certain term of a contract is void or unenforceable for uncertainty, it may be possible to 'separate' that term from the rest of the contract, and leave the contract, as a whole, intact and enforceable.

Contractual intention

It is sometimes thought that Scots law reflects English law in making the validity of a contract dependent on the parties involved having the intention of creating legal relations.

More accurately, however, Scots law may demand less, namely that the parties must simply be 'serious about their agreement'.[8] Whether, in practice, there is in many instances much difference between these two approaches is debatable.

Remaining dispute

Quite apart from the essential matters to be agreed, as discussed above, failure to agree on a particular material issue may lead to the contract being unenforceable. In other words, the parties may have reached agreement on the issues traditionally thought to be essential to the formation of a contract, but remain in negotiation over other issues which they require to have resolved before they can be said to have reached an overall agreement. This should be distinguished from a contract which leaves a certain matter to be agreed in the future. Each case will turn on its particular facts.

Further, a contract may contain a suspensive condition, making the existence of the contract (or at any rate its enforceability – the current interpretation remains unclear under Scots law) dependent upon its satisfaction.

Not otherwise unenforceable

There are a number of reasons why a contract may be unenforceable, quite apart from its failure to satisfy the four requirements listed above. For example, the subject matter of the contact may be illegal or contrary to public policy, or one or both of the parties may not have had the requisite capacity to enter the contract. The latter issue is dealt with below.

Housing Grants, Construction and Regeneration Act 1996

Many engineering contracts entered into after 1 May 1998 are now subject to the Act. The Act's application falls into two principal categories: (i) that relating to dispute resolution; and (ii) that relating to payment provisions. These aspects of the Act are dealt with elsewhere in this book.

The provisions of the Act must now also be considered, therefore, when looking at the essential elements of a construction contract.

Unfair contract terms

Whilst there are certain essential elements required for the formation of any contract, there are also certain legal restrictions placed on the freedom of the parties to contract. In particular, the Unfair Contract Terms Act 1977, Parts II and III of which apply to Scotland, imposes restrictions on the use of clauses seeking to exempt or limit one party's liability under a contract. The Act applies to most contracts for the supply of goods or services[9] and therefore applies to engineering contracts. The Unfair Contract Terms Act renders some contractual provisions void and some ineffective unless they satisfy a 'fair and reasonable' test.

Void terms include those which seek to exclude or limit liability for death or personal injury as a result of the breach of duty arising in the course of business;[10] those which purport to exclude or limit liability for any loss or damage (but including death or personal injury) arising from the use of defective goods and resulting from the breach of duty by a manufacturer or distributor;[11] and any term in a standard form contract seeking to exclude or restrict liability to the customer for breach of a contractual obligation.[12]

Terms requiring to satisfy the 'fair and reasonableness' test include any term purporting to exclude or restrict liability for breach of a duty arising in the course of any business, other than in respect of death or personal injury.[13]

Offer and acceptance

How is it possible to assess if there has in fact been **agreement** on a particular issue? This will be a question of fact in each case. One method of analysing this question is to break the agreement down into terms of offer and acceptance and to determine whether, on an objective basis, agreement was reached between the parties (thus even though the parties may not, **in fact**, have been in agreement).

The offer

An offer should be distinguished from a mere 'puff' or an invitation to treat and must be communicated by the person making the offer (the offeror) to the person to whom the offer is made (the offeree) before it has legal effect.

An offer becomes incapable of acceptance if: (i) rejected by the offeree; (ii) withdrawn by the offeror; (iii) a reasonable time passes without it being accepted; (iv) there is a material change of circumstances; or (v) on the death or insanity of the offeror.

It is sometimes said that, as a general rule, acceptance must be communicated to the offeror. The rule, more accurately, however, is that there must, at the end of the day, and on an objective analysis, be *'consensus ad idem'* (a meeting of minds) between the parties. Thus acceptance of an offer can be 'communicated' in a variety of ways:

- **Expressly** – no particular form of acceptance is required, unless stipulated in the terms of the offer. As a general rule, express acceptance by post takes effect when the acceptance is posted. Silence does not amount to acceptance. Remaining silent however, incurs risk, as acceptance can be inferred therefrom.
- **Conduct** – this will be a question of fact in each case. Very often in the construction industry work will start on site before there otherwise appears to be a completed contract, and the very existence of the contract may be inferred from one party's actings in commencing work.

The terms of the acceptance must match the offer in question. If not, there is no consensus and therefore no agreement. If the acceptance contains conditions, it is likely to amount to a 'counter-offer', which itself requires acceptance by the original offeror before any contract can be said to exist. In a sophisticated negotiation of a commercial engineering contract, there will be protracted exchanges of offers, qualified acceptances and counter-offers. This can lead to difficulties in assessing at what precise point a contract came into existence, and on what terms. Where each party is, in a simpler scenario, seeking to rely on its own set of standard terms and conditions, a 'battle of the forms' may arise, which has to be analysed to determine, again, when and on what terms the contract, if any, was formed.

The possible results of the battle are that a contract containing either one or the other party's conditions or a mixture of both is found to apply, failing which either a contract exists comprising common law implied terms, or no contract exists at all. Frequently, therefore, each side attempts to have the 'last say' before a contract can be said to have come into existence but careful drafting of the conditions to the effect that the contract cannot be subject to any other standard conditions can often preclude victory for either party.[14]

Capacity

Unless the parties to a contract have the requisite capacity to enter that contract, the contract shall be invalid. Although an individual who is under age, insane or, in some circumstances affected by drink or drugs, will lack the requisite capacity to contract, more important, for the purposes of this book, are the cases of certain legal entities lacking the required capacity. For example, a company may only enter a contract if acting within its powers to do so (as prescribed in its Memorandum and Articles of Association). If not, the company's act would be *ultra vires*, and the contract void.

Whilst a contracting party should clearly be aware of the limitations on its own powers, it is less likely to be aware of those on the contracting powers of the other party to the contract. How would it know, therefore, if the other party to the contract had the requisite authority to enter into the contract in question? Some protection is afforded by the Companies Act 1985, section 35 of which provides (in relation to companies to which the Act is applicable):

(1) In favour of a person dealing with a company in good faith, any transaction decided upon by the directors is deemed to be one which it is within the capacity of the company to enter into, and the power of

the directors to bind the company is deemed to be free of any limitation under the memorandum or articles.

(2) A party to a transaction so decided on is not bound to enquire as to the capacity of the company to enter into it or as to any such limitation on the powers of the directors, and is presumed to have acted in good faith unless the contrary is proved.

For the purposes of section 35, the term 'person' includes a body corporate or incorporate. This section would prevent a company which had contracted *ultra vires* its powers from relying on its own excessive act as a foundation for declaring the contract void. The protection to the innocent party would, however, be at risk of being undermined if that party were anything other than completely ignorant of the limits of the other party's contracting powers.

The contracting capacity of other bodies, for example local Authorities, Unions, Associations and Societies, will also be circumscribed by the particular regulations or charters to which each is subject.

A partnership is (in Scotland but not in England) a separate legal entity, and falls to be treated differently. Its capacity to contract in any particular case will be determined, essentially, by principles of agency. Every partner (or individual held out by the partnership as being a partner) is an agent of the partnership and can contract on behalf of the firm unless he in fact had no such authority to do so *and* the entity with whom the partner is dealing knows or believes the partner (or supposed partner) to lack the requisite authority.[15]

Best practice, generally, is to ensure the inclusion in any contract of a warranty from the other party that it has the necessary capacity to enter the contract. This protection often becomes particularly acute in international contract situations where the ability to determine the other party's capacity may otherwise be more restricted. While obtaining such confirmation from a foreign state-owned corporation it is also advisable to obtain a waiver from the corporation confirming that it will not rely on any sovereign immunity protection it might otherwise be afforded in any action to be brought against it in the future arising out of the contract in question.

Letters of intent

It is often the case that parties will enter a relationship or embark on the provision of services or execution of works without yet having executed an appropriate contract. They will often, however, have exchanged 'letters of intent', or one will have issued to the other a 'letter of comfort' designed to form the basis of the relationship pending the execution of a contract. What legal status, if any, do such letters have?

There is no clear legal authority on the effect of such letters (the term 'letter of intent' or 'letter of comfort' has no definite meaning itself), principally, it seems, because their effect will depend very much on their individual terms and the individual sets of circumstances in which they were issued.[16] A letter of intent, together with the subsequent provision of services or execution of works may well, for example, constitute a binding contract, so long as all essential requirements of the contract (see above) are present. On the other hand, such a letter may indeed just amount to an expression of intent without more; or perhaps to an offer which requires yet to be accepted and all other essentials for the formation of a contract to be established.[17]

If all goes according to plan, of course, the letter of intent will in due course be superseded by the detailed and negotiated terms of a formal contract. All work done or services provided in the meantime will be treated as having been carried out under the terms of the detailed contract if that is clearly the intention of the parties. The need to dissect and analyse a letter of intent will normally only arise in the event that the parties find themselves in dispute before any formal contract is entered into.

Thus, for example, a contractor may seek payment for work done, but no contract can be held to have been established. In such event it is likely that a letter of intent issued by the employer will be seen to constitute a request to carry out work, for which the employer should be liable to make reasonable payment to reflect the value obtained – that is, on a *quantum meruit* basis subject to any exclusion or limitation of liability contained within the letter of intent itself. This may in fact turn out to be better for the contractor, as a reflection of the value obtained by the employer may well exceed any price for the works that would otherwise have been included in any completed contract.

A contractor's readiness to argue that no contract exists, on a job that is unlikely to earn any profit, may, however, now be tempered by the comments made by Reese J in *Birse Construction Limited* v. *St David Ltd*.[18] There Reese J suggested that the price offered by a contractor, even where no contract had been entered into, should cap the level of remuneration to which the contractor might otherwise claim to be reasonably entitled.

What if, however, the employer then requested the contractor to do additional work not envisaged by the letter of intent? If no formal contract is entered into, then clearly such additional work will not be governed by any detailed formal contractual terms. Once again, however, the contractor is likely to be entitled to payment on a *quantum meruit* basis, albeit for work not envisaged by the letter of intent but rather instructed separately. However, in this case the employer would be unable to take advantage of any exclusion or limitation of liability provision as it is unlikely that any such provision would be interpreted as being applicable to any work other than that envisaged by the letter of intent.

Given the lack of any general guiding principle to the status of letters of intent, if they are to be used their drafting requires careful consideration. The focus should be maintained on the expectation that the letter is to have as short-term an effect as possible, and thus perhaps for incentives to be built in to encourage the early execution of a formal contract.

Any discussion of the concept of a 'letter of intent' and the essentials for the formation of a contract would not be complete without at least a passing reference to the expression 'subject to contract'. The use of this expression, by itself, holds no magic, but must be looked at in the context in which it is employed. A court asked to determine whether, in any given set of circumstances, a contract existed, will always consider the existence or otherwise of the essential elements described above. To the extent they are all found to exist, then it is unlikely that the use of the expression 'subject to contract' (the deployment of which will already have been taken into account in the consideration of whether the parties were serious about their agreement) will have any great impact. At most it may simply hold the effective date of the already existing contract in suspense until such time as a formal contract is drawn up and executed.

On the other hand, the existence of the words, when taken together with all other circumstances, may indicate that the parties did not intend to create legal relations, or to be serious about their agreement until such time as a formal contractual document is executed.[19] In short, each case will be looked at in the context of its own circumstances.

Implied terms

Terms can be implied into a contract either as a matter of general law (sourced in statute or case law) or in the individual circumstances of a particular contract, usually to impute an intention to the parties to give business efficacy to the contract, or, in other words, to make the contract work.[20]

Terms which have been held to have been implied terms of contracts between Employers and Contractors for works are further considered in Chapter 9.

Terms implied by Statute or General Law

The scope of the former category is beyond that of this book. However, it is worth mentioning that as far as statutory law is concerned, by virtue of the Sale of Goods Act 1979, the Supply of Goods and Services Act 1982 and the Sale and Supply of Goods Act 1994 there is implied into every applicable contract of sale or contract under which property in goods is transferred an implied term that the goods are of 'satisfactory quality'. The 1982 and 1994 Acts are likely to apply to many engineering contracts and contracts for the supply of materials. One generally implied term which will be relevant to engineering contracts is that relating to time. Where the contract does not stipulate any time for performance either of the whole or any part of the works a court is likely to imply that performance should take place within a reasonable time.

Terms implied in the individual circumstances of the contract

The latter category of case arises from a nineteenth-century English case[21] in which the court stated that:

> The implication which the law draws from what obviously must have been the intention of the parties, the law draws with the object of giving efficacy to the transaction and preventing such a failure of consideration as cannot have been within the contemplation of either side; . . . the law is raising an implication from the presumed intention of the parties with the object of giving to the transaction such efficacy as both parties must have intended that at all events it should have.

The reference to 'consideration' may well be inapplicable in a situation governed by Scots law. In short, however, a term is likely to be implied by the courts when required to give 'business efficacy' to the contract.

A court will look for evidence as to why, in the particular circumstances of a contract, it is in fact necessary to imply a term. It may be possible to imply a term into one contract, but not another. The court will not 'improve' or rewrite a contract for the parties, however desirable that may seem.[22]

Formalities of signing engineering contracts and electronic signatures

Advice should always be taken on the requisite formalities of executing a contract in any particular case. Reference may need to be made, for example, to the Requirements of Writing (Scotland) Act 1995, the Companies Act 1985, and the constitutional document of any corporation, partnership or other organisation executing the contract. A summary of the requirements for formally executing documents in Scotland is provided in Appendix 6.

There are no special rules governing the formalities of signing engineering contracts over and above those applicable to the formalities of executing any other contract.

How does the growing use of e-commerce impact on such requirements? Requirements for a contract to be 'in writing' or 'signed' may not be satisfied by the electronic conclusion of a contract.

Essentially, as we have seen, the formal requirements for the execution of an engineering contract are intended to ensure the admissibility of the executory part of the contract for the purposes of proving the same in court. A handwritten signature of a witness provides some link between the signatory and the document bearing the signature. Arguably, this link is missing in the case of electronic communications. A number of initiatives are being taken to deal with the development of e-commerce and problems such as that identified which arise.

An EC Directive on a Framework for Electronic Signatures[23] requires member States to ensure that a signature will not be inadmissible as evidence before the courts of that State simply because it is electronic rather than manual.[24]

The EC Directive does not stipulate that a signature is to be admissible as evidence simply because it is electronic. Rather, it sets out a list of objective criteria to which the courts of member States should refer in assessing admissibility. In short, the Directive provides that an 'advanced electronic signature', which is based on a 'qualified certificate' and which is created by a 'secure signature creation device', will be automatically admissible (though if it fails strictly to qualify with these criteria it will not be automatically inadmissible and may yet satisfy the general objective principles for admissibility). An electronic signature is an 'advance electronic signature' if it is:

- uniquely linked to the signatory
- capable of identifying the signatory
- created using the means that the signatory can maintain under its sole control
- linked to the data to which it relates in such a manner that any subsequent change of the data is detectable.

A 'qualified certificate' is a certificate which meets the requirements set out in Annex 1 of the Directive and is provided by a certification service provider fulfilling the requirements laid down in Annex II.

In the UK, the Electronic Communications Act 2000 has implemented some of the provisions of the Directive. In particular, both electronic signatures, and certification of an electronic signature, are made admissible in evidence in any legal proceedings in relation to any question as to the authenticity of the communication or data or as to the integrity of that communication or data. The Electronic Signatures Regulations 2002,[25] which came into force on 8 March 2002, implement provisions relating to the supervision of certification-service-providers, their liability in certain circumstances and data protection requirements concerning them.

It is estimated that there are approximately 40 000 references in current UK legislation to requirements for documents to be 'in writing' or signed. Under the 2000 Act, the Secretary of State may by statutory instrument revise any such reference to allow for the electronic equivalent of writing or signatures.

Third-party rights

Under English law, a contract cannot (as a general rule) confer rights or impose obligations arising under it on any person other than those who are party to it. This doctrine is known as 'privity of contract'.

In Scotland the privity of contract doctrine does not apply. Under Scots law, a third party, in certain circumstances, acquires rights under a contract to which it is not a party. Thus, if a contract exists between parties A and B, C may acquire, and can enforce as against A and B, rights. This right is known as the *Jus Quaesitum Tertio*. It is vital to the acquisition of such rights that the parties to the contract intended the third party to benefit. Such intention can either be expressed in the contract itself or, alternatively, inferred by implication. Clear identification of the third party is thus also required. There is, further, much legal debate as to whether or not the grant of a *Jus Quaesitum Tertio* must be irrevocable.[26]

The use of collateral warranties will be familiar to all readers of this book. The purpose of a collateral warranty is, effectively, for one party to a contract (A) to confer on a third party (C) certain rights enforceable by C against A in the event of A's default under its contract with B. It will readily be seen that, in simple terms, the effect of a collateral warranty is thus (i) to avoid the restrictions of the privity of contract doctrine, where applicable, and (ii) very similar to that of a *Jus Quaesitum Tertio*.

The use of collateral warranties, whilst having its origin in England, has spread to and is now equally prevalent in Scotland; despite the view that they are, arguably, unnecessary given the possibility of conferring a *Jus Quaesitum Tertio*. In any event, and consistent with that view, the law of England and Wales has recently played 'catch-up' with the law of Scotland by the enactment of the Contracts (Rights of Third Parties) Act 1999 ('the 1999 Act'). The principal effect of the 1999 Act is to confer on a third party the right to enforce a term of a contract to which he is not a party if: (i) the contract expressly so provides; or (ii) the relevant term purports to confer a benefit on him.[27] The 1999 Act only applies, generally speaking, to contracts entered into after 1 May 2000.

Similarly to the law relating to *Jus Quaesitum Tertio*, the 1999 Act provides that the third party must be expressly identified in the contract either by name, or a member of a class or as answering a particular description, but need not be in existence when the contract is entered into.[28] Thus, for example, the future corporate tenant of a building could have such rights conferred on it by generic description, even though at the date of the engineering contract it was not even incorporated.

As the 1999 Act does not apply to Scotland, its terms and effect are beyond the scope of this book. Given various uncertainties arising from the 1999 Act most construction and engineering contracts now expressly exclude the operation of it, and continue to rely on the use of collateral warranties to confer third party benefits. The ICE, NEC and JCT[29] standard form contracts, as well as the ACE and RIBA standard form appointments, all seek to exclude the effect of the 1999 Act.

Attempts to exclude the effects of the Act from contracts governed by English law must be made carefully. There is a risk that the wording adopted may, if not tightly drafted, affect the right of an assignee of the contract to rely on its terms and may even affect the rights of the beneficiary of a collateral warranty.

Even in the absence of a collateral warranty it is still possible, in certain restricted circumstances, that a third party may be able to recover losses incurred by it from a party to a contract to which the third party is not itself a party. The House of Lords has recently decided, (by a narrow majority of 3:2) in the case of *Alfred McAlpine Construction Limited* v. *Panatown Limited*,[30] that the employer under a building contract may recover from its contractor damages for defects in the building constructed, even though the losses are not suffered by the employer, but by the building owner. This decision was made on the basis (being an exception to the general rule that a plaintiff can only recover losses that he personally has suffered)[31] that the employer remains accountable to the building owner for such recovered damages.

The House of Lords made it clear that, had the building owner itself had a direct remedy against the contractor (by way, for example, of a collateral warranty) the employer would only have been able to recover nominal damages. The *Panatown* ruling has yet to be applied in Scotland, but as House of Lords decisions are of high persuasive authority it is quite likely that it will be so in due course. Any Scottish Court considering the issue might well also then express an opinion as to whether the existence of a *Jus Quaesitum Tertio* in the building owner's favour might also exclude the application of the *Panatown* exception.

Formation of the contract – best practice and common pitfalls

It is impossible to offer guidance for each and every situation as to how the formation of a contract should be approached, but the following points may assist in avoiding the most commonly encountered problems.

- Where at all possible the contract should be agreed and formally executed before works commence on site. It may of course prove to be impossible to achieve this due to programming constraints, but this is the 'ideal', which should be strived for. No gaps or uncertainties should be left in the parties' contractual arrangements before commencing works. A logical and orderly process of tender documents submission, qualification, amendment and, if necessary, incorporation into a final, complete document embodying all the conditions of contract and incorporated documents, should be devised and adhered to.

- Avoid, where possible, the incorporation into sub-contracts of the main contract conditions simply by reference. This topic is discussed in more detail in Chapter 12 on sub-contracts, but it is often the case that such an approach will not successfully import the main contract conditions into the sub-contract conditions. The court will not 'make the parties' contract' for them and will not materially alter the main contract conditions in order to make them compatible with the context of the sub-contract. The better approach is to adopt a standard form of sub-contract or a bespoke set of sub-contract provisions.
- When completing contract documentation care should be taken to insert the full and correct names of the parties. Often contract documentation simply refers to trading names and not the full name of the limited company. The limited company is the legal entity with whom the contract is entered into. Inaccurate completion of sub-contract documentation can lead to problems in pursuing claims in adjudication, arbitration or court proceedings.
- Ensure the counterparty to the contract has the necessary capacity and, if relevant, authority to enter the contract.
- Proceeding with contract works on the basis of a letter of intent is unsatisfactory. The full contractual arrangements should be agreed and tied down prior to commencement of contract work.
- Ensure the correct formalities required for execution of the contract are adhered to in order to avoid dispute at a later date as to the validity of the contract and the evidential value of the contract document.

Notes

[1] *May & Butcher Limited* v. *The King* [1934] 2KB17, per Lord Dunedin at page 21.

[2] 1964 SC 308, per Lord Guthrie at P332.

[3] See Viscount Dundedin in *May & Butcher Ltd* v. *The King* [1934] 2KB17 at page 21.

[4] *Walford* v. *Miles* [1992] 2 AC 128.

[5] See *Hescorp Italia SPA* v. *Morrison Construction Limited* 75 Con LR 51 for further discussion.

[6] Gloag described such an agreement as being 'void from uncertainty'. There are a number of authorities, however, demonstrating the courts' reluctance to hold an uncertain agreement to be 'void'.

[7] *Investors Compensation Scheme Limited* v. *West Bromwich Building Society and Others* [1997] CLL 1243; see also the decision in *Demolition Services Limited* v. *Castle Vale Housing Action Trust* [1979] Con LR 55 for an example of such an approach being applied to a building contract.

[8] Stair, I, X, 13: 'In the act of contracting, it must be of purposes to oblige, either really or presumptively, and so must be serious, so that what is expressed in jest or scorn makes no contract.'

[9] But not all, the notable exception being insurance contracts.

[10] Section 16(1)(a).

[11] Section 19(2).

[12] Section 17(1).

[13] Section 16(1)(b).

[14] In the 1980 Vienna Convention a distinction is drawn between those terms in the acceptance materially changing the terms in the offer, and those which do not. The former compromises a counter-offer, and the latter potentially becomes part of the contract, subject to any objections from the offeror. The Scots Law Commission has drafted a Bill (see Scot Law Com No. 144) on the Formation of Contracts, which followed the approval in the Vienna Convention, but the Bill has not reached the Statute Books.

[15] The law relating to partnership is codified in the Partnership Act 1890.

[16] In *British Steel Corporation* v. *Cleveland Bridge and Engineering Co. Ltd* [1984] All ER 504 Goff J said 'Now the question whether in a case such as the present any contract has come into existence must depend on the true construction of the relevant communications which have passed between the parties and the effect (if any) of their actions pursuant to those communications. There can be no hard and fast answer to the question whether a letter of intent will give rise to a binding agreement: everything must depend on the circumstances of the particular case.'

[17] *Monk Construction Limited* v. *Norwick Union Life Assurance Society* (1993) 62 BLR 107l; *Carillion Construction Ltd* v. *Ballast plc.*

[18] (1999) BLR 194; (2000) BLR 57, CA.

[19] See *Stent Foundation Limited* v. *Carillion Construction (Constructs) Ltd (formerly Tarmac Construction (Contracts) Limited)* (CA) 78 Con LR 188.

[20] *Luxor (Eastbourne)* v. *Cooper* [1941] AC 108.

[21] *The Moorcock* (1889) 14 P.964. The English case of *Liverpool City Council* v. *Irwin* [1977] AC 239 also provides useful guidance as to the circumstances in which the courts would be prepared to imply terms. Also see the more recent case of *Prentice* v. *Scottish Power* 1997 SLT 1071.

[22] *Trollope & Colls* v. *North West Metropolitan Hospital Board* [1973] IWLR. 602. See also commentary on implied terms relative to delay and disruption in Chapter 9.

[23] 99/93/EC.

[24] Similar provisions are also found in the Model Law on Electronic Commerce promulgated by the United Nations Commission on International Trade Law ('UNCITRAL') in December 1996 (and amended in June 1998); and in the UNCITRAL Model Law on Electronic Signatures, adopted in July 2001.

[25] SI 2002 No. 318.

[26] See in particular Stair Institutions I, X, 5 and *Carmichael* v. *Carmichael's Executrix* (1920) SC(HL) 195.

[27] Section 1(1).

[28] Section 5.1(5).

[29] Amendment No. 2 to the 1998 edition, as incorporated into the SBCC standard forms.

[30] [2000] EGCS 102.

[31] *The Albazero* [1977] AC 774.

3.   The role of the engineer

Introduction

All of the major standard forms of engineering contract have a party fulfilling the role of the employer's agent or representative but not all such parties are called 'the Engineer'. In the ICE 7th Conditions, ICE Minor Works and FIDIC contracts the party in question is called 'the Engineer', in the ICE Design and Construct Conditions 'the employer's representative' and in the ECC and IChemE contracts 'the Project Manager'.[1]

Although the name changes, the roles undertaken by this party are similar under the various contracts. For convenience, in this chapter the term 'the engineer' is used as a generic term for each of the above mentioned agents of the employer, unless otherwise specified. This chapter considers general matters concerning the appointment of the engineer, the engineer's authority under the construction contract, the engineer's right to appoint delegates and the manner in which the engineer is to carry out the roles he is given under the contract. It is not concerned with any other role an engineer may have on any given project, such as may arise from his appointment by the employer or the contractor to perform specific tasks.

Agent of the employer

The engineer is not a party to the construction contract and carries out his roles under the contract as agent of the employer. There is a substantial body of case law in existence dealing with the existence and role of an agent. Detailed analysis of that body of case law is beyond the scope of this book.[2]

Appointment of the engineer by the employer

Actual authority

The engineer is appointed by the employer. The appointment derives from a contract created between the employer and the engineer.[3] The construction contract itself does not constitute the appointment of the engineer.

The respective rights and duties of the parties and the scope of the services that the engineer is to carry out for the employer are determined by the engineer's appointment. If the engineer breaches that contract his liability will be to the employer in accordance with the usual principles of the law of contract. If the engineer is negligent he may also be liable to the employer outwith the terms of the contract under the law of delict. The appointment contract sets out the authority that the engineer has been given to bind the employer in his duties. This is known as the engineer's 'actual authority' and may vary from contract to contract.

If the appointment contract is in written form then the provisions of the contract can be readily referred to if a dispute arises as to the rights, duties or obligations of the parties under the appointment or, more particularly, the actual authority the engineer has been given as the agent of the employer. If there is no written contract then evidence would have to be provided as to what constitutes the contract and what authority the engineer has been given. In the absence of any provision to the contrary, the courts will imply that an employer has given the engineer such authority as is necessary to enable the engineer to carry out the role given under the construction contract or which is reasonably incidental to this role.[4] The courts may also be prepared to imply other terms of a contract on the basis of, for example, business efficacy or a course of dealing between the parties. Where there is no express agreement and a principal instructs an agent to operate in a particular market place, the principal will be held to have by implication authorised the agent to act in accordance with the custom of that market place.[5] Parties who repeatedly act in the capacity of principal and agent may be taken to have formed such a relationship without ever expressly having stated that this is the case.[6]

The engineer must fulfil the terms of his contract of appointment. Failure to do so could leave the engineer liable to the employer for damages for breach of contract.

It follows from the fact that the engineer derives his authority as agent from his appointment that if the appointment is terminated, or the employer is no longer in existence, his actual authority to continue acting as an agent also comes to an end.[7]

Ostensible authority

It is unlikely that the contractor will ever be made fully aware of the engineer's actual authority as the contractor will not be a party to the appointment contract between the employer and the engineer. The authority that the engineer has to bind the employer in its dealings with the contractor is more likely to depend upon what the contractor has been given to understand is the engineer's authority by the employer. This is known in law as the engineer's 'apparent' or 'ostensible' authority and the parties' words or actings (such as for example in a consistent and regular course of dealing), can all provide the basis for such authority.

It is possible that the engineer's ostensible authority may differ from his actual authority: this can happen when the contractor with whom the engineer is dealing is not made properly aware of the actual authority vested in the engineer. Difficult questions can then arise concerning the contractual obligations of the employer, the engineer and the contractor amongst themselves. An engineer acting within the bounds of his ostensible authority, but beyond the actual authority, will usually bind the employer in any dealings with the contractor.[8] The engineer in such a situation is, however, likely to be acting in breach of his contract of appointment by the employer. Notwithstanding this, a contractor cannot turn a blind eye and rely on an engineer's ostensible authority without making enquiries where circumstances should reasonably have made him doubt the scope of that authority.[9]

In order to avoid difficulties of this nature, the standard form engineering contracts seek to clearly define the extent of the engineer's authority under the contract and also any limits to such authority. The terms of the construction contract will form the ostensible authority and reduce the need for the contractor to look to the engineer's actual authority. Such express provision should also narrow the scope for there to be any difference between the engineer's actual and ostensible authority.

An engineer may on occasion act beyond both his actual and ostensible authority. The law allows an employer to opt to ratify those unauthorised acts, but only: (i) when the employer knows of the engineer's unauthorised actings; and (ii) when the employer would at the time of the act have had the legal capacity to authorise that act in the first place.[10]

Engineer's liability to the contractor under the construction contract

The engineer will have no contractual liability to the contractor under a construction contract. The engineer is not a party to the contract. Where the engineer is acting for an employer who is named and disclosed and is acting within his authority he will incur no personal liability to the contractor, although his actings will bind the employer.[11]

An engineer can become personally liable to the contractor if he acts outwith his actual authority, but it seems that a claim of this nature would not be based on contract but rather on the engineer – as an agent – having breached an implied warranty that he had authority to perform the act in question when in fact he did not.[12] In order to advance such a claim against the engineer the contractor would require to have relied upon the engineer's authority and not to have known that the engineer lacked authority.

Commentators have discussed the liability of the engineer to the contractor in the event of the engineer being negligent in carrying out any certification. Some argue that in such situations the employer is not warranting the engineer's competence but only his fairness and honesty, and that imposing an extra-contractual duty on the engineer would not be desirable.[13]

There is no doubt, however, that the engineer would be liable to the contractor in the event of perpetrating a fraud on the contractor.

Identification of the engineer by the employer

Identification of the engineer under the construction contract

With the exception of MF/1 all the standard form engineering contracts require that an engineer be appointed by the employer and named in the contract.[14] Failure to do so would be a breach of contract by the employer. MF/1 provides that in default of appointment of an engineer, the purchaser shall be the engineer.[15]

The standard forms differ as to who may be appointed as the engineer. All of the standard forms of engineering contract (with the exception of ICE Minor Works)[16] allow for the appointment of a natural person or a legal person (i.e. a company or partnership). ICE Minor Works requires that a 'named individual' be appointed.[17] The ICE 7th Conditions uniquely provide that if the engineer is not a 'single named Chartered Engineer' then the employer must notify the contractor of the name of the individual chartered engineer who will act on behalf of the engineer.[18]

A purported appointment of an engineer that does not comply with the provisions of the relevant construction contract cannot be considered an appointment at all for the purposes of the construction contract. The employer would in these circumstances be in breach of the contract for failing to appoint an engineer. The contractor could refuse to abide by the instructions, orders or decisions of the party whose appointment was not validly made.

Occasionally an employer may name an 'in-house' engineer as the engineer under the contract when in fact the real work of the engineer is being done by an independent private practice which the 'in-house' engineer is supposed to control. Potential confusion may arise as to the authority of the different engineers under the construction contract. Another danger may be that the employer will look to the independent engineer to assist with matters that are more properly the responsibility of the 'in-house' engineer under the construction contract.[19]

Identification of the engineer under sub-contracts

If the ICE 7th Conditions or ICE Design and Construct Conditions form the basis of the main contract between the employer and the contractor, and the contractor is using the CECA sub-contract or the CECA Design and Construct sub-contract then the party fulfilling the role of engineer or employer's representative under the main contract will fulfil any roles also accorded to it by the sub-contract, unless the standard forms are amended.[20]

Engineer's role and authority under contract

Engineer's general role and authority

All of the standard forms of engineering contract differ slightly in their general statements of what the engineer can and cannot do under the contract.[21]

IChemE gives the widest power to the project manager, stating that the project manager has 'full authority to act on behalf of the Purchaser'.[22] This appears to allow the project manager not only to discharge duties expressly reserved for him,[23] but also to act where the obligation is expressed to be an obligation of the Purchaser. The contractor would be entitled to rely upon such actions of the project manager. IChemE also states that obligations of the project manager are obligations of the purchaser, thus allowing a high degree of flexibility as to who is to carry out a particular obligation.

Both the ICE 7th Conditions and ICE Design and Construct Conditions proceed on the basis that the engineer's duties are: (a) as specified in; or (b) are necessarily to be implied from the contract.[24] FIDIC proceeds on a similar basis.[25] MF/1 is more restrictive. It removes any suggestion that the engineer's duties can be implied from the contract, thereby leaving only those that are 'specified' in the contract.[26] ICE Minor Works takes a similarly narrow approach to the powers of the engineer by specifically listing what instructions the engineer has power to give.[27] ECC is different in that it contains no general statement on the authority of the project manager and therefore leaves little room for implication of any duties of the project manager.

Engineer's specific role and authority

Expressly defining the specific roles of the engineer under a particular contract is the best way to achieve clarity for the role of the engineer. The contract should also set out the level of authority given to the engineer to perform those roles.

The role and duties of the engineer as described in the ICE 7th Conditions are manifold. Key specific functions of the engineer under the ICE 7th Conditions are dealt with elsewhere in this book. Certain roles are said to be obligatory, while others are said to be at the discretion of the engineer.

Limits on the role and authority of the engineer

Both FIDIC and the ICE 7th Conditions state that the engineer shall have no authority to amend the contract.[28] Those contracts (as well as the ICE Design and Construct Conditions) additionally provide that the engineer cannot relieve the contractor of its obligations under the contract.[29] The employer needs the comfort of knowing that even the most misguided engineer cannot deprive him of fundamental protections built into the construction contract.

MF/1 provides that where the engineer requires the prior specific approval of the purchaser before exercising any duty the particulars of such requirement will be set out in the contract.[30] If the contractor has been put on notice that the engineer's authority has been limited in this way then the contractor will not be able to rely on the engineer's authority in exercising the duty without having first confirmed that the engineer has obtained the required approval.[31]

Similar provisions appear in the ICE 7th Conditions and FIDIC. Both of these contracts immediately go on, however, to provide that where the engineer exercises an authority for which approval is required, such approval will be deemed to have been given by the employer.[32] While this adds some certainty to the position as far as the contractor is concerned, it does beg the question as to why mention is made in the first place of the engineer requiring to obtain approval. As any such limitation of authority is only then relevant in a question between the employer and the engineer, it is important that such limitation should appear in the engineer's appointment by the employer.

IChemE contains only one specific limitation to the project manager's authority. This limitation prevents the project manager from issuing a notice electing to take over Plant before the contractor is entitled to an Acceptance Certificate in respect of that Plant.[33] ECC contains no general statement on the authority of the project manager.[34]

Employer's liability for engineer's failure to perform

Where the engineer is obliged to carry out a role under the construction contract and fails to do so the employer will be in breach of its contract with the contractor. In situations where the contractor disputes any decision, opinion, instruction or such like of an engineer, the ICE 7th Conditions and ICE Design and Contract Conditions provide that the dispute is to be settled in accordance with the dispute provisions of the contract.[35] If the dispute is ultimately referred to arbitration the arbiter is empowered to 'open up, review and revise' any decision of the engineer with which it does not agree.[36]

Where the engineer misrepresents matters to the contractor (whether negligently or innocently) then, so long as that misrepresentation is made while acting within the bounds of is authority (actual or otherwise), the employer would remain responsible for the engineer's actions and misrepresentation.[37] The question again becomes one of analysing what is or is not the scope of the authority of the engineer. The action which a contractor may take against an employer would depend on the nature and consequences of the misrepresentation. A claim for damages may be possible. The authorities are confused on the question as to whether the employer would be liable where an engineer acts fraudulently (unless the employer made the fraud possible or benefited from it).[38]

Engineer's role under the CECA Sub-contracts

There are numerous references in the CECA Contract and the CECA Design and Construct Contract to the engineer or employer's representative respectively. The nature of the connection between the main contract works and the sub-contract works is mirrored in the inter-relationship between the main contract conditions and the sub-contract conditions.[39] Many provisions and procedures in the sub-contract turn upon decisions made or instructions given by the engineer under the main contract. Accordingly, most references to the engineer fall into the category of setting out the consequences for the sub-contract of such decisions or instructions.[40]

There are also references to the engineer in the sub-contract that do not seem to fall into this category and which suggest that the engineer has a more specific role to play under the sub-contract. One example is Clause 2(1) which provides that the sub-contractor is 'to execute, complete and maintain the Sub-Contract Works ... to the reasonable satisfaction of the Contractor **and** of the Engineer'.[41]

There is, however, no expansion of this provision to explain how or when the engineer is to be called upon to confirm his satisfaction or to express any dissatisfaction with the sub-contract works, or how the sub-contractor would challenge any view expressed by the engineer. It also raises questions over the role of the engineer. Is he still operating as an agent of the employer – in which case is there a conflict between that role and any role he is given under the sub-contract?

A more satisfactory analysis of Clause 2(1) may be that it is simply an acknowledgement that before the Works under the Main Contract are complete the engineer acting under the Main Contract will require to be satisfied as to the completion of each individual part of the works sub-contracted by the contractor.

Engineer's right to delegate

Power to appoint delegates

In many projects it is not practicable or even possible for one person to fulfil all the roles required of the engineer. For that reason all of the standard forms of engineering contracts considered in this chapter allow the engineer to delegate some or all of his duties to one or more other parties.[42] In ICE 7th Conditions, ICE Minor Works, IChemE and MF/1 the delegate is given a title: These are:

(i) the engineer's representative (for both forms of ICE Contract)
(ii) the resident engineer (IChemE)
(iii) the engineer's representative (MF/1).

No title is given to the delegate in the other contracts. In most of the contracts there is provision (or in any event a clear suggestion) that at least one of the roles of the delegate will be as a resident or site engineer supervising and checking the work carried out under the Contract.[43]

The questions of who the engineer is obliged or allowed to appoint to assist him in carrying out his role under the construction contract, and who is responsible for paying for such delegates, fall to be to be resolved between the engineer and the employer and can be dealt with under the engineer's contract of appointment.[44]

There must be a clear understanding between the engineer and the employer as to exactly who should appoint the party to whom the engineer delegates his powers. If the party is not appointed by the engineer (or an employee of the engineer) then ultimately the engineer will not be responsible for that person's actions if the delegate does not perform his role properly (unless the engineer was contracted to deal with the matter personally and failed to properly instruct the delegate).

In order that the contractor knows that he can and should rely on the authority of the engineer's delegate(s), all of the standard forms of engineering contracts provide that the engineer must notify the contractor of the extent of the duties and powers of his delegates. Some forms expressly provide that the delegation is only effective once such notice has been given.[45] A delegate will never have more authority than the engineer.

Role of delegate

With the exception of MF/1, IChemE and ECC, where the engineer's right to delegate is not fettered,[46] all of the other standard forms of engineering contract reserve certain duties and authorities for the engineer alone.[47] The matters reserved to the engineer generally concern the major decisions that require to be made under the contract, such as decisions in relation to the instruction of variations, extensions of time, disputes, and the issue of certificates which the engineer is called to issue (for example, certificates for completion of the works or the making good of defects).

Only the FIDIC form specifies the qualifications that a delegate must possess. Even this stipulation is expressed in very general terms, with the delegate requiring to be '. . . suitably qualified, competent and fluent in the language of the contract'.[48]

Disputing delegate decisions

If the contractor is dissatisfied with decisions or instructions issued to him by the engineer's delegate(s) all of the standard forms of engineering contract provide that he may bring the disputed decision or instruction to the attention of the engineer. It is then up to the engineer to confirm, reverse or amend the disputed decision or instruction.[49]

Engineer's instructions

Form of instructions

Various approaches are taken by the different contract forms. ICE 7th Conditions, ICE Design and Construct Conditions, FIDIC and IChemE are similar in that they each provide that instructions, decisions and orders should be in writing, but also provide for what should happen if oral instructions are given.

In ICE 7th Conditions and ICE Design and Construct Conditions, instructions of the engineer are to be given in writing unless for any reason it is considered necessary to give the instructions orally.[50] The contractor is obliged to comply with an instruction given orally. ICE 7th Conditions and ICE Design and Construct Conditions also provide that the oral instruction must be confirmed in writing 'as soon as possible under the circumstances' and provide a mechanism whereby the contractor can confirm an oral instruction in writing.

These ICE contracts do not specify what happens if no confirmation in writing is given. This prompts the question as to whether that the oral instruction should be treated as invalid. At least one commentator has suggested that the confirmation procedure is directed only at achieving evidential certainty.[51]

FIDIC follows a similar path. The engineer's instructions are to be in writing 'whenever practicable'. There is also a mechanism in place for the contractor to confirm such oral instructions in writing.[52] IChemE states that instructions should be in writing, but provides that an instruction given orally shall be effective from the time given if confirmed in writing within seven days.[53] No reason is given as to why an instruction should be given orally. It would appear that an oral decision which is not confirmed is not effective, making the required confirmation in the IChemE contracts of more than purely evidential value.

ICE Minor Works does not specify that instructions must be in writing. Neither does MF/1, although it does provide that the contractor may require the engineer to confirm an oral instruction in writing. Where that occurs the instruction is not effective until it is confirmed.[54]

ECC provides that every instruction must be 'in a form which can be read, copied and recorded'.

Engineer's power to give instructions

The contractor is able under the ICE forms of contract to ask a party issuing a decision, instruction or order (whether that is the engineer or its delegate) to stipulate under which duty or authority the decision, instruction or order is being made. The contractor will then be in a position to check that the engineer or delegate is acting with the appropriate authority.[55]

When looking at the form in which instructions or other directions are to be given by the engineer it should be observed that if the engineer is giving a notice, the format and service of notices may well be governed by separate provisions of the contract.[56]

Engineer's instructions and the Sub-contracts

Under the CECA forms a sub-contractor must comply with all instructions and decisions of the engineer in relation to the Sub-Contract Works that are notified and confirmed in writing.[57] The decisions of the engineer referred to are decisions made under the main contract rather than decisions given directly to the sub-contractor by the engineer. The contractor must decide whether to confirm such instructions or not.[58] It is not the role of the sub-contractor to question whether the instruction of the engineer has properly been given under the Main Contract.

Impartiality/fairness

As has been stated, the engineer's role under the contract is that of an agent of the employer. What approach should the engineer therefore take when exercising any discretion allowed to him under the construction contract?

The ICE Design and Construct Conditions, ICE Minor Works and ECC are silent on the point. Not so the other forms. ICE 7th provides that the engineer is to act impartially '. . . within the terms of the Contract having regard to all the circumstances'.[59] IChemE also adopts the language of impartiality in providing that in making judgements or forming opinions the project manager must do so 'to the best of his skill and judgement and shall be impartial between the Purchaser and the Contractor'.[60]

MF/1 refers to the engineer exercising his discretion 'fairly within the terms of the Contract having regard to all the circumstances'.[61] Similarly, FIDIC provides that determinations of the engineer are to be 'fair'.[62]

If the engineer is bound to act impartially or fairly and fails to do so then, as with any other failure of the engineer to carry out the role given to him by the contract, the failure would be a breach of contract by the employer. The engineer's liability to the employer in any such situation would turn upon the terms of the contract between them. If the engineer is bound to act impartially and does so, the employer would not be responsible for the decision reached by the engineer.

MF/1, IChemE and FIDIC specify the circumstances in which the question of fairness and/or impartiality should arise. These amount, basically, to instances where the engineer is given discretion as to how to act. That is understandable. If the engineer has a role to play but no discretion as to how to perform that role then his task is more administrative in nature and impartiality would not be an issue. The engineer cannot be said to act impartially where he has specifically been instructed to put the employer's interests first.

Even without express wording imposing a duty of impartiality it is likely that the courts would imply that the engineer has a duty to act fairly, and to balance the interests of the employer and the contractor in exercising what commentators sometimes refer to as his 'quasi-judicial' duties.

In a case involving an architect the English courts were prepared to say that, in circumstances where decisions were made by an architect under the contract which affected the amount of money a contractor was to be paid and the parties agreed to accept his decision, the contract was made on the understanding that in all such matters the architect would act in a fair and unbiased manner.[63]

It is probable that the court's reasoning in this regard would apply equally to contracts which are silent on issues of impartiality and/or fairness, but nevertheless call for the employer's representative to perform quasi-judicial functions.[64]

Replacement of the engineer

The ICE standard forms of engineering contract allow the employer to appoint replacements for the engineer without obtaining the consent of the contractor,[65] whereas MF/1 requires the purchaser to obtain the contractor's consent.[66]

Under the FIDIC contract the employer must: (i) notify the contractor of his intention to replace the engineer; and (ii) provide details of the intended replacement. The employer is not permitted to replace the engineer with a person to whom the contractor raises 'reasonable objection'.[67]

In the IChemE contract the contractor's consent is only required where the project manager's replacement is to be an affiliate or employee of the employer where that was not previously the case.

Notes

[1] In ECC there are two representatives of the employer: the project manager and the supervisor. The project manager is the main representative with the supervisor being given a specific but more limited role relating to monitoring and testing the works. The supervisor is not (as with the other engineering forms who have a subsidiary representative) a party who depends on the delegated authority of the project manager.

[2] For a detailed review of the law of agency see, for example, *Stair Memorial Encyclopaedia* Vol. 1.

[3] For more on the appointment of professionals, see Chapter 13.

[4] *Black* v. *Cornelius* [1879] 6R 581.

[5] *Scott* v. *Godfrey* [1901] 2 KB 726.

[6] *Morrison* v. *Statter* [1885] 12R 1152.

[7] *Tinnevelly Sugar Refining Co. Ltd* v. *Mirrless, Watson and Yaryan Co. Ltd* [1894] 21R 1009.

[8] *Thomas Hayman & Sons* v. *The American Cotton Oil Co.* [1907] 45 SLR 207.

[9] *British Bata Shoe Co.* v. *Double M Shah Ltd* 1980 SC 311.

[10] *Tinnevelly Sugar Refining Co. Ltd* v. *Mirrless, Watson and Yaryan Co. Ltd* [1894] 21R 1009.

[11] *Fenwick* v. *Macdonald, Fraser & Co. Ltd* (1904) 6F 850.

[12] *Anderson* v. *Croall & Sons Limited* (1903) 6F 153.

[13] Hudson para 1.302 and Chapter 6.

[14] ICE 7th Conditions clause 1(c), ICE Design and Construct Conditions clause 1(1)(c), ICE Minor Works clause 2.1, FIDIC clauses 1.1.2.4 and 3.1, IChemE Clause 1, ECC clause 11.1.

[15] Clause 1(1)(d). Interestingly, none of the standard forms of contract expressly prohibit the employer appointing himself or one of his staff as the engineer but how this sits with the engineer's obligation to act fairly or impartially in exercising his discretion is not dealt with by the contracts.

[16] ICE 7th Conditions clause 1(c), ICE Design and Construct Conditions clause 1(1)(c), MF/1 clause 1.1(d), FIDIC clause 1.1.2.4, IChemE clause 1, ECC clause 11.

[17] Clause 2(2)(a): The marginal heading to clause 2(2) of the ICE Design & Construct Conditions suggests similar provision was intended for this form. However, the clause refers only to the employer notifying the contractor of the name of the employer's representative.

[18] Clause 2.1: this requires that a 'named individual' be appointed.

[19] See the discussion of Hudson in this regard, para 2.020.

[20] See CECA Sub-contract and CECA Design and Construct Sub-contracts clauses 1(1) and 2(1).

[21] The specific duties incumbent upon engineers under ICE 7th are commented upon at 3.4.3.

[22] Clause 11.1.

[23] See clause 11.1(a).

[24] ICE 7th Conditions clauses 2.1(a) and (b), ICE Design and Construct Conditions clause 2(1)(a).

[25] Clause 3.1.

[26] Clause 2.1.

[27] Clause 2.3.

[28] FIDIC clause 3.1, ICE 7th clause 2(1)(c).

[29] FIDIC clause 3.1(b), ICE 7th clause 2(1)(c), ICE Design and Construct Conditions clause 2(1)(b).

[30] Clause 2.1.

[31] *Barry, Ostlere and Shepherd Ltd* v. *Edinburgh Cork Importing Co.* 1909 SC 1113.

[32] FIDIC clause 3.1, ICE 7th Conditions clause 2(1)(b).

[33] Clauses 11.1 and 37.9.

[34] It is noteworthy that it contains no general limit either.

[35] See ICE 7th Conditions clause 66 and ICE Design and Construct Conditions clause 66.

[36] See ICE 7th Conditions clause 66(11) and ICE Design and Construct Conditions clause 66(7).

[37] *Laing* v. *Provincial Homes Investment Co. Ltd* 1909 SC 812.

[38] *Thomas Hayman & Sons* v. *American Cotton Oil Co.*, supra, *Robb* v. *Gow* [1905] 8F 90, *Lloyd* v. *Grace Smith & Co.* [1912] AC 716 and more generally Keating paras 13–27 and 13–28.

[39] See generally CECA Sub-contract and CECA Design and Construct clauses 3 and 8.

[40] See for example CECA Sub-contract and CECA Design and Construct Sub-contract clause 8 (variations) or clause 15 (payment).

[41] CECA Sub-contract clause 2(1), which is expressed in very similar form in the CECA Design and Construct Sub-contract clause 2(1).

[42] ICE 7th Conditions clauses 2(4) and 2(5), ICE Design & Construct Conditions clauses 2(3) and 2(4), ICE Minor Works clause 7.2, MF/1 clause 2.3, FIDIC clause 3.2, ECC clause 14.2, IChemE clause 11.5.

[43] ICE 7th Conditions clause 2(3)(b), ICE Design and Construct Conditions clause 2(4)(b), ICE Minor Works clause 2.2, FIDIC 3.2, MF/1 clause 2(3)(b), IChemE clause 11.4.

[44] See Chapter 13.

[45] ICE 7th Conditions clause 20(3)(a), ICE 7th Design & Construct Conditions clause 2(3)(a), ICE Minor Works clause 2.2, MF/1 clause 2.3, FIDIC clause 3.2, ECC clause 14.2, IChemE clause 11.4.

[46] MF/1 clause 2.3, IChemE clause 11.5, ECC clause 14.2.

[47] ICE 7th Conditions clause 2(4)(c) and 2(3)(b), ICE Design and Construct Conditions clause 2(3)(c) and 2(4)(c), ICE Minor Works clause 2.2, FIDIC clause 3.2.

[48] FIDIC clause 3.2.

[49] ICE 7th Conditions clause 2(5)(a), ICE Design and Construct Conditions clause 2(6), ICE Minor Works clause 2.4, MF/1 clause 2(3), FIDIC clause 3.2(b), IChemE clause 11.6.

[50] ICE 7th Conditions clause 2(6)(a), ICE Design and Construct Conditions clause 2(5)(b).

[51] O'Reilly (1999), *Civil Engineering Contracts* 2nd edition, Thomas Telford.

[52] FIDIC, clause 3.3.

[53] IChemE, clause 5.1.

[54] MF/1, clause 2.5.

[55] ICE 7th Conditions clause 2(6)(c), ICE Design and Construct Conditions clause 2(5)(c), ICE Minor Works clause 2.4.

[56] ICE 7th Conditions clause 68, ICE Design and Construct Conditions clause 58, FIDIC clause 1.3.

[57] CECA Sub-contract and CECA Design and Construct Sub-contract clauses 7(1).

[58] CECA Sub-contract and CECA Design and Construct Sub-contract clause 8(2).

[59] Clause 2(7).

[60] Clause 11.1(d).

[61] Clause 2.7.

[62] Clause 3.5.

[63] *Sutcliffe* v. *Thackrah* (1974) AC 727.

[64] See the reasoning in para 5.6, Brian Egglestone (1996), *The New Engineering Contract – A Commentary*, Blackwell Science Limited.

[65] ICE 7th Conditions clause 1(c), ICE Design and Construct Conditions clause 1(c), ICE Minor Works clause 2.1, ECC clause 14.4.

[66] Clause 2.8.

[67] Clause 3.4. Such objection to be given 'with supporting particulars' but there is no specification on what would constitute such particulars.

4.   General obligations

Introduction

General obligations in engineering contracts cover a wide variety of areas. For example, this chapter looks at many areas, including design responsibility, health and safety, ground conditions, programme, copyright, nuisance, workmanship and materials, defective work, variations and tests. General obligations may be owed either by the employer to the contractor (for example, payment and possession of the site) or from the contractor to the employer (carrying out and completing the works). Where express contractual duties are not set out in the contract, terms may be implied into the contract.

The main operative positions in the major standard form engineering contracts provide that the contractor (or where appropriate sub-contractor) shall:

- 'construct and complete the works' [1]
- 'design, construct and complete the works' [2]
- 'execute, complete and maintain the sub-contract works' [3]
- 'carry out, complete and maintain the sub-contract works'. [4]

Further, the contractor/sub-contractor is also obliged to provide all labour, materials, equipment, temporary works and so on so far as it is required for the completion of the works/sub-contract works. [5]

Design responsibility

At common law, where a contractor enters into a contract to design and construct certain works, the law presumes that the works will be fit for the intended purpose. [6] This is a standard that is very difficult for contractors, and indeed their insurers, to accept and as such the obligation is generally tempered in the main standard forms. [7] The major standard forms of engineering contracts address the issue as follows.

ICE Design and Contract Conditions

The contractor's design responsibility is divided into two areas:

- Clause 2(a) states that the contractor is to exercise 'reasonable skill care and diligence' in carrying out its design obligations.
- Clause 2(b) provides that where the employer has provided design input that is contained in the employer's requirements, the contractor shall review the same and accept responsibility for it.

The second area ensures that the contractor is responsible for all of the design elements of the works. This provides the employer with a 'one stop shop' should it have to raise a claim in relation to failure in the design of the works.[8]

In terms of the first area, the contractor's obligations are to exercise 'reasonable skill and care and diligence'. What does this mean in practice? The answer to this question will always be a matter of fact in each case. However, a general statement of the requirement is:

> the standard of the ordinary skilled man exercising and professing to have that special skill. A man need not possess the highest expert skill; it is well established law that it is sufficient if he exercises the ordinary skill of the ordinary competent man exercising that particular art.[9]

There are a number of important points to be borne in mind when considering whether a particular contractor has discharged his obligations in terms of the relevant standard of duty of care:

- The standard is measured against what other members of the profession consider to be sufficient.
- Any litigant would have to show that the professional fell below the standard set by the profession.[10]
- The 'age or stage' of the professional within the profession is not relevant.[11]
- Where there is more than one recognised approach within the profession he must show that he has followed one of these approaches.[12]
- Codes of Practice may reflect what is considered to be fulfilling the obligation.
- A professional should follow new developments within his profession.[13]

ICE 7th Conditions

Clause 8(2) expressly provides that the contractor is not responsible for the design or specification of the permanent works, unless expressly provided for in the contract. However (unless designed by the engineer) the contractor is responsible for the design of the temporary works. Again, should the contractor have such a design responsibility it is to be exercised with '... all reasonable skill care and diligence ...'.

CECA Design and Construct Sub-contract

This form of sub-contract mirrors the provisions of ICE Design and Construct Conditions. Again, there are two areas:

- The sub-contractor shall exercise all reasonable skill care and diligence in designing any part of the sub-contract works.[14]
- Where any part of the sub-contract works has been designed by on behalf of the employer or the contractor the sub-contractor shall check the design and accept responsibility therefore.[15]

For discussion in relation to this wording see the section on ICE Design and Contract Conditions on page 39.

CECA Sub-contract

This form of sub-contract follows a similar approach to that taken in the ICE 7th Conditions. However, there is no express statement that the sub-contractor is **not** responsible for design, rather it provides that the sub-contractor 'shall execute all reasonable skill care and diligence in designing any part of the sub-contract works for which design he is responsible'.[16]

Health and safety

The engineering sector is an inherently dangerous one in which to work, and whilst there has been an admirable focus on improving the health and safety record in recent years, there is still plenty of scope for improvement.

Although a detailed examination of Health and Safety legislation is beyond the scope of this book, it is worth noting that the main legislation affecting the engineering sector in relation to health and safety are the Health and Safety at Work etc. Act 1974, the Management of Health and Safety at Work Regulations 1992, the Construction (Design & Management) Regulations 1994 and the Construction (Health Safety and Welfare) Regulations 1996. Brief outlines of the main provisions of the Act and the Regulations are set out in Appendix 5.

In the absence of any specific contractual provisions relating to health and safety, and notwithstanding the above legislation, contractors on an engineering project will have an implied obligation to provide: (a) staff competent to carry out the work they are asked to do; (b) adequate materials for the project; (c) effective supervision of the works and a proper system of work; and (d) a safe place of work.[17]

Again, although a detailed examination of the Construction (Design & Management) Regulations is beyond the scope of this book, it is worth noting that the CDM Regulations are a sector-specific piece of legislation affecting the construction and engineering industries. It introduced specified roles and responsibilities for clients, designers and contractors. The CDM Regulations also introduced new roles through the creation of the Planning Supervisor and Principal Contractor. It also introduced general duties of cooperation between the parties on site as well as two new documents in the form of the health and safety plan and the health and safety file. The former is prepared by the planning supervisor prior to the tender being issued and is intended to govern, amongst other things, safe operations on site, whilst the latter is issued after completion of the works being designed essentially to ensure that information about the structure is available and to ensure the health and safety of future users of the structure.

ICE Design and Construct Conditions

The CDM Regulations are not referred to in this form of contract. The various obligations of the parties in relation to health and safety are contained within different clauses of the contract. These are as follows:

(a)   The contractor shall take responsibility for the safety of the design and for the adequacy, stability and safety of all site operations and methods of construction.[18]

(b)   The contractor shall have full regard for the safety of all persons entitled to be upon the site and shall keep the site and the works in an orderly state appropriate to the avoidance of danger and shall *inter alia* in connection with the works provide and maintain at his own cost all lights guards fences, etc., when and where necessary for the safety and convenience to the public or others.[19]

(c)   Where the employer carries out any work (or employs another contractor to do work on site) he must:
- have full regard for safety of all persons to be on site and
- keep the site in an orderly state appropriate to the avoidance of damage to such persons.[20]

CECA Sub-contract and CECA Design and Construct Sub-contract

There are no specific provisions in these standard forms of sub-contract that relate to health and safety. However, the sub-contractor is deemed to have full knowledge of the main contract in both forms of sub-contract.[21] Further, the sub-contractor is obliged to carry out, complete and maintain the sub-contract works that no act or omission of his in relation thereto shall constitute, cause or contribute to any breach by the Contractor of any of his obligations under the Main Contract'.[22] Clearly therefore the sub-contractor must adhere to the appropriate provisions in the relative main contract or it will be in breach of the sub-contract.

Ground conditions

Provision of information and inspection of site

ICE 7th Conditions   Ground condition clauses often play a very significant role in the negotiation of engineering contracts. They are one of the employer's primary weapons in ensuring that risk is allocated with the contractor. Contractors in advance of signing a contract containing an onerous ground conditions clause are advised, as a matter of best practice, to ensure that: (a) they undertake appropriate investigations into the ground conditions themselves; (b) they employ a third party to whom they will have recourse to undertake the investigations; or (c) they ascertain whether the employer has undertaken such investigations and if the answer is affirmative they seek to gain either a collateral warranty agreement from the appropriate party or they have the relevant report assigned to them and ask that the third party provide a suitable form of duty of care agreement in the contractor's favour.

Clauses 11 and 12 deal with the respective parties' obligations in relation to ground conditions. In practice, the employer may have commissioned tests in relation to the site. If so (in so far as they are intimated to the contractor prior to the submission of the tender), the contractor is responsible for their interpretation.[23]

However, notwithstanding any information that the employer has intimated to the contractor, the contractor is deemed to have inspected and examined the site (prior to submitting his tender) such that it is satisfied[24] as to:

- the site's form and nature[25]
- the extent and nature of work and materials required[26] and
- the means of communication access and accommodation he may require.[27]

The obligations of the contractor are reinforced in that he is obliged to 'have obtained for himself all necessary information as to risks, contingencies and all other circumstances'. Clearly therefore, the onus on ascertaining whether the site is appropriate for the proposed works is placed firmly on the contractor. The contractor is deemed to have based his tender on all of this information and to be satisfied with the sufficiency of rates and prices.[28] The interpretation of such information where it relates to design should be carried out using all reasonable skill and care.

The wording of this clause is extremely wide and the contractor would be well advised to undertake all appropriate due diligence in relation to the ground, particularly ascertaining from the employer the extent of the information within either its possession or its knowledge.

Adverse physical conditions and artificial obstructions

Whereas the previous section deals with information in relation to the site, this section deals with the contractor's potential right to recover expenses and/or extra time to complete the works in certain circumstances.

ICE 7th Conditions Notwithstanding the obligations upon the contractor contained in clause 11 (see above); there is scope under clause 12 of the ICE 7th Conditions for the contractor to claim additional payment and/or time.[29]

The procedure for such a claim is outlined in detail in Chapter 9.

ICE Design and Construct Conditions The equivalent provisions in this form of contract are the same except that where the contractor considers that there will be a delay/additional cost, the contractor shall include any alternative methods/procedures with comparative estimates of delay/cost when giving notification.[30]

The employer's representative may in response to an application, if he thinks it fit:[31]

(a) give written consent to any measures with or without modification;[32] or

(b) order a suspension (clause 40) or variation (clause 51).[33]

The engineer has four options at this stage in the ICE 7th Conditions; see clause 12(4).

Where the contractor is found to be entitled to additional time and/or money, specific provision is made in relation to the cost of using any additional contractor's equipment.

CECA Sub-contract and CECA Design and Construct Sub-contract

The outcome of the contractor's application for extension of time or additional cost discussed above will impact on any sub-contractor who is involved in such works.

Programme

The precise form of the programme required to comply with clause 4.2 is not stipulated. It should however set out the sequence of the works proposed by the contractor. The programme is required to allow the employer to ensure that the works are being carried out in an appropriate manner.

ICE 7th Conditions

Upon being awarded the Contract (i.e. following the tender process) the successful Contractor is obliged to provide a programme setting out the method/sequence in which the Works will be carried out.[34]

The procedure to be followed to agree the programme is considered in more detail in Chapter 6.

Revision of programme[35]   Where the engineer considers that the works are not proceeding in accordance with the programme, he may seek a revised programme. This is to be submitted in 21 days or in a period agreed by the engineer. Thereafter, the procedures in clauses 14(2) and 14(3) are followed (see table in Chapter 6 for further detail).

Design criteria[36]   The engineer is obliged to provide the contractor with necessary design criteria to enable the contractor to comply with clauses 14(6) and (7), see below.

Methods of construction[37]   If requested by the engineer the contractor shall submit:

- information relating to the methods of construction; and/or
- calculations of stresses, strains and deflections that may arise in the construction

to enable the engineer to ascertain whether the works can be constructed/completed: (a) in accordance with the contract; and (b) without detriment to the permanent works.

Engineer's consent[38]   The engineer shall inform the contractor in writing within 21 days whether:

- the proposed methods are acceptable; or
- in what respects they fail to meet the requirements of the contract or detrimental to the permanent works.

Where the latter occurs, the contractor does what is necessary to obtain the engineer's consent.

Delay and extra cost[39] If the contractor unavoidably incurs delay or extra cost because:

(a) the engineer's consent is unreasonably delayed; or
(b) the engineer's requirements could not have been reasonably foreseen by an experienced contractor at the time of tender,

then the engineer shall take these into account when considering entitlements under clauses 44, 53 and 60 respectively.

Responsibility unaffected by acceptance or consent[40] Notwithstanding acceptance/deemed acceptance by the engineer of any of the matters in clause 14, it shall not relieve the contractor of any of his duties or responsibilities under the contract. This wording is designed to ensure that a contractor cannot seek to absolve itself of responsibility for the works on the grounds that it was accepted by the engineer.

ICE Design and Construct Conditions

The equivalent provisions[41] of this form of contract are the same with the exception that it does not contain equivalent provisions to clauses 14(7)–(9) inclusive.

CECA Sub-contract and CECA Design and Construct Sub-contract

The sub-contractor is not obliged to provide a programme in relation to the works it is to carry out in terms of its sub-contract. However, the sub-contractor is obliged to carry out the works in such a manner as will not cause or contribute to a breach by the contractor of the main contract.[42]

Copyright

ICE 7th Conditions

The copyright of all drawings, specifications and bill of quantities supplied by the engineer or employer shall not pass to the contractor. However, the contractor may at its own cost copy such materials for use in the contract.[43]

The copyright in all documents supplied by the contractor shall remain with the contractor but the employer and the engineer shall have full power to reproduce and use the same for the purpose of completing, operating, maintaining and adjusting the works.[44] This is important for both parties. The employer needs to be in a position that he can make full use of the works during their lifetime. This may, of course, involve repair and extension of the works. However, the contractor will have invested time and money into the design process and as such must have control over the extent to which the design is used. He has been paid for the design in relation to the works, but not other projects.

ICE Design and Construct Conditions

The first tranche, in relation to the copyright in documents produced by the employer, is the same[45] as in the ICE 7th Conditions, see above.

The second tranche, in relation to the copyright in documents produced by the contractor is different[46] from the ICE 7th Conditions. The employer may (at its own expense) make copies of the documents and use the same for the operation, maintenance, dismantling, reassembly, repair, alteration and adjustment of the Works.

Interference with traffic and adjoining properties

ICE 7th Conditions

There is a general obligation that, so far as the contract permits, the works will be carried out so as not to interfere unnecessarily or improperly with:

(a)   the convenience of the public; or
(b)   the access to public or private roads.[47]

Further, the Contractor shall indemnify and keep indemnified the employer in respect of claims arising out of such matters.[48]

Noise and pollution[49]   The work is to be carried out without unreasonable noise disturbance or other pollution. Again, to the extent not unavoidable in the contract, the contractor shall indemnify the employer.[50] However, the employer shall indemnify the contractor in respect of claims as a result of noise/other disturbance or pollution that were unavoidable in carrying out the works.[51]

ICE Design and Construct Conditions

The provisions are the same as those in relation to the ICE 7th Conditions.[52]

CECA Sub-contract CECA Design and Construct Sub-contract

There are no specific provisions in relation to interference with traffic and adjoining properties. Again, the sub-contractor is obliged to carry out the works in such a way as not to cause or contribute to a breach by the contractor of the main contract.[53]

Workmanship and materials

ICE 7th Conditions

All materials and workmanship must be of the nature described in the Contract.[54] Where such matters are not specified in the contract, it is implied that the materials will be fit for their purpose and that the works will be carried out in a workmanlike manner.[55] The engineer may however request that tests be carried out or that samples be provided to ascertain whether the materials and workmanship are of the appropriate quality. The contractor shall provide labour, materials and samples as required for these tests.[56] Where the production of samples is required by or clearly intended in the contract, the contractor is to produce them at his own cost. If it is not so required, then it is at the cost of the employer.[57] The position is the same in relation to the costs of tests.[58]

Access[59]   The engineer (and anyone authorised by him) shall have access to:

- the works
- the site
- workshops where work is being prepared.

The contractor shall give 'every assistance'[60] in obtaining such access for the engineer.

Examination of work before covering up[61]   No work shall be covered up without the consent of the engineer. The contractor must give the engineer the opportunity to examine and measure the works. The engineer shall carry out the examination without unreasonable delay.

Uncovering[62]   The engineer may direct works be uncovered and reinstated to the engineer's satisfaction. Where works were covered up in accordance with the previous section and the works are found to have been carried out in accordance with the contract, the employer shall bear the costs. Otherwise the contractor shall bear the costs.

Removal of unsatisfactory work and materials[63]   The engineer has the power to instruct in writing the:

- removal of materials which the engineer considers are not in accordance with the contract
- substitution with materials in accordance with the contract
- removal and proper replacement of work, which in respect of material, workmanship or design is in the opinion of the engineer not in accordance with the contract.

Default of contractor[64]   Where there is default by the contractor in relation to any of its instructions, the employer may employ another contractor and deduct the cost therefor from any monies due or to become due to the contractor.

Failure to disapprove[65]   Failure by the engineer or any person acting in relation to clause 39(2) shall not prejudice the engineer to subsequently take action under the clause.

ICE Design and Construction Conditions

The equivalent clauses to 37, 38 and 39 respectively of the ICE 7th Conditions (see above) are in the same terms. However the provisions in relation to materials and workmanship[66] shall be considered here.

There are two general statements in this form of contract:

(a)   The works are to be designed, constructed and completed in accordance with the Contract. Where not expressly provided, 'in accordance with appropriate standards and . . . codes of practice'.[67]

(b)   All materials and workmanship are to be as described in the contract, or where not described, shall be appropriate in all the circumstances.[68]

Checks and tests[69]   The Contractor shall:

(c)   submit to the Employer's Representative proposals for checking the design and testing of the materials and workmanship to ensure compliance with the Contract[70]

(d)   carry out such tests and such further tests as reasonably required by the Employer's Representative.[71]

This form of contract has equivalent provisions to clauses 36(2), (3) and (4) of ICE 7th Conditions and these are on similar terms.[72]

Tests following variations[73]   Where a variation is ordered/instructed, the contractor shall advise the employer's representative without delay of whatever tests would be affected or appropriate. The contractor's proposals for such should be submitted as soon as possible.

Costs of tests[74]   Unless provided otherwise, the contractor shall bear the costs of such tests if such test is:

●   required under clauses 8(3) or 36(3)(a); or

●   clearly intended by/provided for in the contract.

Where tests are carried out pursuant to clause 36(3)(b) (see Checks and tests above), the cost is borne by the contractor if the tests show the work has not been carried out in accordance with the contract, but otherwise by the employer.

Defective work

ICE 7th Conditions

Work outstanding[75]   Unless otherwise agreed, all outstanding work shall be completed as soon as practicable during the defects correction period.

Generally, the contractor shall deliver up the works to the employer at or as soon as practicable after the end of the relevant defects correction period, to the satisfaction of the engineer.[76]

Cost of repair[77]   The cost of carrying out the repair work, instructed in accordance with the previous section above, shall be at the expense of the contractor. Any other work shall be paid for as if it were additional work.

Remedies[78]   Where the contractor fails to carry out the remedial work, the employer may have the work carried out by other parties and is entitled to recover/deduct the cost of the same from the contractor.

Contractor to search[79]   The engineer may require the contractor to carry out searches, tests or trials to ascertain the cause of a defect. Unless the defect is one for which the contractor is liable, the costs shall be borne by the employer. Where the contractor is responsible, it shall rectify and make good at its own expense.

ICE Design and Construct Conditions

This form of contract contains the same provisions as the ICE 7th Conditions.[80]

Variations

Most standard forms of engineering contract contain machinery enabling variations to the original contract work scope to be ordered and carried out. The treatment of variations in standard form contracts (and under the common law) and payment for these is dealt with in Chapter 5 on Payment and variations.

Supervision

ICE 7th Conditions

The contractor is obliged to provide all necessary superintendence during the construction of the works and for as long thereafter as may be reasonably required by the engineer.[81] This is to include:

- sufficient persons
- persons having adequate knowledge of operations; and
- persons aware of techniques required and potentially hazardous

to ensure the satisfactory and safe construction of the works. Where the contractor fails to provide such superintendence it is a breach of contract, but no damages will result automatically. The engineer shall be entitled to suspend until such time as it is provided. Persistent failure will entitle the employer to determine the contract; see clause 63(1)(b)(iv).

The contractor is to appoint an individual (with the approval of the engineer) to constantly be on the works. He is in full charge of the works and shall receive instructions from the engineer. The contractor or this authorised agent shall be responsible for the safety of all operations.[82]

ICE Design and Contract Conditions

Again, the contractor is to provide all necessary superintendence.[83] Further, there is a similar role for a contractor's agent[84] as set out under ICE 7th Conditions above.

Contractor's representative[85]   This individual is named in the form of contract. He is to fulfil the following obligations:

- exercise overall superintendence of the works on behalf of the contractor
- receive all comments, orders, approvals etc on behalf of the contractor
- has authority to act for and commit the contractor; and
- he may delegate certain functions with the prior written consent of employer's representative.

Notes

[1] Clause 8(c)(a), ICE 7th Conditions.
[2] Clause 8(1)(a), ICE Design and Construct Conditions.
[3] Clause 2(1), CECA Sub-contract.
[4] Clause 2(1), CECA Design and Construct Contract.
[5] Clause 8(1)(g) ICE 7th Conditions, clause 8(1)(6) of ICE Design and Construct Conditions, clause 2(2) of CECA Sub-contract and 2(2) of CECA Design and Construct Conditions respectively.
[6] *IBA* v. *EMI Limited and BICC Construction Limited* (1980) 14BLR 1(HL).
[7] GC/Works/I Contract 1998 contains an option whereby the obligation imposed upon the Contractor in relation to design may be either one of fitness for purpose or reasonable skill and care (clause 10(2)).
[8] This can be contrasted with standard form building contracts with contractor's design, such as JCT 1998 (with Contractor's Design), where the contractor's responsibility for design is more limited.
[9] *Bolan* v. *Friern Hospital Management Committee* [1957] 1WLR 582.
[10] *McLaren Maycroft Company* v. *Flatcher Development Company Limited* [1973] 2 NZLR 100.
[11] *Wilsher* v. *Essex Area Health Authority* [1987] 2 WLR 425.
[12] *Maynard* v. *West Midlands Regional Health Authority* [1984] 1 WLR 634 (HL).
[13] *Eckersley and Others* v. *Binnie & Partners and Others* (1998) CILL 388.
[14] Clause 2(1).
[15] Clause 2(1).
[16] Clause 2(i).
[17] *Wilsons and Clyde Coal Co. Ltd* v. *English* [1938].
[18] Clause 8(5).
[19] Clause (1).
[20] Clause 1a(2).

[21] Clause 3(1).
[22] Clause 3(2).
[23] Clause 11(1).
[24] Clause 11(2).
[25] Clause 11(2)(a).
[26] Clause 11(2)(b).
[27] Clause 11(2)(c).
[28] Clause 11(3).
[29] Clause 12.
[30] Clause 12(3).
[31] Clause 12(4).
[32] Clause 12(4)(a).
[33] Clause 12(4)(b).
[34] Clause 14.
[35] Clause 14(4).
[36] Clause 14(5).
[37] Clause 14(6).
[38] Clause 14(7).
[39] Clause 14(8).
[40] Clause 14(a).
[41] Clause 14.
[42] Clauses 3(2) and 3(2).
[43] Clause 6(3).
[44] Clause 6(3).
[45] Clause 7(1)(a).
[46] Clause 7(1)(b).
[47] Clause 29(1).
[48] Clause 29(1).
[49] Clause 29(2).
[50] Clause 29(3).
[51] Clause 29(4).
[52] Clause 29.
[53] Clauses 3(2) and 3(2).
[54] Clause 36(1).
[55] *Young & Marten* v. *McManus Childs* [1969] AC 454 (HZ).
[56] Clause 36(1).
[57] Clause 36(2).
[58] Clauses 36(3) and (4).
[59] Clause 37.
[60] Clause 37.
[61] Clause 38(1).
[62] Clause 38(2).
[63] Clause 39(1).
[64] Clause 39(2).
[65] Clause 39(3).
[66] Clause 36.
[67] Clause 36(1).
[68] Clause 36(2).
[69] Clause 36(3).

[70] Clause 36(3)(a).
[71] Clause 36(3)(b).
[72] Clauses 36(4) and (5).
[73] Clause 36(6).
[74] Clause 36(7).
[75] Clause 49(1).
[76] Clause 49(2).
[77] Clause 49(3).
[78] Clause 49(4).
[79] Clause 50.
[80] Clauses 49 and 50.
[81] Clause 15(1).
[82] Clause 15(2).
[83] Clause 15(1).
[84] Clause 15(3).
[85] Clause 15(2).

5. Payment and variations

Introduction

The price payable to a contractor for work carried out under a contract is at the heart of the contract. From the contractor's perspective, payment (and the ability to make a profit) will be the reason he will enter into the contract. From the employer's perspective, knowing how much he will require to pay for the work and when he will require to pay it will be critical in planning and managing the project.

An engineering contract which has been properly negotiated and drafted should provide either a contract price or a mechanism for ascertaining the contract price (the most common types of payment arrangements are considered later in this chapter). If no price or mechanism is agreed it may be that no contract will have been formed. It is possible in certain circumstances to claim payment for work carried out on the basis of payment *quantum meruit* (see later in this chapter). The Scottish Scheme may also assist in determining what sums fall due during the currency of a contract if no contractual machinery has been established to calculate this (see later in this chapter).

The Act is of fundamental relevance to payment. It sets out various requirements which must be adhered to in construction contracts.[1] In particular, contracts affected by the Act must provide 'adequate mechanisms' to determine: (i) what sums fall due under construction contracts; (ii) when these sums fall due; and (iii) when these sums fall to be paid. The Act also prohibits 'conditional payment provisions' (more commonly known as 'pay when paid' clauses). If the Act's requirements are not met, the payment provisions in the Scottish Scheme may fall to be applied to the contract either wholly or in part.

The sections of the Act which legislate on payment are dealt with later in this chapter. This chapter also considers how the Act's provisions are reflected in the ICE 7th Conditions and the CECA Sub-contract, and the payment regimes under these standard forms.

The character of most engineering projects also means that the work initially contracted for will be modified and added to as the contract progresses. Variations to the work scope will occur. This chapter reviews the common law in relation to variations, as well as, where appropriate, how they are dealt with in the ICE 7th Conditions and the CECA Sub-contract.

Performance and payment – the traditional position

Before considering particular types of contractual payment arrangements, it is necessary to comment briefly on how Scots common law has treated performance under building and engineering contracts and how it has linked performance to payment. The traditional 'perspective' on performance and payment is, of course, one that was developed prior to the introduction of the Act.

The basic principle in Scots law is that a contractor is not entitled to payment until all the works he has contracted to undertake have been completed – in other words, until the 'entire' contract has been performed.[2]

This principle is not, of course, absolute. It has always been possible for parties to provide that interim or instalment payments are made during the currency of the contract. The Act now insists on this, but this was in any event commonplace before its introduction. A contract which makes such provision cannot be described as an 'entire' contract as payment is not dependent on completion of all of the contract works.

It has also been accepted by the courts that if minor items of work are left incomplete, or there are immaterial deviations from the contract specification, the contractor would be entitled to pursue payment of the contract price under deduction of an allowance for the value of the work not completed or the cost of repairing any defective work. These principles are set out in the nineteenth-century case of *Ramsay & Son* v. *Brand*.[3] The court in *Ramsay* also expressed the view that if there was material 'non-compliance' with the requirements of the contract then no payment would fall due to the contractor under the contract. The question as to what is material non-compliance in an entire contract has often been a difficult one for the courts to address, and has produced different answers in different circumstances. Much will depend on the nature of the deviation or defect, and how important it is in the context of the construction of all of the works.[4]

A contractor denied the right to claim for payment pursuant to an entire contract due to material non-performance of that contract may not be entirely precluded for making a claim for payment. In certain instances the contractor may be able to make a claim based on *quantum lucratus*. This subject is considered further below.

Other circumstances in which a contractor in an entire contract has been found to be entitled to payment under the contract, even in the absence of complete performance of the contract, are:

- When the contract works are destroyed by, for example, fire and completion is thereby prevented, and the contractor is not at fault. In such circumstances the contractor may be able to pursue payment for work completed prior to destruction of the works.[5] The contractual (and insurance) allocation of risk for destruction of the works during the currency of the contract should, however, be reviewed in such circumstances.
- When the employer's actings prohibit the contractor from carrying out the contract works.[6]

Care should be taken when considering the theory of the 'entire contract' in construction contracts subject to the Act. The Act now stipulates[7] that a party to a construction contract is entitled to payment by instalments, stage payments or other periodic payments.[8] In these circumstances, it seems that reliance on the concept of the 'entire contract', will, at least as far as payment in the modern engineering contract is concerned, be rare.

Classic payment arrangements

There are four main types of payment arrangements used in construction and engineering contracts. The contracts embodying these arrangements are commonly described as:

- lump sum contracts
- measurement and value contracts
- cost reimbursement contracts
- target cost or incentive contracts.

Lump sum contracts

These are contracts for the execution of an agreed scope of works in exchange for payment of a specified sum of money.

If the contractor carries out all of the work specified in the agreed scope of works, he will be entitled to the full contract price. Equally, if the contractor fails to complete all of the work, he will not be entitled to be paid the entire sum (but he will – if the Act applies – be able to seek payment for what he **has** done).

The contractor will not automatically be entitled to additional payment if the works cost him more than he originally estimated. In these circumstances the contractor will have to point to a term of the contract obliging the employer to make payment. It will not assist a contractor to say that he made a mistake in pricing a project. Additional payment will not follow from this, unless it can be demonstrated that the employer was aware of the mistake and took advantage of it.[9]

The amount which a contractor will be paid can of course change in lump sum contracts. Most engineering contracts will provide for the instruction and valuation of changes and variations to the scope of works. Lump sum contracts are no exception. Variations are discussed later in this chapter. The main reasons for adjustments to the amount which a contractor will be paid are variations to the scope of works (additions or omissions), fluctuation in costs (where alteration is allowed), and 'delay and disruption' to the contract works (caused by, for example, unforeseeable ground conditions) which leads to additional costs being incurred (this subject is dealt with more fully in Chapter 9).

Lump sum contracts provide greater certainty in relation to payment than most other types of contract. The employer has control over what changes and additional works he instructs and so can control the contract price and minimise unforeseen increases in the final amount which he will require to pay. For that reason, this type of payment arrangement is often favoured by an employer working to a tight budget which requires careful management.

Measurement and value contracts

In measurement and value contracts (often known as remeasurable contracts), the final contract price is not known at the time of entering into the contract. The contract will provide a method of calculation of the price by reference to measurement of the work actually carried out by the contractor.

The contractor will usually produce a bill of quantities or schedule of rates and prices which the parties will agree. The work carried out will be measured as it is carried out and the rates and prices applied to these measurements to calculate how much is to be paid.

It is common in civil engineering contracts to be unable to ascertain precisely what quantity of work will be required to complete the project until the work has started. The very nature of the work to be carried out – excavation, drilling, formation of foundations, cutting and filling, for example – makes it extremely difficult to predict the quantity and extent of work which will be required. If the contractor cannot ascertain precisely what work and/or quantities will be required to complete the project, he cannot accurately assess how much it will cost to carry out the work. To bind himself to carrying out the project for a fixed lump sum would expose the contractor to unacceptable risk and potentially lead to losses. The solution is, therefore, to agree the rates and prices applicable to the work required and then apply these rates to the work actually carried out to complete the project.

This arrangement will suit a contractor who will be paid for all of the work carried out by him at pre-agreed rates and prices. From the employer's perspective, remeasurement contracts can involve a degree of risk that a significantly greater amount of work and materials than was originally envisaged will be required to complete the project.

Cost reimbursement contracts

Often called 'cost plus', this type of contract allows a contractor to claim for the cost to him of carrying out the project 'plus' an additional fee for carrying it out which will encompass, for example, the contractor's overheads and profit margin. The additional fee is usually based on a percentage uplift over the cost.

A contractor could therefore agree to carry out a project in exchange for payment of his costs plus a pre-agreed additional fee of 5 per cent of those costs.

The contract should stipulate that only 'reasonable' costs will be reimbursed. It will then be for the contractor to demonstrate that it was reasonable in the circumstances for him to incur the costs that he has. The contractor should not in these circumstances be paid for costs incurred unreasonably or unnecessarily.

As with measurement and value contracts, the cost reimbursement contract exposes the employer to the risk that completion of the project exceeds initial estimates. This type of arrangement is often favoured by a contractor who can be sure of his profit margin irrespective of how much the project actually costs to complete.

Target cost or incentive contracts

In order to keep costs to a minimum and to encourage the contractor to carry out the project and manage its costs as effectively as possible, the employer may seek to 'incentivise' the contractor by entering into a target cost or incentive contract.

In this type of arrangement, the contractor's costs will (as in a reimbursement contract) be reimbursed, but he will also be given a target at the beginning of the project to which he should aim to work. If the contractor can carry out the project for less than the target cost, he will receive a bonus over and above the agreed percentage uplift or fee. If, however, the contractor's costs exceed the agreed target, he will be penalised and thereby share the risk of any overrun in the anticipated costs of completion of the project.

This type of arrangement will suit an efficient contractor who may be confident that he can safely agree to a lower target cost than his competitors. However, as the contractor will share the risk of overspend, it is crucial that the target is set at a reasonably achievable level.

Payment under the Act and the New Contractual Payment Regimes

Introduction

The Act has had a significant impact on the payment provisions incorporated in most engineering contracts. The relevant sections of the Act dealing with payment are sections 109–113. These sections can be divided into the following headings:

s 109 – Entitlement to stage/interim payments.
s 110 – (1) (a) What payments are due and when are they due: adequate mechanism
(1) (b) Final dates for payment: adequate mechanism
(2) Notice specifying the sums to be paid.
s 111 – (1) Withholding of payment
(2) Notice of intention to withhold payment.
s 112 – (1) Right to suspend (if no payment and no withholding notice)
(2) Notice of intention to suspend performance.
s 113 – Conditional payment/pay-when-paid clauses.

This section of the chapter considers these provisions and discusses how they are reflected in the ICE 7th Conditions and the CECA Sub-contract. It also reviews the general operation of the payment mechanisms set out in the ICE 7th Conditions and the CECA Sub-contract and comments on the core elements of these mechanisms.

The Act's payment provisions

General   Sections 109–113 of the Act are not designed to favour the position of contractor over that of an employer (or indeed a contractor over a sub-contractor). They are simply intended to bring certainty to how, when and what payments will become due and payable under a construction contract. As with the Act's provisions in relation to adjudication (see Chapter 10), the payment provisions will only apply to the category and type of contracts which the Act is defined as being applicable to (see Chapter 2).

The Act outlines (in relation to payment) requirements that must be adhered to and provides certain rights which apply *irrespective* of what the parties agree in their contract. These requirements and rights are:

- The requirement in section 111 that payment of a sum falling due under the contract must not be withheld without an effective notice of intention to withhold payment being given.
- The right provided to a party in section 112 to suspend performance of its contractual obligations in the absence of payment by a final date for payment (and where a withholding notice has not been issued).
- The prohibition in section 113 which renders conditional payment provisions ineffective.

These provisions will be considered in greater detail, but for present purposes they should be distinguished from, for example, section 110(1) of the Act which requires that a construction contract must provide adequate mechanisms for determining what sums fall due under a contract, when they fall due and the final dates for payment of these sums, as well as the stipulation in section 110(2) that the party making payment should issue a notice specifying how much is to be paid in respect of a given period no later than five days after the date payment becomes due. The Act allows a degree of flexibility to the contracting parties to agree 'adequate mechanisms' to meet the requirements in section 110. There is no such flexibility in relation to sections 111–113 (with the exception of section 111(3) which allows the parties to agree the prescribed period prior to the final date for payment within which a withholding notice must be issued).

If the contract does not in fact provide an adequate mechanism to determine the matters referred to in section 110(1) – whether or not the parties have *attempted* to provide such a mechanism – the payment provisions in Part II of the Scottish Scheme will be implied into the contract to 'fill in the gaps' the parties have left between their contract and the requirements of the Act. The Scottish Scheme is reproduced in Appendix 2.

It is important to understand that the Scottish Scheme's payment provisions only apply *insofar as* the contract does *not* provide what is required in terms of section 110. Section 110(3) provides that 'if or to the extent that a contract does not contain such provision as is mentioned in sub-section (1) or (2) the relevant provisions of the Scheme for Construction Contracts apply'. The contract may therefore provide an adequate mechanism to determine, for example, when a sum falls due, but may not provide what the final date for payment of that sum should be. If this is the case, the paragraph of the Scottish Scheme which determines the final date for payment will apply, but the paragraph dealing with determination of a due date will not apply. The payment provisions of the Scottish Scheme are considered in more detail below.

Section 109 – stage payments

Section 109 is set out in Appendix 1.

The Act does not attempt to set out when or in what circumstances a stage payment should be made. It specifically reserves the parties' right to 'agree the amounts of the payments and, the intervals at which, or circumstances in which, they become due'. The only exception to the right to be paid by instalments or stage payments arises when the duration of the work is to be less than 45 days, or it is agreed between the parties that the duration of the work is estimated to be less than 45 days. Section 109 has brought on to a statutory footing the usual practice in the engineering industry (and the approach taken in standard forms of contract prior to the Act) to make interim or stage payments.

The parties are free to stipulate the mechanism to determine when stage payments will be made. In theory, if the parties so desired, they could agree that the first stage payment would not fall due until after substantial completion or even later. As long as there is certainty in the agreed mechanism, and that mechanism is logical and workable, it will be effective regardless of how unfair or harsh it may seem to either of the parties.

If a contract is silent as to the amounts of interim payments or the intervals for payment, then the relevant provisions of Part II of the Scottish Scheme will apply.[10]

Since the coming into force of the Act in May 1998, it seems there has not been any significant change in the periods generally agreed upon by parties for stage payments. Prior to the Act, it was common for instalment payments to be made monthly or every 28 days. There is nothing in the Act to prevent the use of such periods as the basis for determining the intervals for payment.

Section 110(1) – timing and amount of payments

Section 110(1) is set out within Appendix 1.

As with s 109, s 110 is not designed to favour one particular party. It does not introduce conditions into the contract which give an economically 'weaker' contractor or sub-contractor greater rights under the contract than they would have had prior to 1 May 1998. It does, however, seek to add certainty to a contract as to when payment will be made, thus enabling both parties to more efficiently manage their expenditure and income during that contract.

Section 110(1) is similar to s 109 in that it states that 'the parties are free to agree how long the period is to be between the date on which a sum becomes due and the final date for payment'.

In theory, the parties could agree that a period of 12 months or more should elapse between the due date and final date for any payment. As long as the contract is clear and unambiguous on that point, such a period would comply with the terms of s 110(1). Such an arrangement is, however, commercially unrealistic and unlikely to attract many offers to carry the work out.

Section 110(1) stipulates that there must be an 'adequate' mechanism to determine the two key dates. These are the 'due' date and the 'final' date for each and every payment, whether an interim payment or the final payment under the contract.

A definition of the due date and final date for payment is crucial to achieving the certainty sought by the Act. Each of these dates acts as a trigger for other rights and obligations under the Act. The due date for payment, for example, is necessary in order to calculate when a notice specifying the payment to be made should be issued in terms of s 110(2). The final date for payment is required to allow calculation of: (i) the last date for issuing a withholding notice under s 111 (see below); (ii) the date upon which the payee can suspend performance for non-payment of sums properly due and payable (see below); and (iii) the date from which interest may run in certain circumstances.

The mechanism for calculating the due and final dates for payment need not be elaborate, or to the equal satisfaction of both parties. It must only be 'adequate'. This means that it must be certain, logical and not contradictory. If a contract provided conflicting or contrary terms for calculating one or both of these dates, those terms would probably be deemed 'inadequate' and would bring the Scottish Scheme into operation.

There is, at the time of writing, a paucity of judicial authority in Scotland (and in England and Wales) as to what will equate to an 'adequate mechanism'. Perhaps the best approach is to ask: 'Does it work? Can I determine when sums fall due and when payments should be made? Or is there confusion or silence on one or both of these matters'? It should also be noted that if one party believes the mechanism is more advantageous to the other party to the contract, it does not necessarily follow that the mechanism is inadequate.

It was held by Lord MacFadyen in the case of *Maxi Construction Management Limited* v. *Mortons Rolls Limited*[11] that the requirement that a valuation be agreed by the employer's agent before a claim for payment could be made is not necessarily an inadequate mechanism for determining what payments fall due under a contract. He added, however, that this would only be the case if a timetable for the process of agreement and a means of resolving a failure to reach agreement were provided. He also commented that the absence of such a timetable and a means of resolving a stalemate would have the effect that such a provision would render 'inadequate' the machinery for determining when payments fall due.

Section 110(1) not only requires that the contract provides an adequate mechanism for calculating when payments become due and final dates for payment. It also requires that the contract provides an adequate mechanism for calculating **what** becomes due.

Other than being subject to a prohibition on so-called 'pay when paid' provisions, the parties would appear to be free to agree how the amount of any payment will be calculated. The mechanism for calculating what sums are due can be as simple or complex as the parties wish. It is not uncommon for due dates for payments in engineering contracts to be linked to payment graphs or schedules setting how much will be paid on completion of certain key 'milestones' or phases of construction. These methods are legitimate, even if it may be said that they are more in one party's interests than the other.

If the contract is silent or otherwise fails to provide an adequate mechanism for calculating what payments become due under the contract then the corresponding provisions of the Scottish Scheme will fall to be implemented (see below).

Section 110(2) – payment notices

Section 110(2) is set out within Appendix 1.

This provision is another example of the Act's drive towards clarity and transparency. The Act requires that a payer must give notice to the payee within five days of the due date (calculated in terms of s 110(1)) of the sum, if any, that he intends to pay to the payee. The payer must provide information as to the basis upon which this sum is calculated. It will not be enough for the payer to simply advise the payee of the amount he intends to pay. The prudent paying party will provide sufficient detail in order to allow the payee to understand how he has reached his calculation. For example, a marked up payment application, showing where the paying party disagrees with the value or quantity of measured works, variations or materials, might be sent to the payee.

The Act provides no sanction which will apply to a payer who fails to comply with the notice provisions under s 110(2). This issue has been the subject of much debate since the inception of the Act. Some commentators and adjudicators formed the view that in the absence of a s 110(2) notice the sum applied for by a contractor or sub-contractor automatically falls due. While many took the opposite view that this could not be so unless the contract specifically provided for this to happen, the point was not considered satisfactorily by the courts until the case of *SL Timber Systems Limited* v. *Carillion Construction Limited*.[12]

The Pursuers in that case (SL Timber) raised an action in the commercial court of the Court of Session to enforce an adjudicator's award. It was found by Lord MacFadyen that the absence of a section 110(2) notice does not '. . . in any way or to any extent, preclude dispute about the sum claimed'. The absence of a section 110(2) notice does not, therefore, prevent a party from disputing the amount of the sum claimed and does not automatically lead to the sum claimed becoming payable (unless the contract states otherwise).

The adjudicator in the *SL Timber* case had formed the opposite view to Lord MacFadyen. Lord MacFadyen held, unfortunately for the defenders in the court action, that while he believed the adjudicator to have been in error, this was an error that fell within his jurisdiction in the adjudication and was not one that should prevent payment of the adjudicator's award.[13]

Accordingly, the absence of a section 110(2) notice or its equivalent in a given set of contract conditions should not, unless the contract says otherwise, have any immediate adverse consequences for the paying party. It would, however, be unwise to consistently fail to issue such notices. If the payee is able to understand why a certain payment has been made and how that sum was arrived at it may lessen the prospects of a dispute arising. Furthermore, adjudicators (and indeed arbiters and judges) will not be impressed if it seems to them that there is a general pattern of non-compliance with a requirement of the Act. Best practice dictates that section 110(2) notices should be issued and prepared timeously.

If the contract does not provide for the issuing of section 110(2) notices the relevant paragraph of the Scottish Scheme will apply.[14]

Section 111 – notices of intention to withhold payment

Section 111 is set out within Appendix 1.

Under s 111, every construction contract must provide for the issue of notices of intention to withhold payment. The basic rule is that the contract must provide a provision requiring service of a 'withholding notice' by the payer on the payee no later than the prescribed period before the final date for payment.

The parties are free to agree what that period should be – it may be only one day if the parties agree to this. If they do not agree on a period, the Scottish Scheme will apply and any withholding notice will require to be served no later than seven days before the final date for payment.[15]

In what circumstances should a withholding notice be issued? A withholding notice should be issued when the paying party intends to withhold any amount from a sum which is otherwise due to the payee.

The circumstances in which such a notice should be used are many and varied, but common examples would be:

- When an employer wishes to withhold payment in respect of liquidated damages from a payment due to a contractor.
- Where a contractor wishes to deduct any losses he has incurred as a consequence of a breach of contract by a sub-contractor. The contract may provide expressly for such deductions or allowances to be made in defined circumstances. Alternatively, the contractor may wish to rely on the common law right of retention pending final quantification of his losses. This topic is explored in more detail later in this chapter.

It is important to appreciate that a section 111 notice is *not* required to demonstrate that a particular sum has not fallen due under the contract – a section 110(2) notice would be required for this – but, instead, to demonstrate that a deduction should be made *from* a sum which is *otherwise due*. If the paying party does not believe that certain work for which payment has been applied for has been carried out, or that it has been improperly executed (and the contract provides that such work should not be paid for), or that some other precondition to payment had not been met, then these considerations should, generally speaking, be reflected in the paying party's assessment of the sum falling due to the payee. The conditions governing a contract should, of course, establish how a paying party should ascertain what sums are due.

Lord MacFadyen considered section 111 notices in the *SL Timber Systems Limited* case[16] and found that a section 111 notice relates to '... the situation where a sum is due under the contract, and the party by whom that sum is due seeks to withhold payment on some separate ground'. Some English commentators have stated that the *SL Timber Systems Limited* decision is authority for the proposition that a section 111 notice is not required for 'abatement of price'. Some care should be taken with the concept of abatement, which is a product of the law of England. Abatement is essentially a method by which payment can be reduced as a consequence of work being improperly executed or defective. The nearest common law equivalents to abatement in Scotland are retention and set-off (compensation), both of which are discussed later in the chapter. Some contract conditions, however, allow payment to be made only in respect of 'work properly executed'.

Lord MacFadyen also found that the absence of a timeous notice of intention to withhold payment does not relieve the party making the claim of the ordinary burden of showing that he is entitled under the contract to receive the payment he claims. This proposition is of course entirely consistent with the establishment, in the first instance, of the sum that is due and, if necessary, the deduction of specified amounts from that sum by way of the issue of a withholding notice. The existence of an Engineer's Certificate would be likely to establish that the sum therein certified was due.[17]

Should a withholding notice be reissued for each interim payment following the payment from which a deduction is made? The Act does not specifically require such repetition and it may be thought that the initial notice should remain valid for all subsequent interim payments. The party wishing to be cautious may, however, wish to reissue the withholding notice in respect of future interim payments (or at least refer to the items of the previous notice) in order to reiterate what will presumably be a continuing discrepancy between the sum said to be due to the payee and the sum which has actually been paid.

What information should the notice contain?   The party preparing the notice should take care to include all the information required by the Act or the relevant contract conditions, and that it is issued by the correct party under the contract.[18]

The requirement that the amount proposed to be withheld should be specified speaks for itself, but wherever possible some form of breakdown and analysis of the amounts withheld should be given. The need for the ground for withholding payment to be specified requires more careful consideration. The party preparing the notice should identify exactly *why* the sum is being withheld. If a particular provision of the contract is being relied upon this should be specified. If the payee is said to have breached its contract, the party drafting the notice should, so far as possible, specify which term of the contract has been breached and explain why he believes that term has been breached.

There may of course be more than one reason for withholding payment. Section 111(2)(b) requires that if there is more than one ground for withholding the amount attributable to *each ground* should be specified. Care should therefore be taken to assess the sums attributable to each ground for withholding payment, whether the ground is founded in the express terms of the contract or a breach of a term of the contract.

Clearly, commercial reality must play a role in the preparation of notices. The busy surveyor or engineer will not have time to produce a hugely detailed document on each and every occasion a withholding notice requires to be prepared. As much attention as possible should, however, be paid to the preparation of notices and their timeous issue.[19]

What are the consequences of not issuing a notice?   The consequences of not issuing a withholding notice can be severe. It has been held in a number of reported cases that an adjudicator may not take into account a 'set off' where it has not previously been intimated to the other party via a withholding notice. If, therefore, a party fails to issue a withholding notice at the proper time that party could not plead a 'set off' or other ground for withholding in defence of a claim for payment in an adjudication. The failure to issue a notice will expose a party to payment of claims which may otherwise have been resisted (entirely or partially) by providing a ground for withholding payment in a valid withholding notice.[20]

However, all is not lost for the party who has failed to issue a withholding notice. That party may wish to assert a separate claim against the payee in respect of the sums that it should have withheld in the withholding notice. Clearly, however, by the time such a claim is asserted money will have passed to the payee.

Equally, the timeous issue of a valid withholding notice may not be the 'end of the story' as far as the deduction is concerned. The payee would be perfectly entitled to dispute the *basis* for withholding sums and/or the amount withheld (as opposed to the actual content and timing of the notice). Such a dispute could be taken to adjudication.

Section 112 – The right to suspend performance for non-payment

Another of the mandatory provisions of the Act which the parties are not free to vary by agreement is the right under s 112 to suspend performance for non-payment of sums properly due and payable under the contract.

Prior to the Act, non-payment was not always, unless the relevant contract conditions allowed for suspension on the basis of non-payment, a safe ground for suspending work; the danger for the suspending party being that it may expose itself to a claim that it had repudiated its contract.[21]

Section 112 now allows a claimant to cease working and to 'freeze' his costs and expenses while the disputed claim is resolved (possibly at adjudication). The mechanism for suspending performance requires seven days notice by the suspending party to the party refusing to pay.[22] During these seven days, the suspending party must continue to carry out all of its obligations and meet all of its contractual commitments as if no suspension were being contemplated. This will usually mean that the payee will continue to incur costs and liabilities for which he may not be paid by the other party. A failure by the suspending party to continue working or to 'slow down' in anticipation of non-payment at the end of the seven-day period may be a risky strategy to adopt as the paying party may ultimately pay up, thereby ending the claimant's right to suspend.[23] In that case, the paying party will be entitled to expect the claimant to have continued to work diligently and in line with agreed contractual requirements. Any 'go slow' by the payee in anticipation of non-payment will not justify an extension of time or payment of any consequent acceleration costs.

If, at the end of the seven-day period, payment is not made, then suspension of performance can begin. The payee can stop work. He will of course require to recommence work if payment is eventually made, and, in the absence of some other contractually agreed right, will probably require to meet his own remobilisation costs. The Act does not give the suspending party any automatic right to claim his remobilisation costs in the event of eventual payment.[24]

Under s 112, the suspending party is permitted to deduct any period of suspension from the contract period without penalty. The contract period is effectively extended by precisely the length of the suspension, thereby allowing the suspending party to complete later than originally required without adverse consequence to him.

If suspension is used, the suspending party must of course be able to demonstrate that the sums claimed are **due and payable** under the contract. If this cannot be established, the suspension will not be valid.

Section 113 – prohibition of conditional payment provisions

Section 113(1) provides as follows:

> S 113-(1) A provision making payment under a construction contract conditional on the payer receiving payment from a third person is ineffective, unless that third person, or any other person payment by whom is under the contract (directly or indirectly) a condition of payment by that third person, is insolvent.

The provision essentially prohibits the use of so-called 'pay when paid' clauses in any construction contract. Such clauses, which, for example, made payment by a main contractor to a sub-contractor conditional upon the main contractor having been paid by his employer, were extremely common in the construction and engineering industry prior to the Act. If the main contractor, for whatever reason, decided not to challenge the employer's failure to pay (perhaps in an effort to maintain good relations with the employer), the sub-contractor would effectively have been prevented from obtaining payment for work properly carried out by him.

Clauses which make sub-contractor payment conditional on certification of sums to the main contractor – 'pay when certified' clauses – are still used by many main contractors to protect their cash flow position. These have been the subject of some debate – are they in effect conditional payment provisions struck at by s 113? Some commentators argue that they are, as in the event a certificate is not issued the sub-contractor may well not be paid, while others are of the view that s 113 does not strike at pay when certified arrangements. The courts have not, at the time of writing, yet ruled definitively on the point and it is to be hoped that clear guidance will eventually be forthcoming.

The prohibition on pay when paid clauses is relaxed in the circumstances set out in sub-sections (2)–(5) of section 113. 'Pay when Paid' will be permitted if the ultimate payer is insolvent, as defined by sub-sections (2)–(5). Most standard contract conditions provide for such a position – see, for example, sub-clause 18(3)(e) of the CECA Sub-contract.

The Scottish Scheme – the payment provisions

As has been noted, the Scottish Scheme acts as a 'safety net' if the requirements of the Act are not met in a construction contract. The parties to a construction contract should aim to avoid the application of the Scheme by enshrining the provisions called for by the Act in their own contractual arrangements. Sometimes, however, the complete or partial application of the Scottish Scheme will be unavoidable.

The Scottish Scheme is reproduced in full in Appendix 2. A detailed review of the Scottish Scheme is beyond the scope of this book, but the following summary illustrates its key features. All section references are references to the Act. All paragraphs are within Para II of the Scottish Scheme.

- **Paragraph 2** provides a method of calculating what sum falls due in respect of a stage payment in the absence of an adequate mechanism in the contract to determine this (see s 110(1)(a)).
- **Paragraph 4** provides a method of determining when payments become due in the absence of an adequate mechanism in the contract to determine this (see s 110(1)(a)).
- **Paragraph 5** provides a method of determining when the final payment becomes due in the absence of an adequate mechanism in the contract to determine this (see s 110(1)(a)).
- **Paragraph 8** provides a method of determining the final date for payment in the absence of an adequate mechanism in the contract to determine this (see s 110(1)(b)).
- **Paragraph 9** provides a framework for the issue of a notice specifying the amount of payment in the absence of this being provided for in the contract (see s 110(2)).
- **Paragraph 10** stipulates when a notice of intention to withhold payment should be issued if the contract does not provide for this (see s 111(3)).
- **Paragraph 11** provides for what should replace a conditional payment provision should a contract incorporate this (see s 113).
- **Paragraph 12** provides important definitions for the terms used in paragraphs 1–11. It should be noted that paragraphs 6 and 7 of Part II apply only to construction contracts of less than 45 days' duration.[25]

ICE 7th Conditions and CECA Conditions

What are the payment mechanisms and notice provisions in:

- the ICE 7th Conditions; and
- the CECA Sub-contract?

The ICE 7th Conditions

The provisions contained in Clause 60 set out the payment mechanism under the ICE 7th Conditions. Clause 60(1) requires the Contractor to submit monthly valuations to the Engineer in respect of work carried out[26] and subsequent valuation dates should be at monthly intervals commencing one month after the Works Commencement Date. The Contractor's valuations are referred to as 'statements'. The first statement should be issued by the Contractor one month after the Works Commencement Date. This allows the first and all subsequent valuation dates to be calculated with a 'starting point' of the Works Commencement Date.

The Clause 60(1) statement should show:

(a)   The estimated contract value of the Permanent Works carried out up to the end of the relevant month.
- Clauses 55–57 deal with measurement of the work carried out by the Contractor. This is commented upon further below.

(b)   A list of any goods or materials delivered to the Site for but not yet incorporated in the Permanent Works and their value.

(c)   A list of the goods or materials identified in the Appendix to the Form of Tender which have not yet been delivered to the Site but in which property has vested in the Employer pursuant to clause 54, and their value.

- It is important to note that the list will include not only materials on the Site, but also those materials that are not on the Site which the Employer is deemed to own – see clause 54(4).

(d)   The estimated amounts to which the Contractor considers himself entitled in connection with all other matters for which provision is made under the Contract including any Temporary Works or Contractor's equipment for which separate amounts are included in the Bill of Quantities.

- The most common 'other matter for which provision is made under the Contract' will of course be a variation to the Contract. The subject of variations and the operation of clause 52 of the ICE 7th Conditions is dealt with later in this chapter. The clause also envisages claims in respect of, for instance, reinstatement works (clause 20(3)), damage to highways (clause 30(3)), uncovering (clause 38(2)), and repair work (clause 49(3)).

Certification of payment

The certification and payment process under clause 60(2) works as follows:

- Within **25 days** of the date of delivery of the Contractor's monthly statement to the Engineer (or his representative) the Engineer shall certify what sums, if any, are due in respect of the monthly valuation.[27]
- Within **28 days** of the date of delivery of the Contractor's monthly statement the Employer shall pay to the Contractor:
  (a)   the amount that in the *opinion* of the Engineer is due to the Contractor in respect of works carried out and any other amounts that the Contractor may be entitled to (see clause 60(1)(a) and (d)) less retention (see below); and
  (b)   the amount which the Engineer considers proper in respect of materials on site and materials in which ownership has vested in the Employer.

It can therefore be seen that the period of time between certification and the final date for payment may be as short as three days.

Clause 60(2)(a) refers to the 'opinion' of the engineer. It has been held that the use of this word imports an element of flexibility into the engineer's evaluation of the works and that his measurement need not be absolutely precise.[28]

When do sums fall due? An adequate mechanism to determine this is obviously a requirement of the Act. Clause 60(2) deals with this by stating that payments become due on certification. This amounts to an adequate mechanism to determine when sums falls due. An adequate mechanism to determine the final date for payment is also provided – payment should be made no later than 28 days after the date of delivery of the Contractor's monthly statement.

It should be noted that the Engineer's certificate is a condition precedent to payment becoming due to the Contractor. In other words, if a sum has not been certified as payable the Contractor has no immediate right to payment. This topic is covered in more detail in Chapter 7.

Measurement

Clauses 55–57 of the ICE 7th Conditions allow the works carried out by the Contractor to be remeasured. It is these clauses which give contracts governed by the ICE 7th Conditions their characteristic as measurement and value contracts. The Engineer will rely upon them in assessing – in accordance with clause 60(2)(a) – the amounts due to the Contractor in respect of the works carried out.

The basic principle is that the Contractor is to be paid for quantities of work which he undertakes at the contract rates. Clause 55(1) makes it clear that the quantities set out in the Contract Bill of Quantities are estimated quantities of the work and are not to be taken as the actual and correct quantities of the work to be carried out by the contractor. Clause 56(1) obliges the Engineer to ascertain and determine by measurement the value of the works in accordance with the contract, and by implication the rates in the Bill of Quantities.

Clause 56(2) allows the Engineer to adjust rates and prices applicable to particular items of work in the event that the actual quantities for that item of work transpire to be greater or less than those stated in the Bill of Quantities. This does not of course mean that every increase or decrease in the quantities set out in the Bill of Quantities will merit a change in rate. Additional expense for the Contractor would not constitute a reason for a change to a rate. It seems that there must be an alteration in the character or nature of the work before the rate can be changed.[29] The Engineer is obliged to consult with the Contractor if he believes a change in the relevant rate or price is appropriate.

Clause 56(3) allows the Engineer to call upon the Contractor to send a representative to any measurement and for the Contractor to provide any particulars required by the Engineer. In the event that the Contractor does not send a representative to attend the measurement then the measurement taken by the Engineer in the absence of a Contractor's representative shall be taken to be the correct measure of the work. It would therefore seem prudent for the Contractor to comply with any request by the Engineer to have a representative attend a measurement.

Clause 56(4) makes provision for work carried out on a daywork basis. The rates and prices for work carried out on a daywork basis will sometimes be set out in a daywork schedule incorporated within the contract. If no such schedule is included, reference should be made to the rates and prices contained in the relevant edition of the *Schedule of Day Works carried out incidental to Contract Work*, published by the CECA.

The Contractor should note that it is under an obligation to provide the Engineer with such records, receipts and other documentation as may be necessary to prove the amounts paid and/or costs incurred by the Contractor in respect of dayworks. The Engineer is able to determine when such documentation should be delivered to him and the form in which this documentation should be provided. Such requests should be complied with wherever possible in order to expedite payment. The Engineer is also permitted to require the Contractor to submit quotations for materials before ordering these materials.

Clause 57 deals with the method of measurement to be employed during the contract. Clause 57 provides:

> Unless otherwise provided in the Contract or unless general or detailed description of the work on the Bill of Quantities or any other statement clearly shows to the contrary the Bill of Quantities shall be deemed to have been prepared and measurements shall be made according to the procedure set out in the *Civil Engineering Standard Method of Measurement Third Edition 1991* approved by the Institute of Civil Engineers and the Federation of Civil Engineering Contractors in association with the Association of Consulting Engineers or such later or amended addition thereof as may be stated in the Appendix to the Form of Tender to have been adopted in its preparation.

If there is any dispute about the measurement of work or the techniques employed in carrying this out, reference should be made to the appropriate standard method of measurement, unless the contract indicates that the Bills have not been prepared in accordance with the standard method. This provides important information as to how measurements should be approached and may be germane in resolving any debate or disagreement over measurement.

Notice specifying payment to be made

The requirements of section 110 of the Act are satisfied by clause 60(9). Clause 60(9) states that every certificate issued by the Engineer shall be sent to the Employer and to the Contractor. Clause 60(9) goes on to say that 'by this certificate the Employer shall give notice to the Contractor specifying the amount (if any) or the payment proposed to be made and the basis on which it was calculated', thus meeting the requirements of the Act.

Withholding of payments

Clause 60(8) allows the Engineer to 'delete, correct or modify any sum previously certified by him'. The Engineer is able to reflect any such deletion, correction or modification in any certificate. It has been held in England that the ability to correct a certificate constitutes a defence to an action for payment founded on the certificate.[30] It is not clear how such an approach meshes with the statutory and contractual requirement that a notice of intention to withhold payment be issued where a payment is to differ from a sum certified. If no notice was issued prior to the final date for payment of the sum certified it may be suggested that the subsequent correction of certificate A (in a future certificate B) would not prevent a claim based on certificate A if no payment had, by the time of issue of certificate B, been made of the sum certified in certificate A.

Clause 60(10) provides:

> Where a payment under clause 60(2)(4) or (6) is to differ from that certified or the Employer is to withhold payment after the final date for payment of a sum due under the contract the Employer shall notify the Contractor in writing not less than one day before the final date for payment specifying the

amount proposed to be withheld and the ground for withholding payment or if there is more than one ground each ground and the amount attributable to it.

This clause satisfies the requirements of section 111 of the Act. The notice may be issued up to one day before the final date for payment of a certified sum. It is important to note that it is the Employer, and not the Engineer, who should give this notice.

Final account

Clause 60(4) states:

> Not later than 3 months after the date of the Defects Correction Certificate the Contractor shall submit to the Engineer a statement of final account and supporting documentation showing in detail the value in accordance with the Contract of the Works carried out together with all future sums which the Contractor considers to be due to him under the Contract up to the date of the Defects Correction Certificate.

> Within 3 months after receipt of this final account and of all information reasonably required for its verification the Engineer shall issue a certificate stating the amount which in his opinion is finally due under the Contract from the Employer to the Contractor or from the Contractor to the Employer as the case may be up to the date of the Defects Correction Certificate and after giving credit to the Employer for all amounts previously paid by the Employer and for all sums to which the Employer is entitled under the contract.

> Such amount shall subject to Clause 47 be paid to or by the Contractor as the case may require. The payment becomes due on certification. The final date for payment is 28 days later.

Clause 60(4) allows deduction of 'all sums to which the Employer is entitled under the Contract'. It has been suggested that this means that, for example, liquidated damages (an entitlement to which accrues pursuant to the contract) could be deducted, but that claims for damages as a consequence of a breach of contract could not be taken into account as these do not fall due 'under the contract'.[31] This interpretation of clause 60(4) seems correct. Notwithstanding this, it should be possible to put in place a withholding notice specifying that sums are to be retained from the final account sum otherwise due as a consequence of the Contractor's breach of contract. Such a notice would require to be put in place later than one day before the final date for payment of the sum in the final certificate. The final date for payment of the final account sum is 28 days following the date of certification of the sum to be paid.

Retention

Clause 60(5) deals with the amount of retention which can be retained by the Employer. The Contract should provide for the relevant retention percentage. This will normally be between 3 and 5 per cent. Retention is commonly provided for in order that the Employer has an amount of money to draw upon should the Contractor fail to remedy defects or to finish the works.[32]

Clause 60(6) specifies when retention should be paid. In summary, the position as to payment of retention is as follows:

(a)   The first half of the retention sum falls due to the Contractor upon the issue of the Certificate of Substantial Completion. The exact amount to be paid to the Contractor in respect of the first half of the retention should be certified by the Engineer within 10 days of the date of issue of the Certificate of Substantial Completion.[33]

Clause 60(6) is slightly confusing as to the due date for payment, as it also states that 'payment becomes due on certification of the amount due'. This is presumably distinct from the statement that 'upon issue of the **Certificate of Substantial Completion** . . . there shall become due to the Contractor [one half of the retention fund]'. Payment of the sum certified as due in respect of the first half of retention should be made within 14 days after the issue of the Certificate of Substantial Completion.

If any sums are proposed to be withheld from the first half of the retention fund, a notice of withholding should be put in place no later than one day before the end of the 14-day period.

(b)   At the end of the Defects Correction Period the remainder of the retention fund falls due to the Contractor. Within ten days of the end of the Defects Correction Period the Engineer is obliged to certify the amount due in respect of the remainder of the retention. Payment becomes due on certification of that amount. The final date for payment is 14 days after the end of the Defects Correction Period.[34]

The CECA Sub-contract

Clause 15 payment provisions: general

The provisions contained in clause 15 of the CECA Sub-contract set out the machinery for payment under the sub-contract. The CECA Sub-contract is of course designed to be used in conjunction with a main contract on the ICE main contract conditions.

The CECA Sub-contract has two alternative payment mechanisms.[35] These are:

(a)   payment on the basis of rates and prices specified in the contract; and
(b)   payment by reference to the contract price based on stage and milestone event payments. If this route is chosen, then the stage payment dates or milestone dates should be specified in the Third Schedule to the contract. This permits accurate calculation of what sums are due and when they are payable, as required by the Act.

Application procedure: due dates and final dates for payment

The Sub-Contractor is required under clause 15(1)(a) of the CECA Sub-contract to submit written 'statements' of work carried out by them under the Sub-contract. The first such application must be submitted no later than seven days before the date specified in the First Schedule to the CECA Sub-contract (referred to as the 'specified date'), or any other date as agreed between the parties. This application should detail the value of work done by the Sub-Contractor and the value of materials delivered to site or stored off-site for incorporation in the Sub-Contract Works, if such off-site materials can be included in the Contractor's application for payment under the Main Contract.

It is important to be aware that the statement should be 'in such form and contain such details as the Contractor may reasonably require'. Care should be taken by the Sub-Contractor to comply with any requests by the contractor as to the format and content of the statement (provided those are not unreasonable). A statement in the form requested by the Contractor will be regarded as a 'valid statement' – see clause 15(1)(b). The submission of 'a valid statement' in a form required by the Contractor will oblige the contractor to include the value of work and materials recorded in such a statement in his application for payment under the Main Contract (see clause 15(2)(a)).

The inclusion of the relevant value of work and materials under the Sub-Contract is said in clause 15(2)(a) to be subject to the submission of a 'valid statement'. A statement would not, strictly speaking, be treated as 'valid' if it was submitted less than seven days before the 'specified date' defined in the First Schedule to the Sub-Contract. Adherence to submission dates is therefore important. The certificate issued by the Engineer under the Main Contract should include sums which are ultimately due to the sub-contractor in respect of the Sub-Contract Works.

When will payments fall due to the Sub-Contractor? Clause 15(3)(a) states that:

> Within 35 days of the Specified Date or otherwise as agreed but subject as hereinafter provided, there shall be due to the Sub-Contractor in respect of the value of the work and materials if included in a valid statement payment of a sum calculated and determined by the Contractor in accordance with the rates and prices in this Sub-Contract, or by reference to the price, as the case may require, but subject to a deduction of previous payments and of retention monies at the rate(s) specified in the Third Schedule hereto until such time as the limit of retention (if any) therein specified has been reached.

> The Contractor shall notify the Sub-Contractor in writing to the amount so calculated and determined within 35 days of the Specified Date. The final date for payment shall be 3 days later.

Although this clause does not explicitly say so, there is apparently an obligation upon the Contractor to calculate and determine what sums are due to the Sub-Contractor in respect of a 'valid statement'. The wording of the clause may have been improved if this obligation had been made absolutely clear. If the Contractor does *not* calculate and determine the sum due, then presumably no sum can fall due to the Sub-Contractor under the Sub-Contract conditions. If the conditions imposed a positive obligation upon the Contractor to calculate and determine the sum then presumably it would be easier for a Sub-Contractor to assert that, in the absence of any calculation and determination (and accordingly no sum falling due in accordance with the conditions), the Contractor was in breach of its contractual undertaking to so calculate, and that an adjudicator (or arbiter) could instead calculate the sum due to the Sub-Contractor. A strict interpretation of clause 15(3)(a) might suggest that without the imposition of a firm obligation upon the Contractor to 'calculate and determine' the clause does not provide an adequate mechanism to determine *when* sums fall due. Equally, however, it may also be argued that it is at least implicit in sub-clause 15(3)(a) that the Contractor should do so, and that accordingly there is an adequate mechanism.

There is perhaps a further question mark over precisely when the sum *falls due* to the Sub-Contractor. Is it at the end of the 35-day period? Is it the date the Contractor actually calculates and determines the sum due? Or it is the date the Contractor notifies the Sub-Contractor in writing of the amount calculated and determined? The condition simply says 'within 35 days . . . there shall be due to the sub-contractor . . . a sum calculated and determined by the contractor'. The position is not, it is submitted, entirely clear. It may be prudent for parties – if possible – to clarify this point by amending the CECA Sub-contract to stipulate exactly when the sum falls due.

The importance of the submission of a valid statement by the Sub-Contractor is again emphasised in clause 15(3)(a). The statement that '. . . there shall be due to the Sub-Contractor in respect of the value of the work and materials . . . payment of a sum calculated and determined by the Contractor . . . ' is qualified by the words '. . . is included in a valid statement . . . '. In other words, if a claim for work and materials is not recorded in a valid statement, no sum can fall due to the Sub-Contractor in respect of the value of work and materials. In the case of *Enco Civil Engineering Limited* v. *Zeus International Developments Limited* the court held that judgment could not be granted as, despite the presence of a Certificate, it was unable to determine when the 28-day period expired in the absence of a statement.[36]

The final date for payment of the sum calculated is not completely certain. Clause 15(3)(a) states: 'The Contractor shall notify the Sub-Contractor in writing of the amount so calculated and determined within 35 days of the Specified Date. The final date for payment shall be three days later.' It may be asked 'later than when'? Common practice seems to suggest that payment is made three days later than the end of the 35-day period, but on one reading of the sub-clause, payment should be made three days later than the date the notice specifying the payment to be made is issued. This notice need not – according to clause 15(3)(a) – be issued at the end of the 35-day period, but only *within* the 35-day period. Again, the cautious approach may be simply to make a minor adjustment to the conditions to make the position absolutely beyond doubt.

The mechanism set down in clause 15(3) for determination of when the sum due to the Sub-Contractor falls due is not dependent on payment being made under the Main Contract, a feature of clause 15 of the old FCEC Conditions of Contract.[37]

Notices: payment due and withholding of payment

As discussed, clause 15(3)(a) does make provision for the issue of a notice specifying the amount due to the Sub-Contractor. S 110 (2) calls for a notice to be issued specifying: (i) the amount (if any) of the payment to be made; and (ii) the *basis* on which that amount was calculated. Clause 15(3)(a) only requires, however, that the amount 'so calculated and determined' be specified, and not the *basis* for that calculation. The clause does not comply with s 110(2) in this respect, and may lead to the operation of the Scottish Scheme which will oblige the paying party to specify the basis on which the amount is calculated.[38] This criticism of clause 15(3)(a) may of course be academic if in any event the Contractor provides – as good practice dictates – a description or breakdown of how the amount said to be due was calculated.

Clause 15(9) provides:

> In the event of the Contractor withholding any payment after any final date for payment hereunder, he shall notify the Sub-Contractor of his reasons in writing not less than one day before the final date for payment specifying the amount proposed to be withheld and the grounds for withholding payment or if there is more than one ground each ground and the amount attributable to it.

This sub-clause complies with the requirements of s 111 of the Act.

The CECA Sub-contract (at clause 15(3)(b)) in fact provides five bases for a Contractor to withhold or defer payment of all, or part of, any sums otherwise due. It seems logical that if payment is to be withheld for any of those reasons a timeous withholding notice referring to the relevant ground should be issued. The CECA grounds for withholding payment can be summarised as follows:

(a)   The interim claim is for an amount that is less than the minimum amount stated in the Third Schedule to the Contract (i.e. the minimum payment).

(b)   The information provided in the Sub-Contractor's application is inadequate and insufficient to justify the issuing of an interim certificate by the Engineer to the Contractor under the Main Contract.
   - This again stresses the importance of providing information requested by the main Contractor (and good record keeping).

(c)   The Engineer has refused to certify the sums claimed by the Sub-Contractor within the Contractor's application (providing that the Engineer's failure was not due to any act or default on the part of the contractor).
   - This appears to link payment to certification of the relevant amount by the Engineer under the Main Contract. Accordingly, it may be described as a pay when certified clause. The question as to whether such a clause is rendered ineffective by the Act is dealt with in the above commentary on s 113 of the Act.

(d)   the Employer has failed to pay sums duly certified under the Main Contract, where that failure to pay is due to the insolvency of the Contractor.

- this is unquestionably a pay when paid clause, but one which is permitted by s 113 of the Act as it is predicated on the ultimate paying party becoming insolvent.[39]

(e)   the valuation submitted by the Sub-Contractor is in dispute either between the Contractor and the Sub-Contractor or between the Contractor and the Employer.

The Contractor would not be precluded from asserting a ground for withholding *other* than these specified. For example, the Contractor's right to deduct the cost of completing the Sub-Contract Works from sums due (clause 17(3)), and its right to deduct any sum it is prevented from recovering from the Employer by reason of a Sub-Contractor breach (clause 10(3)), are explicitly preserved. Common law rights (such as retention and set-off) which would allow withholding are also preserved by clause 15(3)(b).

Retention

Retention is payable to the Sub-Contractor in line with certification of payment of retention by the Employer to the Contractor.[40] The precise payment mechanism in relation to retention will depend on whether or not the works are to be completed by sections or not. The first moiety is due 'within 35 days' of the issue of the relevant Main Contract Certificate. The Contractor must notify the Sub-Contractor in writing of this certification. Payment should be made 'seven days later'.[41] The final retention payment will be due 28 days from the issue of the Defects Correction Certificate under the Main Contract. The Contractor must once more notify the Sub-Contractor of this in writing. The final date for payment is, again, 'seven days later'. The Contractor will not be obliged to make payment of retention to the Sub-Contractor if, due to its insolvency, the Employer has not made payment of retention to the Contractor.

Final account

The final payment under the Sub-Contract is calculated and will fall due and payable in terms of sub-clause 15(6) of the CECA Sub-contract. Sub-clause 15(6) provides that if one month has expired since the submission by the Sub-Contractor of his final account, the Contractor must advise the Sub-Contractor in writing of the amount (if any) he intends to pay to the Sub-Contractor on the earlier of: (i) three months after the Sub-Contractor has attended to any clause 13 outstanding work and defects; or (ii) 14 days after full payment has been made to the Contractor under the Main Contract.

Sub-clause (6) requires the Sub-Contractor to provide – as an apparent pre-condition to payment – an undertaking (to either the Employer or the Contractor) as to 'the completion or maintenance' of the Sub-Contract Works if the Contractor is required to produce such an undertaking under the Main Contract. The same wording as to when payment should be made used in sub-clause 15(5) – 'seven days later' – is used here.[42]

Sub-clause 15(7) requires the Sub-Contractor to give timeous notice of any claims that it may have against the Contractor. All relevant claims must have been intimated in writing prior to the issuing of the Defects Corrections

Certificate by the Engineer under the Main Contract. This interpretation of Clause 15(7) was upheld in the Scottish case *Loudonhill Contracts Limited* v. *John Mowlem*.[43] In the case of sectional completion, intimation must be given by the sub-contractor prior to issuing of the Defects Corrections Certificate in respect of the section to which the claim relates.

Failure to intimate a timeous claim by the Sub-Contractor will bar such a claim from being made. The reason for this is obvious. The Contractor would be unable to include the value of such claims in its statement of final account to the Engineer and may otherwise be prejudiced by the Sub-Contractor's failure to give timeous notice of such claims.

Interest on late payments

Contractual provisions

Parties will often include a contractual provision relating to interest on overdue payments. Clause 60(7) of the ICE 7th Conditions provides:

In the event of:

(a)   failure by the Engineer to certify or the Employer to make payment in accordance with sub-clauses (2) (4) or (6) of this clause, or

(b)   any decision of an adjudicator or any finding of an arbitrator to such effect

the Employer shall pay to the Contractor interest compounded monthly for each day on which any payment is overdue or which should have been certified and paid at a rate equivalent to 2 per cent per annum above the base lending rate of the bank specified in the Appendix to the Form of Tender.

If in an arbitration pursuant to clause 66 the arbitrator holds that any sum or additional sum should have been certified by a particular date in accordance with the aforementioned sub-clauses but was not so certified this shall be regarded for the purposes of this sub-clause as a failure to certify such sum or additional sum. Such sum or additional sum shall be regarded as overdue for payment 28 days after the date by which the arbitrator holds that the Engineer should have certified the sum or if no such date is identified by the arbitrator shall be regarded as overdue for payment from the date of the Certificate of Substantial Completion for the whole of the Works.

The provisions of clause 60(7) entitle the contractor to interest on sums which should have been paid *under the contract*, in other words in accordance with the contractual mechanisms for payment.[44] It does not entitle the Contractor to interest on damages for breach of contract at common law; this topic is covered separately in Chapter 9.

The right to contractual interest exists irrespective of the powers of an arbiter or an adjudicator in the resolution of a dispute: the right arises from the contractual relationship of the parties, and not from the functions of the arbiter or adjudicator.

The right to contractual interest under clause 60(7) will arise in three types of circumstance:

- Firstly, where the Engineer has certified payment, but the Employer has failed to make payment in accordance with that certification by the final date for payment.
- Secondly, where the Engineer has failed to certify. Clause 60(7) now states that if an arbiter holds that any sum or additional sum should have been certified by a certain date, that shall be regarded as a failure to certify. In other words, if an arbiter finds that previous certification was inadequate, this will trigger an entitlement to interest. This is in contrast to the previous position (in, for example, the *ICE Conditions of Contract* 6th edition), where it was thought there would only be a failure to certify in situations where the Engineer had done something which he ought not to have done under the terms of the contract.[45]
- Where an arbiter or an adjudicator has made a finding that there has been a failure by the Engineer to certify or the Employer has failed to make payment in accordance with Sub-clauses 60(2), (4) or (6).

Statutory interest

A detailed examination of The Late Payment of Commercial Debts (Interest) Act 1998 ('the Late Payment Act') is outside the scope of this book.[46] It is, however, useful for those in the engineering industry to have a basic knowledge of its essential provisions. The Late Payment Act applies not only to Scotland but also to England and Wales and Northern Ireland and provides at Section 1 that:

> It is an implied term in a contract to which this Act applies that any qualifying debt created carries simple interest subject to and in accordance with this Part . . . Interest carried under that implied term . . . shall be treated . . . in the same way as interest carried under an express contract term.

The effect of Section 1 is therefore to add an implied term to contracts to which the Late Payment Act applies thus allowing simple interest to be claimed on debts. The right to interest on late payments introduced by the Late Payment Act cannot be contracted out of. However, Part II of the Late Payments Act provides, amongst other things, for the parties to agree (subject to being in a form necessary to satisfy the Late Payment Act) their own contract terms for dealing with the application of interest on debts, which will in effect oust (or at least vary) the term implied by the Late Payment Act.

The Late Payment Act provides that the 'default' rate of statutory interest will be 8 per cent above the base rate of the Bank of England applicable at the time the debt falls due. It would be possible, it is submitted, to contract for a lower rate of interest which would still satisfy the requirement of the Late Payment Act that a 'substantial remedy' be provided to deal with late payments. The rate of interest used in the ICE 7th Conditions of Contract and the CECA Sub-contract probably satisfy the requirement of the Late Payment Act that for a substantial remedy to be provided.

The Late Payment Act applies to contracts for the supply of goods or services where the purchaser and the supplier are each acting in the course of business.[47] In essence this will cover most engineering contracts, sub-contracts and consultant appointments, but excluding contracts and appointments with domestic purchasers of goods or services. The Late Payment Act does though exclude certain contracts including contracts of service or apprenticeship[48] and consumer credit agreements.

As with much legislation which affects the engineering industry the Late Payment Act was introduced in phases. Initially the Late Payment Act only applied between small business suppliers and either large business purchasers or UK public authority purchasers.[49] It can now be relied upon by any business contracting with any other business provided that the contract under which the debt in question arises was entered into on or after 7 August 2002. A party pursuing interest on late payments is also now entitled to claim 'compensation' in addition to interest on the debt. The statutory compensation is as follows:[50]

- for a debt of less than £1000, **£40**;
- for a debt of £1000 or more, but less than £10 000, **£70**;
- for a debt of over £10 000, **£100**.

Treatment of variations in engineering contracts

Introduction

By their very nature engineering projects often involve work which was not envisaged prior to commencement of work at site or is different in character to that originally described to the contractor in the tender documents.

Common law position

The word 'variation' will often have a defined meaning in a standard form contract. It is also, however, commonly used to describe an adjustment to the scope of works originally agreed between the parties or the introduction of extra work. It is also used, although perhaps less commonly, to describe works which are removed from the original work scope – an 'omission'. In this section, the word 'variation' is used in the broader sense of a change to the scope of works, whether this be by way of modification of work originally contracted for, the addition of extra work or an omission.

It is critical to understand that not only will a contract expressly provide that certain works be carried out, but that some work will *impliedly* fall within the four corners of the agreed work scope. This 'implied' work is also often described as 'necessary incidental' work. Such work would not amount to a variation of the contract work scope. Whether a particular piece of work is truly a variation to the work scope or in fact encompassed by that body of work will be a question of fact and circumstance. Expert evidence from an engineer or surveyor may be required to answer the question and industry custom and practice will be relevant.

In some contracts the work to be carried out is precisely defined (for example, in a contract incorporating detailed bills of quantities) and the scope for a variation to the scope of works to arise is wide.[51] In other contracts, such as design and build contracts where the work is not precisely defined and an 'end result' is specified by way of performance aims or design parameters, there is perhaps less likelihood that variations will arise – see, for example, the case of *Williams* v. *Fitzmaurice*[52] where the contract provided only that a house be constructed. This was held to include an obligation to fit floorboards. The question of whether an item of work constitutes a variation to the agreed work scope will fall to be answered by construing the contractual work requirements in each case.

At common law, an employer has no right to insist upon a variation to the contract work scope. If a contractor wished to, he could refuse an instruction to carry out the works in question. Of course, even in contracts where there is no 'variations clause' a contractor will generally carry out the work if he is requested to do so in the expectation that he will be paid for it. As discussed earlier, this situation has frequently given rise to the analysis that there is an implied agreement to pay for the extra work on a *quantum meruit* basis (unless of course the parties have come to an express agreement in relation to payment). As explained previously, however, if the Scottish Scheme's provisions governing the calculation of sums due under a construction contract apply, payment for the extra work may well be governed by these rules, and in particular paragraph 2 of Part II on the element of omitted work. Omissions of work will at common law also allow a contractor to seek payment. If no agreement is reached on payment the contractor would be entitled to seek damages for loss of profit – the instruction to omit an element of work contracted for would be regarded as a breach of contract.

If works which are additional to the contract work scope are carried out by the contractor, but have not been instructed by the employer, the contractor would have difficulty in establishing an entitlement to payment for these works unless he could show that the employer either expressly or impliedly agreed to pay for the work (or a claim based on *quantum lucratus* was possible – see below). Wherever possible, written or documentary evidence of the instruction of a variation should be sought and preserved. In the absence of such evidence it may not be possible to establish an entitlement to payment.

Variations under the ICE 7th Conditions of Contract

The ICE 7th Conditions of Contract provide machinery for (i) the instruction of variations (clause 51); and (ii) the valuation of variations (clause 52).

Clause 51 Clause 51(1) describes what variations under the ICE 7th Conditions may include – additions, omissions, substitutions, alterations, changes in quality, form, character, kind, position, dimension, level or line, and changes in any specified sequence, method or timing of construction required by the contract. These words are not, however, exhaustive of what might be construed as a variation. More generally, a variation has been described as being an 'instruction that imposes any new obligation or constraint'. This is a useful generic definition to bear in mind when considering the ICE variations clauses.[53]

A change in *programme* to be submitted by the Contractor under clause 14 will not equate to a variation. The programme is not generally incorporated into contracts governed by the ICE 7th Conditions and an adjustment to it would not equate to an alteration of a contractual obligation.

The Engineer is obliged, in accordance with clause 51(1)(a), to order a variation that is, in his opinion, **necessary** for the completion of the work. Such situations may arise, for example, where the work becomes physically or legally impossible to complete without a variation or where a method statement has become redundant or impossible to comply with.

In terms of clause 51(1)(b) the Engineer *may* order any variation which, in his opinion, is '**desirable** for the completion and/or improved functioning of the Works'. This provides the Engineer with some discretion to vary the Works for reasons other than those stated in clause 51(1)(a). It does not, however, constitute 'carte blanche' for the Engineer. For example, the Engineer is not permitted to order variations in order to achieve a saving for the Employer, nor to assist in the Employer's financial management.

It should be noted, however, that the Engineer is empowered to give instructions under clause 13(1) which may allow him to circumvent the requirements of cause 51(1)(b). Clause 13(1) allows the Engineer to give instructions on any matter connected with construction and completion of the works to his satisfaction. If an instruction is issued in accordance with clause 13(1) any additional cost to the Contractor can be claimed via clause 13(3). Clause 13(3) requires any additional cost related to an instruction under clause 13(1) to be valued in accordance with clause 53.

Clause 51(2) requires all variations to be ordered in writing. Any variation ordered orally requires to be confirmed in writing (see clause 6(b)). The Contractor may confirm any instruction in writing to the Engineer and if not contradicted in writing by the Engineer forthwith it will be deemed to be an instruction in writing by the Engineer.

The Contractor is not entitled, in terms of clause 51(3), to claim the cost of any variation to the extent that it is made necessary by his own default.

Clause 52   The process of valuation is explained at length in clause 52. For present purposes, it is perhaps most readily illustrated by way of an abbreviated flow chart (Figure 5.1).

Clause 52(4) states that if the Contractor or Engineer considers that any rate or price of work which is not being varied is rendered unreasonable or inapplicable, either party may notify the other. The Engineer shall fix the rate as in the circumstances he shall then think reasonable and notify the Contractor.[54]

The Contractor may consider that it is entitled to a higher rate than that notified by the Engineer in terms of clause 52(3) and (4). If so, it must follow the procedure set out in clause 53 which is summarised in Figure 5.2. Clause 53 is principally concerned with records, notices and other details to be maintained by the Contractor.

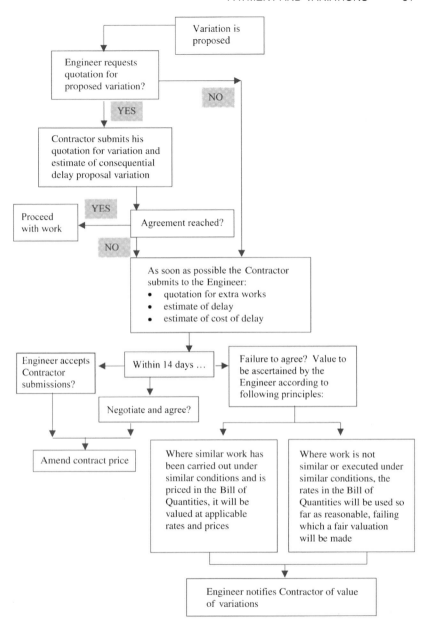

Figure 5.1. Clause 52(1)–(3): summary of process of variation valuation.

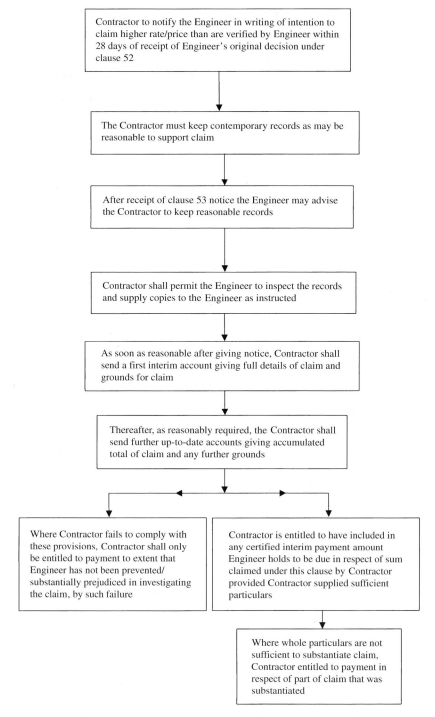

Figure 5.2.   Clause 52(3): summary of additional payments procedure.

Variations under the CECA Sub-contract

This form of sub-contract provides its own mechanism for both ordering and valuing variations. The relevant clauses are clauses 8 and 9 respectively. The procedure for ordering variations can again be illustrated in diagrammatical form in Figures 5.3 and 5.4.

It should also be noted that if so required the Sub-Contractor should submit a quotation for the work as varied and an estimate of delay (clause 9(1)).

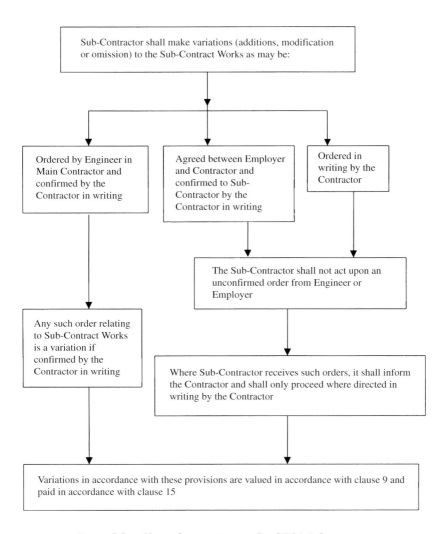

Figure 5.3.   Clause 8: variations under CECA Sub-contract.

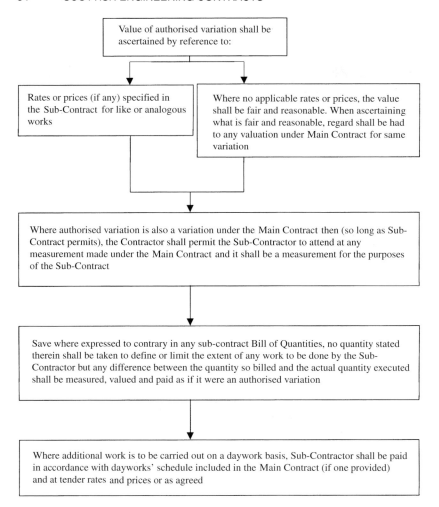

Figure 5.4.   Clause 9: valuation of variations under CECA Sub-contract.

No price agreed

Quantum meruit and the Scottish Scheme

In the absence of agreement on price or a mechanism for establishing a price, it may well be that no contract will be held to have come into existence.[55] In many instances, however, the courts have intervened to hold that payment is due for work which one party has carried out for another and to hold that, in fact, there is an 'implied contract' in place.[56] The basis for payment in such circumstances has been held to be payment *quantum meruit* – in other words, payment of a reasonable sum in return for the work which has been carried out.

There is an important conceptual point which must be borne in mind when considering if payment should be made on the basis of *quantum meruit*. For *quantum meruit* to apply, a contract (whether express or implied) must exist.[57] If a contract does not exist, then payment may instead be pursued on the basis of *quantum lucratus*, which is a remedy based in the Scots law of recompense, and not the law of contract. *Quantum lucratus* is considered further below. If, for example, work is carried out by one party while the parties are still discussing – and have not reached consensus on – price, a court may hold that there is an implied contract and that payment is due on the basis of *quantum meruit*.[58] Preparatory works (which are not carried out speculatively) carried out in advance of the main contract may fall to be paid for on the basis of *quantum meruit*. For example, an architect was found entitled to claim a reasonable sum for preliminary drawings prepared by him in the hope of winning a commission.[59] The court found in this case that there was an implied contract to pay.

To succeed with a claim in respect of an implied contract, it is important that the party seeking payment should be able to prove that the employer did actually intend to contract for the additional work, or that the employer so conducted himself as to give the contractor a reasonable belief that a contract did exist. If a contractor carries out work without authority or instruction and the employer has not given his consent to the work being done, then there may be no contract and, therefore, no requirement for the employer to pay.[60]

Payment *quantum meruit* cannot be claimed in addition to, or in combination with, the payment of the original contract price. Furthermore, a claim based on *quantum meruit* will not arise simply because work proved to be more complex or more difficult to execute than was anticipated at the time of tender. It has been established, however, that if a party to a contract is in material breach of contract such as to entitle the other party to rescind, then the contract can be brought to an end and, if the party choosing to rescind so elects, a claim made for payment *quantum meruit*.[61] Such an election must be made as an alternative to a claim for damages.

How much is 'a reasonable sum' for the purposes of a *quantum meruit* claim? There is no definitive description of what is a reasonable sum. The meaning of this phrase will depend on the nature of the work involved. If there are established customary rates for the type of work involved, these could be referred to in ascertaining what is reasonable. Tables of professional fees can be looked at if the work involved the employment of professionals, as could rates or prices agreed upon between the parties in abortive negotiations or earlier contracts between the parties in which rates or prices were agreed in respect of similar work. The rates and prices deemed reasonable by expert witnesses familiar with the particular type of work may also be persuasive, as would rates and prices contained in trade publications.

Prior to the coming into force of the Act payment for alterations or additions to the contract scope of works[62] instructed by an employer had in certain circumstances been held to be due on the basis of *quantum meruit*.[63] It is submitted that if the contract is one to which the Act applies, the absence of a mechanism to determine the value of such altered or additional work should not lead to payment *quantum meruit*, but, instead, the application of the Scottish Scheme. Where a construction contract fails to provide an adequate mechanism for determining what payments become due, paragraph 2 of Part II of the Scottish Scheme should apply. The Scottish Scheme is considered briefly elsewhere in this chapter, but it allows for payment of, among other things, an amount equal to the 'value of any work'. The 'value of work' is defined at paragraph 12 of Part II as '... an amount determined in accordance with the construction contract under which the work is performed, or where the contract contains no such provision, the cost of any work performed in accordance with that contract, together with an amount equal to any overhead or profit included in the contract price'.

It is submitted that 'the work' contemplates not only work carried out pursuant to the original work scope, but also works which are additional to or alterations of the original work scope. Variations to the scope of work would therefore be payable on the 'cost plus' basis outlined in paragraph 2 of Part II of the Scottish Scheme.

Quantum lucratus

Payment *quantum lucratus* may be made if one party has been enriched by services rendered by another and where payment of the party rendering the services would be equitable. The owner of land upon which construction works have been carried out or a structure erected will often (provided he does not insist on removal of the works) be taken to have benefited from – or be enriched by – such works. As has previously been noted, a claim for payment *quantum lucratus* cannot be prosecuted if a contract exists for the work in question.[64] Moreover, if any other remedy exists (such as, for example, one in the law of delict) a claim *quantum lucratus* will not be possible. A *quantum lucratus* claim is very much a 'last resort' for payment. The courts have also held that the party seeking to make the claims must have incurred a loss such as, for example, the actual cost of the work and must not have:

(a)   carried the work out gratuitously, i.e. without any intention that payment be made for the work; and
(b)   carried the work out for his own benefit.

The use of *quantum lucratus* as a basis for making claims for payment is relatively unusual. The courts have been reluctant to hold that where a significant amount of construction work has been carried out there is no express or implied *contractual* right to payment. The availability of this 'last port of call' should not, however, be forgotten if the pursuit of a claim on a contractual basis is likely to prove problematic.

'Set-off' – retention and compensation

The term 'set-off' is commonly used in the construction industry to refer to situations where one party withholds or makes a deduction from payment due to the other party to a contract because it considers it has a legal entitlement to do so. Care must be taken, however, with the legal basis for such a step. It is always helpful, and frequently important, to analyse precisely the basis for such deduction or withholding.

In Scots law, there are two main legal remedies applicable to the withholding of payment. These are:

- compensation (or 'true' set-off)
- retention.

Compensation

In simple terms, compensation allows a 'liquid debt' owed by party A to party B to be 'set off' against a liquid debt owed by party B to party A. The effect of such set-off is the extinction, either partially or completely, of the debts. The obligation to pay is not postponed or suspended (see Retention, below), but eliminated. The source of compensation in Scots law is the Compensation Act 1592.

Compensation is not, however, easy to operate. In order for it to be applied there must be two *liquid* debts. A liquid debt is a debt which is capable of immediate ascertainment, fixed in amount and payable immediately and not contingent on the occurrence of a future event. It would not be possible, for example, for party A to seek to extinguish a liquid debt presently due to party B by relying on a debt owed to it by party B which will only fall due at a future date.

As is discussed below, a claim for damages arising from a breach of contract would not be classified as a liquid debt but, instead, an *illiquid* debt or claim. Examples of liquid debts include a sum certified for payment and an undisputed invoice for the sale of goods.

Retention

Retention is an equitable remedy in Scots law founded on the principle of 'mutuality of contractual obligations'.[65] What does this mean?

At its most basic level, a contract is made up of groups of obligations and counter obligations. The most obvious example of this concept (and one of the most relevant in the context of engineering contracts) is the obligation to pay a party in return for that party's performance and execution of work in accordance with all the express and implied terms of a contract.

If, therefore, a party breaches its contract by, for example, failing to complete an element of the contract works in accordance with the terms of the contract, the employer may wish to retain a payment falling due to the contractor (or a portion of it) until the sum due to the contractor in damages for the defective work is established. Such an approach would be legitimate provided that the contract did not expressly exclude this right, but would not be appropriate if the sum due arose from a separate contract from the contract which was breached. In other words, retention is not – at least at common law – available on a 'cross-contract' basis. It is possible to adopt a contract condition which makes retention (or a bespoke contractual equivalent) possible between separate contracts.

Care should be taken, however, to ensure that if sums are to be retained from a payment certificate the breach of contract relied upon has occurred prior to the date upon which payment of the certified sum should be made in terms of the contract. The court in the case of *Redpath Dorman Long* v. *Cummins Engine Co. Ltd* considered this point and held that a claim for losses arising under a contract (as a result of its breach by *Redpath*) must be 'contemporaneous' with the corresponding obligation to pay sums certified under the contract.[66]

In the *Redpath* case the Defenders had withheld payment of sums certified in five interim architect's certificates. The court considered that it would be necessary to look at when the alleged breaches of contract took place and compare these occurrences with the dates upon which payment under the certificates fell to be made (in this case 21 days after the issue of each certificate). The case of *Redpath* was later approved by the House of Lords in *Bank of East Asia Limited* v. *Scottish Enterprise and Another.*[67] It was held in that case that in a contract to be performed in stages the 'counter-obligation' for payment of a stage of work was the completion of work for that stage in accordance with the contract. It followed that retention might be operated in respect of corresponding obligations which fell due to be performed at the same time, but that it has no relevance to an obligation which had *previously* been performed. Accordingly, a party could not withhold payment for work done on the basis of a failure to complete works in accordance with the contract if that failure had occurred *after* the date upon which the payment in question fell to be made. It should also be noted that the amount of payment to be retained should not exceed the amount of the paying party's claim.[68]

A withholding notice would also of course be required where sums are to be retained from a payment which is otherwise due to a party under a contract. It will obviously be important that the notice specifies the date when the breach of contract relied upon occurred, and relates that breach to the date when the payment being withheld fell to be made.

Retention is distinguishable from compensation in that it does not extinguish a debt once and for all. The application of retention merely postpones payment until the 'illiquid claim' (for example, the cost of rectifying defective works) is finally and definitively quantified. Frequently, a court's decree as to the amount of loss incurred as a consequence of a breach of contract will transform an illiquid claim for damages into a liquid debt. Retention is often combined with a counterclaim for damages which may, in turn, eventually produce a court decree for a specific amount. The situation may arise, therefore, where a court will hold that a party's claim under the contract for payment of a particular sum is valid, but also that a counterclaim for another sum should be granted. In these circumstances the damages established by the court as due in respect of the counterclaim would fall to be 'set off' against the sum due under the principal action for payment.[69]

Contract conditions very often provide specific mechanisms for deduction and withholding of sums where, for example, the payee has breached its contract and the paying party has suffered loss as a consequence of this. Clearly such clauses are desirable for a paying party as they can more easily be referred to and relied upon in a notice of withholding than the common-law remedy of retention. If such a clause is relied upon it should be specifically described in the relevant withholding notice.

If a party owed money under a contract becomes insolvent it may, upon the application of the Scots law principle of 'balancing of accounts', be possible for the debtor to retain payment on the basis that it has an illiquid claim (for example, in relation to losses incurred because of defective work) which arises under a separate contract. The normal prohibition on cross-contract retention is relaxed in the context of insolvency. Detailed consideration of this issue is outwith the scope of this book, but caution should be exercised when considering a demand for payment from, for example, the liquidator of a company if there is also a claim which could be asserted against the company in liquidation. Advice should be sought as to the appropriate approach in such circumstances.

Notes

[1] Sections 109–113 of Part II of the Act.

[2] *Readdie* v. *Miller* (1841) 3D 488; *Muldoon* v. *Pringle* (1882) 9R 915; *Ramsay & Son* v. *Brand* (1898) 25R 1212.

[3] *Supra cit.*

[4] For examples of how the courts have approached this issue, see the cases of *William Steel* v. *R L Young* 1907 SC 360; *Speirs Ltd* v. *Peterson* 1924 SC 428; and *Forrest* v. *Scottish County Investment Co.* 1916 SC (HL) 28.

[5] *Richardson* v. *Dumfriesshire Road Trustees* (1890) 17R 805.

[6] *Duncanson* v. *Scottish County Investments Co. Ltd* 1915 SC 1106.

[7] Section 109(1).

[8] NB: this provision does not apply to contracts of less than 45 days in duration – see s 109(1) of the Act.

[9] *Seaton Brick and Tile Company Ltd* v. *Mitchell* (1900) 2F 550; *Brooker-Simpson Ltd* v. *Duncan Logan (Builders) Ltd* 1969 SLT 304.

[10] Section 109(3).

[11] 2001 GWD 26–1001.

[12] 2001 SCLR 935; (2000) BLR 516.

[13] The subject of jurisdiction and the enforceability of adjudicators' decisions is covered in more detail in Chapter 10.

[14] Part II of the Scottish Scheme, para 9.

[15] Paragraph 10 of Part II of the Scottish Scheme.

[16] *Supra cit.*

[17] See *Clark Contracts Ltd* v. *The Burrell Co. (Construction Management) Ltd*, 2002 GWD 14 462.

[18] See the case of *Muir Construction Ltd* v. *Hambly Ltd* 1990 SLT 830 where Lord Prosser held that precise words in carefully constructed provisions were intended by the parties to have a precise effect in carefully structured procedures (in the context of determination). If a withholding notice is issued by a party other than one authorised to do so under the notice may not be regarded as valid. But see, by way of contrast, comments by Judge Bowsher in the case of *Discarn Project Services Limited* v. *Opecprime Development Limited* (2000) BLR 402.

[19] In the case of *Strathmore Building Services* v. *Greig* 2000 SLT 815 it was held that an effective section 111 notice did require to be in writing and that a telephone message referring to earlier correspondence was insufficient. It was also held in this case that a letter which suggested payment would be withheld that had been issued prior to an application for payment would not constitute

a valid withholding notice. The court held that section 111 envisaged a notice in response to an application for payment.

[20] See cases of *VHA Construction plc* v. *RBSTB Trust Company Limited* (2000) BLR 187 and *Northern Developments (Cumbria) Limited* v. *J & J Nichol* (2000) BLR 158. Also see *SL Timber Systems Limited* v. *Carillion Construction Limited*. Compare with *The Construction Centre Group Limited* v. *The Highland Council* 2002 GWD 27–932. See, however, *Parson Plastics (Research and Development) Ltd* v. *Purac Ltd*, Court of Appeal 12 April 2002 where it was found that a counterclaim could be 'set-off' against an adjudicator's decision even in the absence of a withholding notice. Care should be taken with this case as (i) the contract was not subject to the Act and (ii) there was a specific clause which made the requirement to issue a withholding notice subordinate to Purac's common law right of set-off.

[21] See Chapters 8 and 9 for further commentary on repudiation.

[22] Section 112(2).

[23] Section 112(3).

[24] See Chapter 6 for further commentary on this issue.

[25] See the definition in para 12 of 'relevant construction contract', and by extension 'construction contract' as referred to in paras 6 and 7.

[26] Clause 60(1).

[27] The sum to be stated in the certificate is to be exclusive of VAT. The responsibility for establishing the VAT element and making payment of this belongs to the employer.

[28] *Royal Borough of Kingston upon Thames* v. *AMEC Civil Engineering* (1993) 35 Con LR 39.

[29] *Keating*, 7th edition, para 20–260.

[30] *Enco Civil Engineering* v. *Zeus International* (1991) 56 BLR 43.

[31] See para 20–286 of *Keating*, 6th edition.

[32] The Term Version ICE Conditions of Contract (published 19 September 2002) does not include a retention clause, a position which may be welcomed by many contractors and possibly reflected in future editions of standard Forms of Contract.

[33] See clause 60(6)(a)–(b).

[34] See clause 60(6)(e).

[35] See clause 15(3)(a).

[36] (1991) 56 BLR 43.

[37] See for example, *Taymech Limited* v. *Trafalgar House Construction (Regions) Limited* 1995 SLT 1003.

[38] The Scottish Scheme, Part II, para 9.

[39] Section 113(1) of the Act.

[40] Clause 15(5)(a) of the CECA Sub-contract.

[41] Again, the question arises: 'later then when'?

[42] See commentary on clause 15(3)(a) for analysis as to what the 'final date' for payment is.

[43] 2000 SCLR 1111.

[44] See Chapter 5.

[45] See *Hall & Tawse* v. *Strathclyde Regional Council* 1990 SLT 771.

[46] See Scott Johnston (1999), *Debts and interest in the construction industry*, Thomas Telford.

[47] Section 2(1)–(3) Late Payment of Commercial Debts (Interest) Act 1998.

[48] Section 2(4) Late Payment of Commercial Debts (Interest) Act 1998.

[49] The Late Payment of Commercial Debts (Interest) Act 1998 (Commencement No. 1) Order 1998. Small businesses were designed as, broadly speaking, those businesses with less than 50 employees.

[50] See *The Late Payment of Commercial Debts (Scotland) Regulations 2002* and *The Late Payment of Commercial Debts (Interest) Act 1998 (Commencement No. 6) (Scotland) Order 2002*. It should also be noted that calculation of the relevant interest rate has also been simplified. Six-month interest rate 'reference periods' have been created. If a debt falls due within a given 6-month period the relevant rate of interest will be the Bank of England interest rate applicable at the beginning of that period.

[51] An increase or decrease in the quantities set out in incorporated bills will constitute a variation.

[52] (1858) 3H&N 844.

[53] *English Industrial Estates* v. *Kier* (1991) 56 BLR 93.

[54] The Engineer may consider that additional works be carried out on a dayworks basis, and instruct the same. See clause 52(5).

[55] See Chapter 2.

[56] See, for example, the English Court of Appeal decision in *ACT Construction Limited* v. *E. Clarke & Sons (Coaches) Limited*, Court of Appeal, 16 July 2002 (unreported).

[57] *Alexander Hall & Son (Builders) Ltd* v. *Strathclyde Regional Council* 1989 GWD 9–401.

[58] *Avintair Limited* v. *Ryder Airline Services Limited* 1994 SLT 613.

[59] *Robert Allan and Partners* v. *McKinstry* 1995 SLT (Sh Ct) 63.

[60] *Murray* v. *Fairlie Yacht Ship* 1975 SLT (Sh Ct) 62.

[61] See the cases of *Boyd & Forrest* v. *Glasgow & South Western Railway Company* 1915 SC(HL) 20 and *ERDC Construction Limited* v. *H M Love & Co.* 1995 SLT 254.

[62] More commonly referred to as 'variations'.

[63] See for example *Taylor* v. *Andrew Weatherford* 1991 GWD 28–1647.

[64] A claim *quantum lucratus* may be appropriate if the contract purportedly entered into is void – see *Lawrence Building Co. Ltd* v. *Lanark County Council* 1978 SC 30; or where the agreement entered into cannot be proved – see *Mackay* v. *Rodger* 1907 15 SLT 42.

[65] See *Johnston* v. *Robertson* (1861) 23 D 646.

[66] 1982 SLT 489.

[67] 1997 SLT 1213.

[68] *Dick & Stevenson* v. *Woodside Iron & Steel Co.* 1888 16 R 242.

[69] See *Ballantyne* v. *East of Scotland Farmers Ltd* 1970 SLT (Notes) 50 for an example of this in practice.

6. Commencement, completion and delays

Contractual works periods, commencement and possession

Amongst the essential ingredients of any construction or engineering contract – required in the very formation of the contract itself – are likely to be the scope of work to be undertaken under the contract, the price to be paid to the contractor and the time in which the works must be undertaken. The time element of any construction or engineering contract is important in creating certainty for both parties to the contract. The contractor will want to know precisely when he has to mobilise resources (and in particular labour), when essential plant and equipment required for the execution of the works should be available at site, and, critically, the outside time limit in which he has to programme the contract works. For the employer, he must know the date by which he is required to provide the contractor with possession of the site. There may also be many reasons why he has to have certainty as to the date on which he can expect to take over the completed site – for example, a developer may have entered into a contract for the sale or lease of the development, a school may require to be ready by the commencement of a new school term, or a pipeline may require to come on stream at a particular date.

It is therefore vital that a contract sets out clearly the time at which a contractor may commence his works, and the period within which he has to execute and complete those works. Standard forms of contract deal with this feature of a contract in different ways and often specify a particular date at which completion is due in an appendix to the contract. Civil engineering forms, on the other hand, usually specify a period for completion and determine the completion date by reference to the commencement date and a specified period. Clause 41(1) of the ICE 7th Conditions, for example, defines the 'Works Commencement Date' as:

(a) the date specified in the Appendix to the Form of Tender or if no date is specified

(b) a date between 14 and 28 days of the award of the Contract to be notified to the contractor by the Engineer in writing or

(c) such other date as may be agreed between the parties.

Clause 43 then requires that the works shall be completed '. . . within the time stated in the appendix to the Form of Tender] . . . calculated from the Works Commencement Date'.

The CECA Sub-contract (clause 6(1)) provides that the sub-contractor must commence the sub-contract works within ten days (or such other period as may be agreed in writing) of receipt of the contractor's written instructions to do so, and that it shall complete the sub-contract works within the period for completion specified in the schedule to the sub-contract form.

NEC, on the other hand, follows the conventional building contract approach by providing at clause 30.1 that:

> The **Contractor** does not start work on the Site until the first **possession date** and does the work so that Completion is on or before the Completion Date.

The 'Completion Date' is defined, arguably rather unhelpfully, as '... the **completion date** unless later changed in accordance with this contract' (clause 22.2(12)). The terms printed in bold are identified in the Contract Data. The contractor must therefore start and complete the contract works between a defined possession date and a defined completion date.

It can be seen that a difference in terminology exists between 'commencement' and 'possession' of the site. Under the ICE 7th Conditions clause 41(2), the contractor is under an obligation to start the Works 'on or as soon as is reasonably practicable after the Works Commencement Date'. The assumption is that possession of the whole of the site together with necessary access to it will be given to the contractor by the employer on the Works Commencement Date (clause 42(2)). If the employer cannot give possession and appropriate access on the agreed date it will be in breach of its contractual obligation to do so under clause 42(2) of the ICE 7th Conditions. Clause 42(1) also envisages provision in the Contract for, amongst other things,:

(a) the extent of portions of the Site of which the contractor is to be given possession from time to time[1]

(b) the order in which such portions of the Site shall be made available to the contractor

(c) the availability and the nature of the access which is to be provided by the Employer . . .

It will be important, therefore, for any contractor to assess carefully not only the contractual commencement date and period for completion of the works (or the defined works completion date) but also the extent of his right of access to the site and the time at which he is to be given possession of the site (in whole or in part). The site boundaries must be clearly and comprehensibly described in the contract documents.

The essence of time

A question often encountered in the industry is whether time for completion of works can be said to be so critical that it is 'of the essence' or, in other words, that no excuse will permit completion beyond the specified date or period in the contract. Were this to be the case, and the contractor failed in its obligation to complete the works by the specified date, it is likely that the employer would be able to treat the contractor as having repudiated the contract, thus allowing the employer to accept the repudiation and terminate the contract (although it is highly unlikely that, by the time the completion date under a contract was reached and breached, it would benefit the employer to terminate the contractor's employment and bring on a new contractor to complete the job). The contract would have to make quite clear that time was to be regarded as of the essence, and in most engineering contracts, this is unlikely to be the case, especially where other provisions dictate against it (for example, where the contract contains provision for the awarding of extensions of time and the imposition of liquidated damages).

The programme

It is usual for building and engineering contracts to oblige the contractor to produce a programme describing how it intends to progress and complete its works within the time period allowed under the contract. It is a popular misconception that the contract programme is, generally, a contract document. Under most standard forms it is not, and cannot be if the (already established) contract requires its production. Clause 14 of the ICE 7th Conditions requires the contractor within 21 days after the award of the Contract to submit to the engineer for his acceptance a programme 'showing the order in which he proposes to carry out the Works'. The engineer is given an opportunity either to accept or reject the programme, or to request the contractor to supply further information to clarify or substantiate the programme or to satisfy the engineer as to its reasonableness. If the engineer does none of this, he is deemed to have accepted the contractor's programme.

The procedure to be followed to agree the programme can be summarised as shown in Figure 6.1.

As the contract programme will, generally, not be a contract document, failure to progress the works in accordance with the programme does not in itself amount to a breach of contract by the contractor.[10] The purpose of the programme is to provide a tool by which to measure rates of progress during the contract works for the efficient and smooth-running execution of the works. It will, ultimately, also become a critical tool in establishing the entitlements of the employer or the contractor arising out of any delay to the contract works. Under clause 14(4) of ICE 7th Conditions the engineer, if at any time concerned that the actual progress of the work does not conform to the accepted programme, shall be entitled to require the contractor to produce a revised programme showing such modifications to the original programme as may be necessary to ensure completion of the works within the contractual time for completion.

It should also be borne in mind that clause 13(2) of the ICE 7th Conditions states that the mode, manner and *speed* of construction of the works are to be of a kind and conducted in a manner acceptable to the engineer.

Programming under NEC takes on an added importance, as the scheme under that contract relies on the existence of an accepted programme. In a similar way to the ICE 7th Conditions, clause 31 of NEC provides for the contractor to submit a programme to the project manager for acceptance within a period stated in the contract data. In such circumstances, the contract programme will have the same contractual effect as that under the ICE 7th Conditions. However, clause 31 also envisages the possibility of the programme under NEC already being identified in the contract data and thus, presumably, having been agreed

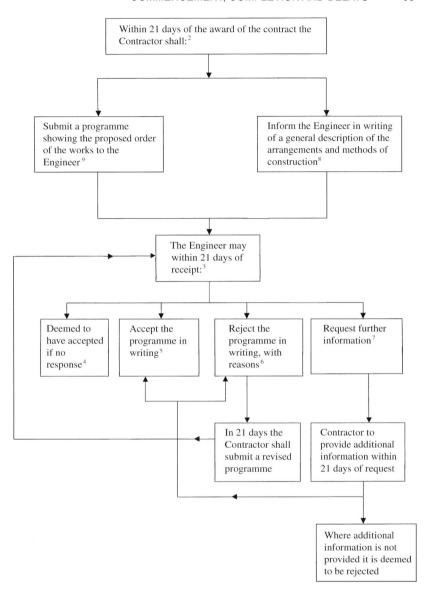

Figure 6.1.   The procedure to be followed to agree the programme of works.

prior to the date of the contract. Indeed, the definition section of NEC defines the accepted programme as 'the programme identified in the Contract Data or . . . the latest programme accepted by the Project Manager'.

In certain circumstances, therefore, it seems that the programme being used under an NEC contract may well have the status of a contract document. Unlike the position under the ICE 7th Conditions, there is no provision deeming the project manager to have accepted the programme in circumstances where he does not expressly do so or does not expressly reject the programme tendered by the contractor. The likelihood of this event occurring is, perhaps, slight given that such an event may constitute a 'compensation event' for the purposes of clause 60 of NEC in relation to which the contractor may be entitled to compensation and additional time (see below). In such circumstances, the employer may well be deemed to have accepted the programme where the contractor has been working to the programme without any dissension from the employer.

Early completion

The principal obligation on the contractor is to complete the works within the time allotted under the contract and, subject to that restriction:

> . . . the general principle applicable to building and engineering contracts, [is] that in the absence of any indication to the contrary, a contractor is entitled to plan and perform the work as he pleases . . .[11]

This latitude does not, however, entitle a contractor to assert a claim against the employer in circumstances in which he finishes within the overall time period allowed under the contract, but later than the period in which he had programmed the works to complete. Certainly, the contractor is entitled (subject only to any requirements for acceptance of his programme under the applicable contract provisions) to programme his works to finish earlier than the contractual completion date. However, the obligation on the employer remains simply to allow the contractor to complete the works within the original contract period. The contractor's programme does not impose any obligation on the employer to assist the contractor to complete in accordance with that programme.

In *Glenlion Construction Limited* v. *The Guinness Trust*[12] the contract completion period was 104 weeks, and the contractor submitted a programme showing completion of the works in 101 weeks. The case came to the courts on appeal from an arbitration, and the Judge confirmed that the contractor was entitled to complete the works earlier than the contract completion date, whether or not his programme in fact showed an earlier completion date, and whether or not the contractor was under an obligation under the contract to produce a programme. However, in answer to the question:

> Whether there was an implied term of the contract between the Applicant and the Respondent that, if and in so far as the programme showed a completion date before the date for completion by the employer by himself, his servants or agents should so perform the said agreement as to enable the contractor to carry out the works in accordance with the programme and to complete the works on the said completion date . . .

the Judge ruled that:

> . . . the answer . . . must be 'no'. It is not suggested by [the contractor] that they were both entitled and obliged to finish by the earlier completion date.

If there is such an implied term it imposed an obligation on [the employer] but none on [the contractor]. It is unclear how the variation provisions would have applied. Condition 23 operates, if at all, in relation to the date for completion stated in the appendix. A fair and reasonable extension of time for completion of the works beyond the date of completion stated in the appendix might be an unfair and unreasonable extension from an earlier date.

It is not immediately apparent why it is reasonable or equitable that a unilateral absolute obligation should be placed on an employer.

The Judge then proceeded to quote from the 10th Edition of *Hudson's Building and Engineering Contracts* as follows:

In regard to claims based on delay, litigious contractors frequently supply to architects or engineers at an early stage in the work highly optimistic programmes showing completion a considerable time ahead of the contractual date. These documents are then used: (a) to justify allegations that the information or possession has been supplied late by the architect or engineer; and (b) to increase the alleged period of delay, or to make a delay claim possible where the contract completion date has not in the event been extended.

In short, therefore, the only real effect of a programme showing a completion date earlier that the contractual completion date is to build 'float' into the programme, which then becomes important in the assessment of extensions of time and/or liquidated damages (see below).

It is, of course, equally possible for the employer, for whatever reason during the course of the contract, to request the contractor to complete earlier than the contractual completion date (to accelerate). By so doing, the employer is, effectively, seeking to amend the terms of the contract, and it is likely that the contractor's consent would be required. Thus, for example, clause 46(3) of ICE 7th Conditions provides as follows:

If the contractor is requested by the employer or the engineer to complete the works . . . within a revised time being less than the time or extended time for completion prescribed by clauses 43 and 44 as appropriate and the contractor agrees so to do then any special terms and conditions of payment shall be agreed between the contractor and employer before any such action is taken.

It can therefore be seen that a contractor would, if appropriate, be entitled to seek recompense from his employer in the event that he agreed to work to an earlier completion date.

If, however, the engineer forms the view that for any reason 'which does not entitle the contractor to an extension of time' the rate of progress of the works or any section of the works is too slow to ensure the contractual completion date is achieved the engineer can send a written notice to the contractor insisting that progress be accelerated (clause 46(1) of the ICE 7th Conditions). In such circumstances the contractor will not be entitled to seek any additional payment.

Similarly, clause 36.2 of NEC envisages opportunity for the contractor to refuse to comply with any instructions issued by the project manager, for the contractor to submit a quotation for 'an acceleration to achieve Completion before the Completion Date'.

Substantial completion and dealing with time over-run

Time provisions in an engineering contract are crucial and the consequences of over-run can be significant. What will constitute over-run? The obligation under ICE 7[13] Conditions is for the works to be 'substantially completed in accordance with the Contract' within the contractual period. Under the CECA Sub-contract the obligation[14] is to '. . . complete the Sub-Contract Works which shall satisfactorily pass any performance test or other final test that may be prescribed by the Sub-Contract or by Statute within the Period for Completion . . .'.

What constitutes substantial completion?

The equivalent standard in building contracts is that the works should reach 'practical' completion. There is no definitive description from case-law of what has to be satisfied to achieve practical/substantial completion, although the existence of patent defects will preclude certification thereof. However, as long as the owner can enter into occupation, the existence of minor or trivial defects will not preclude the achievement of substantial completion. This is perhaps even more likely to be the case where there is provision in the contract for a defects liability period. Thus the works will be substantially complete if 'finished' or 'done' in the usual sense of those words.[15] Moreover, it might also be relevant to take into account the nature of any defects that do exist and the difference between the cost of fixing such defects and the contract price.[16] It is unlikely that the word 'substantial' adds much to the principal 'completion' obligation. In each case the proper definition of the term will be a matter of interpretation of the particular contract, and a question of fact. 'Substantial' and 'practical' completion might be described as being like elephants – difficult to describe but generally recognisable when accosted.

Under NEC, 'completion' is described as:

. . . when the contractor has

- done all the work which the Works Information states he is to do by the Completion Date and
- corrected notified Defects which would have prevented the employer from using the works.

Over-run

The risk of over-run is one of many risks that must be allocated between the parties to the engineering contract. Time over-run can, essentially, arise from:

- default by the contractor
- default by the employer
- circumstances arising which are neither the responsibility of the contractor or the employer (for example, weather, third-party delay (for example by building control or planning authorities) or political forces).

The manner in which such risk allocation is dealt with, and in particular in the standard form contracts, is dealt with below.

Liquidated damages

Definition

Where the contractor, without any valid contractual excuse, delays the contract works (that is, does not complete the works within the contractual period) he will be in breach of contract. Subject to the terms of the contract, the employer would be entitled to pursue a claim against the contractor for his unliquidated (common law) damages.[17] In order to avoid the need to undertake such an exercise, the parties will often agree, before execution of the contract, what the employer's losses are likely to be in the event of a delay to the contract, and for provision to be made within the terms of the contract for automatic payment of such damages (generally referred to as 'liquidated damages') in the event of delay. The benefit to the employer of such a scheme is that he does not then have to prove his actual losses (which may be greater or less than the stipulated liquidated damages, in which case the employer will either be out of pocket or likely to receive a 'windfall'). In one sense, the employer's right to liquidated damages is simply derivative of the general rule on recoverability of damages, as suggested by the Court in *Temloc* v. *Errill*:[18]

> The damages payable in respect of late completion of the works are one head of the general damages which may be recovered by an employer for the contractor's breach of a building contract. Their character is not in any way altered according to whether the rate at which they are payable is agreed by the parties in advance, so that they become liquidated, or determined by the court after breach, so that they remain unliquidated until so determined.

Distinguished from penalties

In order to be enforceable, the sum stipulated in the contract by way of liquidated damages must constitute a genuine pre-estimate of the employer's loss rather than a 'penalty', the intention of which is to ensure timeous completion of the contract under threat of 'punishment' for delay. Lord Dunedin gave the definitive statement of the law in this area in the House of Lords decision in *Dunlop Pneumatic Tyre Company* v. *New Garage and Motor Company Limited*.[19] The key elements of his decision can be summarised as follows:

1. The description of the sum stipulated in the contract as 'liquidated damages' or a 'penalty' is not conclusive. The court must look at the

substance of whether the payment stipulated is, in truth, a penalty or liquidated damages.

2. A penalty is a payment of money stipulated '*in terrorem*' of the defaulting party, whereas the essence of liquidated damages is a genuine covenanted pre-estimate of damage. This principle was confirmed in the case of *City Inn Limited* v. *Shepherd Construction Limited*.[20]

3. The question as to whether a sum stipulated is a penalty or liquidated damages will be answered by construction of the particular contract on a case by case basis, judged as at the time of making the contract and not as at the time of the breach.

4. By way of a guide to construction:

    4.1. the sum will be held to be a penalty if 'extravagant and unconscionable in amount' as compared to the greatest loss that could conceivably be proved to have followed from the breach

    4.2. there will be a *presumption* that the stipulated sum is a penalty when a single sum is made payable by way of compensation on the occurrence of one or more events, some of which may result in serious and others in more trifling damage

    4.3. the sum stipulated can be construed as a genuine pre-estimate of damage even where the consequences of the breach (in this case delayed completion) are such as to make precise pre-estimation almost an impossibility.[21]

The ICE 7th Conditions clause 47(1)(a) attempt to put beyond doubt the question of whether the sum stipulated is, in truth, a penalty or, properly so-called 'liquidated damages' by providing that:

> . . . the Form of Tender shall include a sum which represents the employer's genuine pre-estimate (expressed per week or per day as the case may be) of the damages likely to be suffered by him if the whole of the works is not substantially completed within [the contractual period for completion].

Clause 47(3) further stipulates that:

> All sums payable by the contractor to the Employer pursuant to this Clause shall be paid as liquidated damages for delay and not as a penalty.

On the basis of Lord Dunedin's remarks as summarised above, however, it is unlikely that this provision will be of any particular significance in aiding in the construction of the contract.

Clause 47 of the ICE 7th Conditions provides that liquidated damages, where applicable, shall either be paid 'forthwith' by the contractor to the employer or alternatively shall be deducted from any amounts due by the employer to the contractor (clause 47(5)). In order to comply with the Act (as reflected in clause 60(10) of the ICE 7th Conditions), any attempt by the employer to set off against a certificate any amount purportedly payable by way of liquidated damages must be preceded by a Notice of Intention to Withhold Payment.

It is crucially important for the employer operating under the ICE 7th Conditions to ensure that the question of liquidated damages is properly addressed in the Appendix to the Form of Tender, as if no sum is inserted by way of liquidated damages, or if the sum is stated to be 'nil', then '. . . to that extent damages shall not be payable' (clause 47(4)(b)). It is arguable that, in such circumstances, the employer is deprived of any right to claim damages, whether liquidated or unliquidated, in the event of the contractor completing late.

By virtue of the 'back to back' and indemnity provisions of clauses 3(2) and (3) of the CECA Sub-contract, a sub-contractor operating on that standard form will be equally subject to liquidated damages:

> The Sub-contractor shall indemnify the contractor against every liability which the contractor may incur to any other person whatsoever and against all claims . . . made against or incurred by the contractor by reason of any breach by the Sub-contractor of the Sub-contract (clause 3(3)).

Under NEC (Option R), the contractor's liability to liquidated damages is, perhaps unsurprisingly for that form, stated in plainer language:

> The contractor pays delay damages at the rate stated in the Contract Data from the Completion Date for each day until the earlier of:
>
> - completion and
> - the date on which the employer takes over the works.

In May 1999 the Scottish Law Commission published Report on Penalty Clauses,[22] making various recommendations to reform the law on penalty clause through legislation. Such recommendations include

- that penalties which are not manifestly excessive should be enforceable even if they cannot be regarded as based on a genuine pre-estimate of loss
- that the enforceability of a penalty should be judged according to all the circumstances, including circumstances arising since the contract was entered into.

The Report's recommendations have not yet reached the statute book.

Acts preventing timeous completion

In the next section, Extension of time, the contractual mechanism for granting extensions of time will be considered, which, if operated, will, as the name suggests, extend the time in which the contractor has to complete the works, and reduce its liability to damages for late completion (whether unliquidated or liquidated). Such clauses are, in effect, the 'flip-side' of clauses providing for liquidated damages. However, where no such extension of time provisions exist to assist the contractor, his principal defence to the imposition of liquidated damages will be to demonstrate that he has been prevented by the employer from completing on time and that the employer should not be entitled to benefit from that act of prevention by subsequently receiving damages for late completion. It is sometimes suggested that an act of prevention by the employer will put time under the contract 'at large', as there is no provision allowing for the contract completion date to be extended as a result of the act of prevention. In effect, the expression 'time at large' can simply be equated to the invalidity of the liquidated damages provision caused by the act of prevention, with the employer then having to resort to proof of his unliquidated damages on the basis that the contract works would still have to be completed within a reasonable time.

In order to protect against any such defence by the contractor, the employer should ensure that provision is made for an extension of time to be granted to the contractor in circumstances in which the employer has prevented the contractor from progressing the works. A useful summary of the position is given by the Court of Appeal in *Peak Construction (Liverpool) Limited* v. *McKinney Foundations Limited*:[23]

> If the failure to complete on time is due to the fault of both the employer and the contractor, in my view, the [liquidated damages] clause does not bite. I cannot see how, in the ordinary course, the employer can insist on compliance with a condition if it is partly his own fault that it cannot be fulfilled . . . I consider that unless the contract expresses a contrary intention, the employer, in the circumstances postulated, is left to his ordinary remedy; that is to say, to recover such damages as he can prove flow from the contractor's breach.

> No doubt if the extension of time clause provided for a postponement of the completion date on account of delay caused by some breach or fault on the part of the employer, the position would be different. This would mean that the parties had intended that the employer could recover liquidated damages, notwithstanding that he was partly to blame for the failure to achieve the completion date. In such a case the architect would extend the date for completion, and the contractor would then be liable to pay liquidated damages for delay as from the extended completion date.

> The liquidated damages and extension of time clauses in printed forms of contract must be construed strictly *contra proferentem*.[24] If the employer wishes to recover liquidated damages for failure by the contractor to complete on time in spite of the fact that some of the delay is due to the employer's own fault or breach of contract, then the extension of time clause should provide, expressly or by necessary inference, for an extension on account of such fault or breach on the part of the employer.

Extension of time

As part of the risk allocation process, most standard form engineering contracts will allow for the time in which the works are to be completed to be extended in certain circumstances. It is, perhaps understandably, easy to jump to the conclusion that such provision is for the benefit of the contractor, by way of reducing his exposure to liquidated damages. However, in truth, the ability to grant extensions of time benefits the employer, first by being able to maintain the obligation on the contractor to complete within a specified time period, but also (as has been seen above) to ensure that an act of prevention by the employer does not invalidate the liquidated damages provisions.

Circumstances entitling extensions

Allocation of the risk of delay is treated differently under the various standard forms. Clause 44(1) of the ICE 7th Conditions allows the contractor to apply for an extension of time in the event of:

(a)   any variation
(b)   increased quantities
(c)   any cause of delay referred to in the Conditions
(d)   exceptional adverse weather conditions
(e)   any delay, impediment, prevention or default by the employer
(f)   other special circumstances of any kind whatsoever which may occur.

It will immediately be seen from item (c) that a trawl through the contract conditions may be required in order to identify occurrences which may justify an extension of time application (unlike, for example, in the JCT standard form of building contract, in which such events have been listed together for ease of reference). Such occurrences include:

- physical conditions (other than weather) not reasonably foreseeable by the contractor (clause 12)
- delay in the issue of drawings, specifications or instructions (clause 7(4))
- the issue of instructions from the engineer explaining or adjusting contract documents (clause 13(3))
- failure to give timely possession of the site (clause 42(3))
- delay caused by default by a nominated sub-contractor (clause 59(4)(f)).

The risk of any act of prevention by the employer invalidating the liquidated damages provisions is avoided by the widely drafted wording of items (e) and (f) in clause 44(1) which entitle the contractor to an extension of time in those circumstances.

In the CECA Sub-contract, the listing at clause 6(2) is more comprehensive (albeit dependent to a large extent on the terms of the main contract). It lists the bases for entitlements to an extension of time as:

(a)   . . . any circumstances or occurrence (other than a breach of this sub-contract by the sub-contractor) entitling the contractor to an extension of his time for completion of the main works under the main contract; or
(b)   . . . the ordering of any variation of the Sub-contract works to which paragraph (a) of this sub-clause does not apply; or
(c)   . . . any breach of this Sub-contract by the contractor.

Determination of the extension

Under ICE 7th Conditions, the engineer is obliged, upon application for an extension of time from the contractor (and may in the absence of any application) to 'make an assessment' of any delay suffered by the contractor which may entitle the contractor to an extension of time. The engineer is obliged, under clause 44(3), to grant an interim extension of time where the delay suffered 'fairly entitles' the contractor to an extension of time. He must make a similar assessment within 14 days after the due date or extended date for completion of the works, and, in accordance with clause 44(5) shall, within 28 days of the issue of the certificate of substantial completion, determine the overall extension of time (if any) to which the contractor may be entitled, subject to that extension of time being no less than any extension of time already granted on an interim basis.

Correspondingly, the CECA Sub-contract entitles the sub-contractor to an extension of time '... as may in all the circumstance [sic] be fair and reasonable' (clause 6(2)).

Under NEC, the assessment of any delay to the completion date is stated, simply, as:

> ... the length of time that, due to the compensation event, planned completion is later than planned Completion as shown on the Accepted Programme (clause 63.3).

Application procedure

It has been seen that the contractor (or sub-contractor as the case may be) may make an application for an extension of time. A question sometimes arises as to whether or not such application, in accordance with the various requirements in the contract, amounts to a *condition precedent* to the granting of an extension of time, failure to comply with which will undermine any right to any extension. Determination of this issue will depend on the construction of the particular contract on a case by case basis. Clause 44(1) of the ICE 7th Conditions requires the contractor 'within 28 days after the cause of any delay has arisen or as soon thereafter as is reasonable' to deliver to the engineer full and detailed particulars in justification of the period of extension claimed in order that the claim may be investigated at the time. However, it has already been noted that the engineer may, in the absence of any claim, make an assessment of the delay, and it may therefore be unlikely that the obligation on the contractor amounts to a condition precedent. This interpretation is consistent with the clear intention of clause 44(1)(e) and (f) (see above) to avoid the risk of acts of prevention invalidating the liquidated damages clause on the basis that they do not constitute sound grounds for an extension of time.

The CECA Sub-contract is, to the extent that an application is being made for an extension of time on the basis of circumstances entitling the contractor to an extension of time under the main contract, much clearer. Clause 6(2) of the CECA Sub-contract states:

> ... it shall be a condition precedent to the Sub-contractor's right to an extension of the Period for Completion that he shall have given written notice to the contractor of the circumstances or occurrence which is delaying him within fourteen days of such delay first occurring together with full and detailed particulars in justification of the period of extension claimed in order that the claim may be investigated at the time ...

NEC operates in an altogether different manner. Reference has already been made to the listing in the contract of 'compensation events' (at clause 60). In the event of a compensation event occurring, the contractor submits to the project manager, for agreement, a 'quotation' that, in accordance with clause 62.2, comprises '. . . proposed changes to the Prices and any delay to the Completion Date assessed by the contractor' arising out of the proposed method of dealing with the compensation event.

In certain circumstances, the project manager himself must assess the compensation event. In particular, if there is no accepted programme or the contractor has not submitted a revised programme for acceptance as required by NEC, the project manager must assess the compensation event '. . . using his own assessment of the programme for the remaining work . . . ' (clause 64.2).

Delay analysis

Assuming there is a dispute between the parties as to the correct extension of time to be granted to the contractor, on what basis is the assessment to be carried out by an adjudicator, arbitrator or court (as the case may be)? As has been suggested above, accurate records of the rate of progress and the events impacting on that rate of progress, and in particular the accurate revision and maintenance of an ongoing programme of the works, will be critical to the success of the contractor's attempts to prove its entitlement.

The starting point of any delay analysis will be the construction programme. The analysis will involve a determination of the impact of the employer's risk event on the critical path through the programme. The critical path has been defined as

> the sequence of activities which needs the longest total time to complete the project or an element thereof. A delayed progress of any activity on the critical path causes a delay to the completion of the project.[25]

There may be several critical paths through the construction programme, but it is the overriding critical path which leads to the contractual completion date with which this discussion is concerned.

An event for which the employer bears responsibility and risk may delay a particular construction activity but, unless that delay impacts upon the critical path there would be no entitlement (that is, it would not be 'fair and reasonable') to postpone the completion date.

There are many sophisticated approaches to delay analysis, but two are used more frequently than others, namely: (a) 'time impact analysis' (or 'time slice' analysis); and (b) the 'collapsed' as built analysis.

Time impact analysis   Time impact analysis requires, first and foremost, the base or master programme. Ideally, use will be made of the detailed comprehensive programme submitted at, or before, commencement of the works. However, it may be possible to recreate the base programme from contemporaneous documents. In any event, the programme 'logic' (that is, the sequence in which events are planned to follow previous events) and the anticipated durations of each activity will have to be validated, and the critical path identified. Progress of the relevant construction activities through-out their duration is then measured, and the effect of the employer's risk events measured on those relevant activities.

Collapsed as built analysis   The 'collapsed' as built analysis requires, as its starting point, the 'as built', or '**actual**' programme which records what took place, when, and for how long. The delay caused by the employer's risk events is then transposed onto the as built programme, the programme logic tested, and the as built programme 'shrunk' or 'collapsed' to try to arrive at the programme by which the contractor *would* have executed the works had he not sustained delay as a result of the employer's risk events.

A comprehensive and robust analysis of the effect of the relevant event upon the construction programme may be a complex and technical process. It demands an understanding of construction workflow and the sequencing of activities. However, the goal of the delay analysis is simple – to identify the date by which, starting from the date of possession, the contractor ought fairly and reasonably to have completed the works.[26]

That exercise might involve consideration of a number of difficult concepts, including, for example: (i) concurrent delay; (ii) 'float'; (iii) 'net' or 'gross' extensions of time; and (iv) global claims. These are reviewed below.

Concurrent delay   If the construction programme is delayed over a single period by two or more events and the responsibility for the delay can be attributed to both the contractor and the employer, is the contractor entitled to an extension of time?

In *Henry Boot Construction (UK) Ltd* v. *Malmaison Hotel (Manchester) Ltd*[27] it was agreed by the parties that, in these circumstances, the contractor would be entitled to an extension of time for the period by which the completion date was delayed *as a result of the employer's risk event*. That was so notwithstanding that there was a concurrent effect of a delay event *other* than an employer's risk event.

Although not expressed in that decision, the logic supporting that statement of principle might be that as the contractor has a responsibility to mitigate its delays, if it were *not* entitled to an extension of time because *it was itself* in delay at the time of an event for which the employer is responsible, the contractor would then effectively be compelled to accelerate to overcome the effects of the contractor delay *and* that for which the employer is responsible in order to avoid liquidated damages.

Although this chapter is not concerned with money, it should be noted that, whilst the contractor would, in the circumstances of concurrent delay described, be entitled to an extension of time (thus reducing its exposure to liquidated damages), it would not be entitled to recover any losses incurred as a result of such delay.

What if a contractor suffers a delay that does not entitle it to an extension of time and, during the period of that delay, an employer's risk event occurs that would *not* have delayed it if it was not already in delay? This question was considered in the case of *Royal Brompton Hospital* v. *Hammond & Others*.[28] In this case it was held that in order to determine whether an employer risk event can be truly held to be a cause of delay an analysis of the critical path and effect of the employer risk event would have to be undertaken. If by reason of the existing delay the employer risk event made no difference to the overall completion of the works, in such a situation the employer risk event would have no effect on the completion date. The court distinguished this situation from the situation in which '. . . as it were, the works are proceeding in a regular fashion and on programme, two things happen, either of which had they happened on their own, would have caused delay, and one is [an employer risk event] while the other is not'. The law in this area is evolving and some care should be taken with the application of the decision in the *Hammond* case.

'Float'   As has been described above, the contractor's programme might include 'float'. 'Float' can be described as the period allowed by the contractor in its master programme to complete any particular activity or the contract as a whole in excess of the period the contractor genuinely, and reasonably, anticipates will be required to complete.

There is an ongoing debate in the industry in relation to 'ownership' of such float. Is the contractor entitled to apply the float exclusively to periods of delay for which he is responsible or, for example, should the float be 'set off' against delays as they arise throughout the project, irrespective of the attribution of responsibility for those events?

Although there is no definitive statement on the question, some guidance is given in *Ascon Contracting Ltd* v. *Alfred McAlpine Construction Isle of Man Ltd*.[29] In that case His Honour Judge Hicks, QC, rejected the contention that: the 'benefits' of the float, and therefore the residual liability, fell to be allocated among the parties responsible for delay and that that allocation was entirely in the main contractor's gift as among sub-contractors, or as between them and the main contractor where the latter's own delay was in question. The case suggests that the float belongs to the party which uses it first.

'Net' or 'gross' analysis   If the contractor overshoots the completion date and, during his period of culpable delay, an employer's risk event occurs, does the extension of time arising as a result of that event serve to accelerate the *actual* date of completion (i.e. the gross analysis), or add to the (extended) completion date **only** the period of critical delay caused by the employer's risk event (i.e. the net analysis)?

In *Balfour Beatty Building Ltd* v. *Chestermount Properties Ltd*,[30] it was held that the net approach is correct. This may be also described as the 'dot-on' approach, whereby the critical delay caused by the new employer's risk event is 'dotted on' to the (extended) completion date. Employer's risk events in general, and variation instructions in particular, are to be treated according to the same principles, depending on whether they occur before or during a period of culpable delay.[31]

A contractor cannot therefore rely on an instruction after substantial completion (during his period of culpable delay) to obtain an extension of time up to the date of that instruction. He will be entitled to an extension of time only in respect of the period of *critical delay* attributable to that instruction which will then be added to the existing (extended) Completion Date.

Global claims   It will be apparent that the approaches to delay analysis previously outlined are technical and potentially artificial.

The delay analysis will require to consider the original and/or the 'as built' programme, the programming logic which has been used and, in particular, the duration of each relevant construction activity. It may also be necessary, for example, to demonstrate the reasonableness of the allowances in the original contract programme.

It is tempting, especially from the contractor's point of view, simply to identify the period of delay for which an extension of time can be sought as being the difference between actual completion and the contract completion date and to attribute that period to the effect of all of the employer's risk events throughout the project.

Such an approach has come to be known as a 'global' or 'total time' claim.

A 'global (money) claim' has been defined as being put forward where:

> ... a global or composite sum, however computed, is put forward as the measure of damage or of contractual compensation where there are two or more separate matters of claim or complaint, and where it is said to be impractical or impossible to provide a breakdown or sub-division of the sum claimed between those matters.[32]

or

> ... where a plaintiff does not seek to attribute specific loss to specific breaches of contract, but rather alleges a composite loss as a result of all the alleged breaches.[33]

The definition applies equally to claims for time.

Global claims were criticised in the landmark (Privy Council) case of *Wharf Properties* v. *Eric Cumine Associates*,[34] upon which Defenders have historically relied as authority for the proposition that a pleading which fails to identify the term breached the facts amounting to breach and the effect of such breach (including the loss caused) is an abuse of process. However, the combined effect of this and other cases seems to be that where a claim is made for delay-related costs as a result of various events and it is impossible or at least impracticable to link each element of loss to each such event, then a global claim may be permitted.

The overriding concern is the requirement to give fair notice of the claim. That will depend upon all of the circumstances including the forum, the knowledge of the parties, and the complexity of the project. For the purposes of persuading the engineer under an engineering contract, the level of particularity should be such as to facilitate a reasonable audit of the submission and an opinion as to entitlement to be formed. In court or arbitration, the required degree of particularisation may be higher.

Some recent consideration has been given to the question of global claims by Lord MacFadyen in the case of *John Doyle Construction Limited* v. *Laing Management (Scotland) Limited*. The case is the subject of an appeal and further judicial pronouncements may be expected. Nonetheless, the decision provides a useful discussion of this topic. The Court made it clear that it was proceeding on the assumption that contractors are, as a matter of principle, entitled to advance global claims for loss: that point was common ground between the parties for the purposes of the debate. The point that was central to the case was whether a global claim must necessarily fail in its entirety because one of the factors causing the loss and expense on the part of the contractor was not the liability of the employer.

There were two reasons why Lord MacFadyen decided that the global claim did not necessarily have to fail in these circumstances. The first was that the contractor actually averred concurrent causes of delay – in other words, on the face of the contractor's written pleadings there were no causal factors which the contractors did not say that the employer was not responsible for, even if on a concurrent basis. The second reason was that the contractor was entitled to bring evidence which might be able to show that he had a proper basis of being awarded some lesser sum than the full global claim – effectively, that the claim might have some partial success, rather than proceeding only on an 'all or nothing' basis. The contractor was therefore entitled to have its evidence heard. There was, however, a warning from the Judge that if there was no 'rational basis' for the award of the lesser sum, their entire Global claim was at risk of failure. The case is therefore not a carte blanche for the contractor to present its claims on a global basis without any regard to issues of underlying causality.

The delay protocol

In November 2001 the Society of Construction Law issued its draft Protocol for Determining Extensions of Time and Compensation for Delay and Disruption. The intention of the Society is to produce a protocol acceptable to all quarters of the construction and engineering industry which could be employed as a contract document, and to provide answers to some of the common issues that arise in the analysis of entitlements to extension of time (and/or compensation for the additional time spent and resources used) to complete the project. In summary, the draft protocol's principles so far as they relate to issues discussed in this chapter are as follows:

- **The programme** – an approved programme (using industry standard critical path method project planning software) should be established.
- **Purpose of extension of time** – an extension of time serves only to relieve the contractor of liability for liquidated damages for any period prior to the extended contract completion date.
- **Procedure for granting an extension of time** – the updated programme should be the primary tool used to determine the length of the extension of time. The goal of the extension of time procedure is the ascertainment of the appropriate contractual entitlement to an extension of time, and is not to be based on the question of whether or not the contractor needs an extension of time in order to avoid liquidated damages. It will also be necessary for the parties 'to apply intelligence and experience' to the process to ensure that all relevant factors are taken into account and that any anomalous results generated by the programme analysis are managed properly.

- **Float** – an extension of time should only be granted to the extent that the employer delay is predicted at the time of the employer's risk event to reduce to below zero the total float on the activity paths – in other words, only to the extent that the activity paths were (or are anticipated to be) critical to completion on the then prevailing contract completion date at the time the employer's risk event occurs.
- **Concurrent delay** – where contractor delay to completion occurs concurrently with employer delay, the contractor's concurrent delay should not reduce any extension of time.
- **Delay analysis** – 'time impact' analysis should be utilised wherever possible, both for prospective and retrospective analysis.
- **Global claims** – these are 'strongly discouraged' by the Protocol and noted as being rarely accepted by the courts.

A revised version of the Protocol was due publication in October 2002.

Suspension

Section 112 of the Act allows the contractor to suspend performance of his obligations under the construction contract where a sum due under the contract is not paid in full by the final date for payment and no effective notice to withhold payment has been given. Section 112(4) provides that:

> Any period during which performance is suspended in pursuance of the right conferred by this section shall be disregarded in computing for the purposes of any contractual time limit the time taken, by the party exercising the right or by a third party, to complete any work directly or indirectly affected by the exercise of the right.

In other words, the suspending contractor will, effectively, receive an extension of time for the period during which it suspends performance. As has been noted by other commentators, however,[35] there is no entitlement to additional time which may be required for remobilisation of labour and plant to return to site and recommence the works, nor can any recompense be claimed in respect of this. It is nevertheless possible for parties to cater for such entitlements in their contract.

The ICE 7th Conditions and the CECA Sub-contract make no specific provision for suspension of performance, but the statutory right to suspend is still available.

Notes

[1] Site is defined in clause 1(i)(v) of the ICE 7th Conditions.
[2] Clause 12(1)(a).
[3] Clause 14(2).
[4] Clause 14(2).
[5] Clause 14(2)(a).
[6] Clause 14(2)(b).
[7] Clause 14(2)(c).
[8] Clause 14(1)(b).
[9] Clause 14(1)(a).

[10] Such a failure may, however, be relevant to a consideration of whether a contractor has proceeded with its works with due diligence in the context of contractual determination provisions.

[11] *Pigott Foundations Limited* v. *Shepherd Construction Limited* (1993) 67 BLR 48.

[12] (1988) 39 BLR 89.

[13] Clause 43 and 48(2).

[14] Clause 6(1).

[15] *Hoening* v. *Isaacs* [1952] 2 All ER 176.

[16] *Bolton* v. *Mahadeva* [1972] IWLR 1009.

[17] And, in so doing, would have to prove that the delay caused his losses and that his losses are not too remote. The test of remoteness turns on whether losses arose as a natural result of a breach or whether they would have been within the contemplation of the parties at the time the contract was entered into – see the classic case of *Hadley* v. *Baxendale* [1854] 9 Ex 341.

[18] (1988) 39 BLR 30.

[19] [1915] AC 79.

[20] 2001 SCLR 961.

[21] 'On the contrary, that is just the situation when it is probable the pre-estimated damage was the true bargain between the parties' – Lord Dunedin in *Temloc, supra*.

[22] Scot Law Com No. 171.

[23] (1970) IBLR 114.

[24] If there are two possible constructions of a contract provision the construction to be preferred is the one which does **not** favour the party who drafted and put forward the condition.

[25] Pickavance, K. *Delay and Disruption in Construction Contracts*, 2nd edition, page 74.

[26] *Henry Boot Construction (UK) Ltd* v. *Malmaison Hotel (Manchester) Ltd*, 70 Con LR 32, at page 37, following *Balfour Beatty Building Ltd* v. *Chestermount Properties Ltd*. See also the case of *Royal Brompton Hospital NHS Trust* v. *FA Hammond and Others* (2001) BLR 317 which also deals with concurrent delay but probably does not advance matters much beyond what was said in the *Malmaison* case.

[27] 70 Con LR 32.

[28] Technology and Construction Court, 2000.

[29] 66 Con LR 118.

[30] 32 Con LR 139.

[31] 32 Con LR 139 at pages 160–164.

[32] *Hudson*, 11th edition, para 8.200.

[33] *Bernhard's Rugby Landscape Ltd* v. *Stockley Park Consortium Ltd* 82 BLR 32.

[34] 52 BLR 1.

[35] See, for example, Redmond, J. (2001) *Adjudication in Construction Contracts*, Blackwell Science, Chapter 10. Redmond also suggests that recovery of common law damages in respect of the costs of suspension and remobilisation might be possible on the basis that such a possibility should have been within the parties' contemplation at the time of formation of the contract.

7. Certificates

Introduction

Certificates play an important role in the majority of Scottish engineering contracts. A number of rights, and indeed responsibilities, are triggered by the issue of a certificate. Perhaps the most significant of these is a contractor's right to payment. This is crucially important to a contractor: cash flow is the lifeblood of the industry.

A certificate, once issued, governs the relationship between the parties. In addition, certificates act as 'markers' as to the particular stage work has reached under the contract. It should be noted at the outset that there is no common-law decision or statutory provision which creates a right to receive a certificate for any given event. Certification can only arise where there are express terms to that effect in the contract. The requirement to certify (whether this be a payment of or a stage reached during the contract works) cannot be implied into a contract in Scotland.

It is intended in this chapter to give guidance on the following issues:

- types of certificate
- recovery of monies with/without a certificate
- the immunity of the certifier.

Types of certificate

As mentioned already, the certificates that need to be issued (if any) depend upon the express terms of the contract. In this chapter, the general principles surrounding certification will be considered together with the various certificates that come into play under the ICE 7th Conditions.

The ICE 7th Conditions

There are four key types of certificates provided for by the ICE 7th Conditions. The four types are:

- interim payment certificates
- final certificates
- Certificates of Substantial Completion
- Defects Correction Certificates.

All certificates must be issued by the engineer. Copies of certificates have to be given to the employer and the contractor.

Interim certificates Clause 60 of the ICE 7th Conditions deals with 'certificates and payment'. Clauses 60(1) to 60(3) are relevant for the purposes of interim certificates. It should be noted that 'interim certificates' are not expressly defined under the conditions.

The process of payment and certification under clause 60 is dealt with more fully in Chapter 5.

The Engineer must certify the amount he considers due to the Contractor, if any, within 25 days of receipt of a monthly statement by the Contractor. Upon certification by the Engineer, the sum so certified is due to the contractor by the Employer. The final date for payment for the sum certified is 28 days after the monthly statement is received. Payment pursuant to the issue of certificates is more fully dealt with in Chapter 5.

If the Employer fails to pay before the final date for payment, then interest will be due on the certified sum. Again, this subject is covered more fully in Chapter 5.

Final certificates The second form of certificate found in ICE 7th Conditions is a final certificate. Clause 60(4) is the most important clause for this type of certificate. Final certificates are explained in more detail in Chapter 5.

The Contractor must submit a final account not more than three months after the date of the Defects Correction Certificates (explained further below). Once this has been received, the Engineer must issue the fnal certificate within three months 'after receipt of this final account and of all information reasonably required for its *verification*'.

Unlike the final certificate under JCT Standard Form Contracts, the final certificate under the ICE 7th Conditions has no evidential status insofar as the contractor's compliance with contractual obligations is concerned.

Payment becomes due to the Contractor on certification, with the final date for payment being 28 days later.

Clause 60(4) is also considered in Chapter 5.

Certificate of Substantial Completion The Certificate of Substantial Completion is defined in ICE 7th Conditions (clause 1(1)(r)) as a certificate issued under clause 48. The Contractor notifies the Engineer when he believes that the works are substantially complete and have passed any prescribed final tests. The term 'substantially complete' does not have a contractual definition. That is a matter for judgment in each individual case.[1]

After notification, the Engineer then has 21 days to reach a decision. At that point he can either issue a certificate of Substantial Completion or issue an instruction specifying all the work that requires to be done for a Certificate of Substantial Completion to be granted. If the latter route is taken, the Certificate of Substantial Completion must be granted within 21 days of completion of the specified work.

There are two additional circumstances in which a Certificate of Substantial Completion can be issued. These are 'premature use' and 'partial completion', found respectively at clauses 48(3) and 48(4) of the conditions. In the first example, if the Employer uses or occupies any substantial part of the works (other than provided for in the contract), the engineer shall provide a certificate upon the contractor's written request. Second, if the Engineer considers that any part of the works is substantially complete, he can issue a certificate to that effect, or, in other words, that a certain part is substantially complete. In both these scenarios, the Contractor is deemed to have undertaken to complete any outstanding work during the defects correction period.

A number of rights and obligations are triggered by the issue of the Certificate of Substantial Completion. If the project has continued (due to non-completion) past the completion date agreed in the contract, then liquidated damages for delay in completion may be due. For every day/week (depending upon the contract) that the date of completion contained in Certificate of Substantial Completion is later than the contractually agreed completion date, a pre-ascertained amount of damages will be due from the Contractor to the Employer.

The total sum due will be decreased if an extension of time is granted to the Contractor. The decrease in liquidated damages due will depend upon the length of the extension of time. In terms of clause 44(5) of the conditions, the Employer must review all extension of time claims within 28 days of the granting of the certificate.

Liquidated damages and extensions of time are reviewed more comprehensively in Chapter 6.

The issue of the certificate marks the beginning of the defects correction period, and also triggers the entitlement of the Contractor to payment of the first half of the retention fund.[2]

Once the certificate is issued, the Contractor no longer has full responsibility for the care of the works; see clause 20(1)(a) of the ICE 7th Conditions. The contractor must maintain the necessary insurance cover until that point.

Defects Correction Certificates   This certificate is defined in clause 61 of the conditions. It is issued at the end of the defects correction period, so long as all the outstanding work, above rectification of defects and other faults etc., have been completed. As stated above, the Contractor must submit his final account no later than three months after the certificate has been issued. During the defects correction period, the Contractor must complete all outstanding work as soon as is practicable.

It should be noted that the certificate does not relieve the Contractor or the Employer from any liability towards each other arising out of or in connection with their respective obligations under the contract.

Certification – general principles

What constitutes a certificate?

A number of important rights and obligations flow from the issue of a certificate. Accordingly, there should be no room for doubt that the purported 'certificate' *is* in fact a 'certificate'.

The certifier should make it clear that a certificate has been issued. It is useful, and certainly best practice, if the document bears the word 'certificate' on its face. Some certifiers will actually refer to the clause in the contract which empowers them to grant the certificate – for example, clause 48 of the ICE 7th

Conditions in the case of a Certificate of Substantial Completion. It should be straightforward for a Contractor to distinguish between ordinary correspondence and a certificate. The covering letter with the certificate may assist in this regard (see *H. Fairweather Ltd* v. *Asden Securities Ltd*).[3] If the contract is prescriptive as to the content and/or format of the certificate, the relevant requirements should obviously be adhered to.

Clause 60(9) of the ICE 7th Conditions stipulates that the interim payment certificate sent to the Contractor shall not only give notice specifying the amount of payment, but also the basis on which the amount was calculated. It therefore seems that the certificate will not only act as the notice required by the Act specifying the sum to be paid to the contractor but that it should also provide an explanation as to the basis on which the sum was calculated.[4] The certificate should therefore contain, or at least attach, some form of analysis or breakdown as to how the sum specified as payable has been reached.

The ICE 7th Conditions do not require reasons to be specified for the timing or basis of issue of certificates of substantial completion or defects correction certificates.

Express preconditions

If the contract stipulates any preconditions for the issue of a certificate, then these must be satisfied. The most likely preconditions that a contract will contain are as follows:

- who has the role of certifier
- who the certificate should be served upon
- when the certificate should be served
- the mechanism by which the certificate should be issued.

The following preconditions are all required under clause 60 of the ICE 7th Conditions for the issue of interim payment certificates:

- the certificate must be issued by the Engineer
- the certificate must be issued to the Contractor and the Employer (clause 60(9))
- the certificate must be prepared within 25 days of the date of delivery of the Contractor's statement
- the Contractor must issue the monthly statement to the Engineer or the Engineer's representative.

The certifier should also ensure that any conditions *vis-à-vis* delivery of the certificate are satisfied.

Errors

A minor error in a certificate can be corrected by the certifier (see *Euston Contractors Ltd* v. *Protea Estates*). That is especially so with interim certificates under the ICE 7th Conditions where errors can be corrected in the following certificate (clause 60(8)). It is submitted, however, that an error may lead to one party obtaining a right to be paid interest. For example, if an Engineer under-certifies by adopting the wrong approach to payment (based on a mistaken view of the contract) then he would have failed to certify in accordance with the contract. Interest would therefore be triggered (see *Blaenau Gwent Borough Council* v. *Lock (Contractors' Equipment) Ltd*).[5]

Recovery with/without a certificate

If a Contractor has a certificate the task of recovering those sums will be far easier. If the contractor is satisfied with the sum certified he could seek payment on the basis of that certificate through adjudication (or arbitration or litigation if appropriate). In the absence of a withholding notice such a claim would be extremely difficult to defend.

The Contractor may, however, disagree with the sum certified. He could in these circumstances seek a revisal of the certificate. An adjudicator appointed under the ICE 7th Conditions will operate under the ICE Adjudication Provisions which expressly allows him to:

> open up, review and revise any decision (other than that of an adjudicator unless agreed by the Parties), opinion, instruction, direction, certificate or valuation made under or in connection with the Contract and which is relevant to the dispute.

An adjudicator under the Scottish Scheme may also open up and revise certificates under the Scottish Scheme. Section 20(2)(a) of the Scottish Scheme states as follows:

> he (the adjudicator) may . . . open up, review and revise any decision taken or any certificate given by any person referred to in the contract, unless the contract states that the decision or certificate is final and conclusive.

It is submitted that interim certificates issued under the ICE 7th Conditions are not final and conclusive (unless parties have amended the Conditions).

Clause 66(ii)(a) of the ICE 7th Conditions also allows a review of certificates. It states:

> Such arbitrator (arbiter) shall have full power to open up review and revise any decision opinion instruction direction **certificate** or valuation of the engineer or an adjudicator . . .

How then does a contractor recover sums for work done without a certificate, where the contract demands the issue of one? The key question to be answered is this: is a certificate a condition precedent to payment? If the answer is no, recovery ought to be relatively straightforward. The contractor could raise adjudication or arbitration to recover what he believed to be due under the contract.

It is far more cumbersome for a contractor to recover payment in the absence of a certificate. Much of the relevant case law relates to instances where the would-be certifier has acted improperly. Issues have arisen in relation to many forms of contract regarding the certifier's 'dual' role – as an agent of the employer on the one hand, but an 'assessor' on the other. The result, in a number of cases, has been that the certifier has been disqualified and the contractor has been entitled to recover payment in the absence of a certificate.

The leading case on this area of law is *Panamena Europea Navigation* v. *Frederick Leyland and Company Limited*.[6] In that case the certifier insisted upon the work being done economically. However, the contract only stipulated that the certifier had to determine if the work was satisfactory. The Court held that

> on the true construction of the contract the surveyor, in relation to certifying that the work had been satisfactorily carried out, was confined to passing the actual quality of the work, without regard to the amount or value of the materials and labour expended thereon.

It is submitted, therefore, that if the certifier has acted improperly, recovery can be made without a certificate.

Furthermore, under the majority of 'standard conditions' a certificate is a condition precedent to payment. In essence, that means that a contractor has no immediately enforceable right to payment unless a sum has been certified. The debt is contingent on certification. In *Costain Building & Civil Engineering Limited* v. *Scottish Rugby Union*[7] it was held that on the true construction of the ICE Conditions of Contract, 5th Edition a certificate of the engineer was a condition precedent to the right of the contractor to be paid. Lord Clyde stated as follows:

> Essentially as it seems to me the question whether certification or arbitration is a condition precedent to payment under a contract should be a matter of construction of the particular contract. As a matter of construction of the present contract, I am prepared to hold that the contractor does not have an immediately enforceable right to payment of sums which have not been certified and which are open to dispute.

It is submitted that the position is exactly the same under the ICE 7th Conditions.

The *Costain* decision was considered in the case of *Karl Construction Limited* v. *Palisade Properties plc*.[8] Lord Drummond-Young in this case stated that

> ... under the JCT and ICE Standard Forms payment is due by an employer conditionally on the issue of a certificate by the architect or engineer, or on a decree of an arbiter, or on a decree of the court.

Lord Drummond-Young also considered what should be done in the event of a failure in the certification mechanism set out in a contract. He offered the example of an architect refusing to certify sums payable to a contractor and an employer not compelling him to do so. It was held that in these circumstances, and in the event that the contract said nothing about a failure to issue certificates, the party adversely affected could resort to arbitration, if the matter fell within the terms of an arbitration clause, and, if not, litigation in order to have the amount that should have been certified determined. In other words, the correct approach to take in the situation where there has been a refusal by the certifier to certify sums for payment is to seek that an arbiter (or if appropriate a court) operates the contractual machinery in relation to certification in order to determine what is due to the contractor.

A decree of the arbiter or the court would, according to Lord Drummond-Young in *Karl Construction Limited*, be equivalent to a certificate and payment will be due by the employer to the contractor in the same way as it would have been had the certified issued a certificate. It would not be correct to approach a failure to certify on the basis that this constituted a breach of contract and to seek damages from the employer. The provisions of the contract could, held Lord Drummond-Young, always be enforced using arbitration (or if appropriate by asking the court to operate the contractual certification machinery).

Role and immunity of certifier

It is important to bear in mind that the certifier is normally engaged by the employer for a particular project. The certifier cannot truly be described as independent. He is the agent of the employer.[9]

Equally, however, the certifier is obliged to act independently, honestly and fairly in carrying out certification duties.[10] The employer should not seek to unduly influence a certifier nor act in such a way as to put at risk the certifier properly exercising his duties under the contract. While this principle does not prevent the certifier from liaising with the employer and discussing matters arising under the contract with him, the certifier should be aware that if he oversteps the boundaries of impartiality he may be vulnerable to disqualification as certified.

Any act, omission or failure by the certifier could result in a breach of his contract with the employer. That would, of course, depend upon the express and implied terms of the particular contract. If the certifier has failed in his duties to the employer then the employer would be entitled to pursue a damages claim against the certifier. Depending upon the breach by the certifier, the resulting situation might put the employer in breach of his contract with the contractor. The contractor, however, could not pursue the certifier because there is no contractual relationship with the certifier. He would only have a right of action against the employer.

The most likely situation to arise is one where the certifier certifies work which does not actually conform to the contract. If this occurs as a consequence of a failure by him to exercise reasonable supervision then the employer will be able to pursue a claim against him. The leading case in this regard is *Sutcliffe* v. *Thackrah and others*. In that case the employer raised an action against the certifier for negligence and breach of duty in supervising the building of a house and for certifying works not done or improperly done by the builders. The Court held that in issuing interim certificates the certifier did not act as an arbitrator between the parties. Accordingly he was under a duty to act fairly in making his valuation and was liable to an action in negligence by the building owner.

It is therefore obvious that a certifier must at all times exercise due skill and care. He should not assume there is absolute immunity for a certifier.

Notes

[1] See Chapter 6 for further discussion on this issue.
[2] The release of retention is covered in greater detail in Chapter 5.
[3] (1979) 12 BLR 40.

[4] Section 110 of the Act.

[5] (1994) 3 Con LR 121.

[6] [1947] AC 428.

[7] (1994) SLT 573.

[8] Citation.

[9] *Beaufort Developments (NI) Limited* v. *Gilbert-Ash NI Ltd & Another* 2 All ER 778.

[10] *Sutcliffe* v. *Thackrah & Another* [1974] 1 All ER 859.

8. Ending the engineering contract

Introduction

Terminology

The ending of a contract is often equally as important and often even more difficult than entering into a contract. The ending of a contract may be carried out in two ways:

- under the common law
- contractually.

It is an area of law that is made more impenetrable by the use of a variety of differing terms meaning essentially the same thing. This chapter will follow the guidance of *Hudson's Building & Engineering Contracts* (11th edition) which states '... forfeiture, determination, termination, renunciation [and] recission ... have been variously used in the cases and elsewhere. In context the different descriptions should generally be regarded as synonymous, with no significant differences of consequential effect'.

ICE

Both the ICE 7th Conditions and the ICE Design and Construct Conditions contain clauses under which either the employer, the contractor or both may terminate the contract. The purpose of such clauses is two-fold:[1]

- to ensure that it is clear when a termination event arises. The situation otherwise would mean that the employer or contractor would be seeking to reply on common law provisions which may prove to be difficult to establish
- to ensure that the consequences of the termination are clear. For example the right to or calculation of any compensation on termination may not be clear, or there may be no requirement to leave the site or to deliver relevant papers or intellectual property rights to the employer.

This chapter will look at the basic common law provisions regarding termination, the ICE contractual provisions, and also take a brief look at the ancillary termination clauses in the ICE contract. Because of the complex factual and legal matrix that exists when common law and contractual termination rights co-exist, it follows that although this chapter will give an indication of some of the basic and more practical issues which can arise in this area, it should be stressed that this is an area of great complexity, and suggested further reading is set out in the list of publications and further reading.

Common law

There are four main ways in which a contract can be ended under the common law:

- completion of the performance of the contract
- frustration
- material breach of the contract
- agreement of the parties to the contract.

Completion of performance

Completion of performance under a contract (for example, the completion of the works and expiry of the defects liability period) will bring to an end many aspects of the parties' contractual relationship. Some obligations will, however, continue to subsist and be enforceable. Examples would include an obligation to complete the works in accordance with the terms of the contract (which might be relied upon in the event of a latent defect becoming manifest), and an obligation upon both parties to allow an arbiter to finally determine any dispute which may arise under the contract.

Frustration

In very unusual circumstances it is possible for an event to occur which changes the nature of the original contract to such an extent that, if the contract were to continue, it would involve the performance of something 'radically different from that which was undertaken by the [original] contract'.[2] In other words the parties would be performing something other than what they had originally agreed to perform. For the doctrine of frustration to apply, the intervening event must not be the fault or within the control of either party to the contract.

To stress the extent to which frustration is a very unusual method of determination, Lord Justice Harman stated 'Frustration is a doctrine only too often invoked by a party to a contract who finds performance difficult or unprofitable, but it is very rarely relied on with success. It is in fact a kind of last ditch'.[3]

Examples of cases where frustration has been held to have occurred include:

- A change of law occurs after entering into the contract, where the change in law would prohibit the completion of the works.[4]
- The destruction of, for example the ground on which the works were to have been carried out.[5] It follows therefore that a landslip may lead to frustration of a contract.
- Exceptional weather can, but only rarely lead to the frustration of the contract.

A contract can only very rarely be capable of being frustrated where the contract contains an express term dealing with circumstances of the event.[6]

The effect of frustration is to automatically discharge both parties to the contract from any further performance of their obligations under that contract.

Any money paid under the contract before the event of frustration occurred would be recoverable and future payments would no longer be payable. However, if the employer under the contract derives some benefit from any works carried out prior to the event of frustration, the employer may be unable to recover any monies paid.

Both the ICE 7th Conditions and ICE Design and Build Conditions contain at clause 63(1) a clause dealing with frustration. Interestingly although 'Frustration' is the side heading of the clause, it does not feature in the operative part of the clause, which simply refers to circumstances rendering it 'impossible or illegal' to perform the obligations. Clause 1(3) of both sets of conditions provides that 'headings and marginal notes in the conditions of contract shall not be deemed to be part thereof or be taken into consideration in the interpretation or construction thereof or of the contract'. Because the clause provides for 'deemed abandonment' in these circumstances the effect is that the contractor would be entitled to payment under clause 63(4).

Force majeure

Many standard forms, including FIDIC, refer to force majeure and use it as a ground either for extensions of time or else for termination. The rationale behind its inclusion in contracts is that it attempts to provide contractual clarity where otherwise there may be difficulties in interpreting whether or not an event of frustration has occurred. As noted above, frustration cannot apply where the parties have contemplated and drafted for a particular event. There is, however, no explicit reference to force majeure in the ICE conditions.

Although force majeure has no precise meaning in the English language, it has been held to cover events such as Acts of God (which themselves have been defined as being events of nature that reasonable foresight and ability could not foresee or reasonably provide against),[7] new laws[8] and wars, riots and strikes. If a project is sufficiently important to merit amendment to the standard ICE Conditions there is a strong argument for the inclusion of a force majeure clause.

Breach of the contract

A breach occurs when one party to a contract fails to perform an obligation under the contract. For example, the employer may consistently not pay the contractor[9] or the contractor may not comply with the assignation provisions. The main consequences of a breach are: (a) the party against whom the breach is committed is entitled to sue for damages; and (b) if the breach is sufficiently serious the innocent party can, but is not obliged to, treat the party in breach as having repudiated the contract. The innocent party can accept that repudiation and in that way end the contract. Whilst acceptance of the repudiation must be communicated to the party in breach, there does not appear to be a set way in which the innocent party communicates the acceptance of the repudiation.[10] Importantly not every breech of a contract will amount to a repudiation of the contract.

A repudiation may comprise either an implied or an express refusal to perform some element of the contract. Alternatively the repudiation may be a material breach which is a breach going to the 'root' of the contract.[11]

The choice between accepting the repudiation or suing for damages will be a function of the seriousness of the breach. Damages for example may not be an appropriate remedy or may be inadequate to compensate the innocent party for the loss it has suffered. Examples of cases where there has been a material breach of the contract include:

- the contractor failing to carry out work without cause[12]
- the contractor producing work of an unacceptable quality[13]
- the employer failing to give the contractor possession of the site[14]
- the contractor failing to provide a bond, when the bond was a requirement of the tender.[15]

Acceptance of a repudiation of a contract will bring to an end the future obligations of the parties to a contract, but will not prevent accrued (pre-repudiation) rights to payment from being pursued or the use of an arbitration clause (or indeed the referral of a pre-existing dispute to adjudication).

Agreement of the parties

There is no prohibition on the parties at any stage in a contract agreeing to end that contract. Should they decide to do so best practice dictates that this is formally recorded to ensure that decisions as to whether all or merely some of their obligations are extinguished are properly recorded.

ICE contracts

Generally

An essential point to make clear about contractual termination clauses is that they do not bring an end to the contract itself. Instead they provide for the termination of the contractor's employment under the contract. The difference, although seemingly small, is in fact very significant. The determination of the employment of the contractor under the contract will not end the contract itself, and so ancillary clauses including, for example, an arbitration[16] clause would continue to bind the parties. For this reason contractual termination clauses will often cover the consequences of such termination.

In terminating the employment of a party under a contract, great care should be taken in exercising such termination rights and in ensuring compliance with the termination procedure set out in the contract.[17] If the party attempting to terminate the employment of the other party does so wrongfully (whether legally or factually wrong) since the terminating party is likely to cease performing its own obligations under the contract it runs the risk of repudiating the contract.[18]

As noted in the introduction to this chapter, in cases where a contractual termination clause exists there will often be a complex factual and legal matrix that makes the operation of that clause potentially very difficult. One reason for such difficulty is that although a contractual termination clause may exist, the factual circumstances that surround a particular purported termination event may not be wholly or adequately covered in the contract, in other words the lines will be blurred. The existence of the contractual clause therefore does not mean that the common-law termination rules have no application. In fact, contractual termination clauses do not exclude common law, unless the contract states that it is to be the exclusive remedy for breaches and thus excludes the operation of the common law.[19]

The main termination provisions in both ICE 7th Conditions and the ICE Design and Build Conditions are as follows:

- abandonment of the works (clause 63), comprising frustration and war clause
- employer default (clause 64)
- contractor default (clause 65).

In each case the consequences of termination are dealt with in each clause.

Abandonment

Deemed abandonment of the works is stated to have occurred: (a) when circumstances occur making continued performance of obligations impossible or illegal provided such circumstances are outside the control of either party; or (b) if there is a war resulting in general mobilisation of the armed forces and (i) the contractor continues to carry out the works for 28 days following mobilisation and (ii) if substantial completion has not occurred before the 28-day period expires.

Notice is required for deemed abandonment in circumstances of illegality or impossibility but not for mobilisation. Accordingly clause 68 will apply which provides that notices will be written, and served at the relevant registered office of either party or the contractor's principal place of business or employer's last known address, as appropriate.

The effect of deemed abandonment under clause 63(1) or (2) is covered under clauses 63(3), (4), (5) and (6):

- Clause 63(3) ensures that the contractor removes its equipment from the site with 'reasonable dispatch', failing which the employer shall be entitled to dispose of the equipment pursuant to clause 54(3).
- Clause 63(4) covers payment on abandonment. The payment will cover the value of work carried out prior to abandonment, amounts for preliminary items, cost of delivered materials that the contractor is obliged to accept, reasonable costs for removing its equipment from the site and a catch-all provision designed to cover costs incurred on the assumption that the works would have completed. Excluded from recovery are costs for loss or damage.
- Clause 63(5) provides that a further effect of deemed abandonment is that retention monies are released and, if the contractor allows, an allowance can be made against the retention monies for any costs of making good. It may suit the contractor to make such an allowance rather than run the risk of the employer undertaking such works itself and charging the costs against the contractor.

- Clause 63(6) confirms that despite the deemed abandonment the contract remains in full force and effect.

Employer default

Clause 64 of the ICE 7th Conditions sets out the grounds on which the contractor can, by giving seven days notice (although the contractor can extend the notice period to allow the employer to rectify the situation) terminate its employment under the contract. Unlike clause 65 (which states that 'where a notice of termination is given pursuant to a certificate issued by the engineer . . . it shall be given as soon as is reasonably possible after receipt of the certificate'), clause 64 contains no such indication as to appropriate timing. Once the notice period has expired the contractor should therefore act within a reasonable period in the circumstances. Although the seven days refers to the notice period rather than to the period within which the contractor must act, there is nothing to suggest that the notice period cannot be retrospectively extended. The final paragraph of clause 64(1) makes it clear that such termination does not 'avoid . . . the Contract or release . . . the Employer from any of its obligations or liabilities under the Contract'.

There are essentially two main grounds for termination:

Assignment   The contractor is entitled to terminate its employment if the employer either assigns or tries to assign the contract or a part of it without the prior written consent of the contractor. This is consistent with the provisions of clause 3(1) which prohibits assignment by the employer and contractor without the prior written consent of the other. Unfortunately the ICE Conditions do not reflect the slight difference in terminology between Scots and English law in this area. In England and Wales the correct reference is to 'assignment' whilst in Scotland it is 'assignation'; there are fundamental differences between the two concepts. Perhaps in future editions clause 67 (which deals with the relevant amendments required for using the Conditions in Scotland) will be amended to encompass this required change.

Insolvency   Six separate insolvency events are gathered together under this general heading, including the employer:

- becoming bankrupt or having a petition in bankruptcy presented
- having a receiving or administration order being made against it
- making an arrangement with or an assignment in favour of its creditors
- agreeing to perform the contract under a committee of inspection of its creditors
- where it is a company, having a receiver or administrator appointed or it going into liquidation (excluding voluntary liquidation for the purpose of amalgamation or reconstruction)
- having an execution levied on his goods that is not stayed or discharged within 28 days.

In each case the onus is on the contractor to show that the event has occurred. It should be noted that as with assignation, notice is required and so termination on employer insolvency is not automatic. In the absence of contractual provisions insolvency does not by itself necessarily affect a contract, however, it may lead to the insolvent party being unable to fulfil its obligations (for example to pay the contractor) which in turn leads the other party to withhold its own obligations[20] (to proceed with the work).

The effects of the contractor exercising the right to terminate its obligations under clause 64 are contained in clauses 64(2) and 64(3).

Clause 64(2), as with clause 63(3), requires the contractor, after the seven-day notice period to remove the contractor's equipment with 'all reasonable despatch'.

Clause 64(3) deals with the payments due on termination. Once again the approach adopted under clause 63(4) and 63(5) in relation to payment is adopted here, in that the contractor is entitled to pay for the value of the works carried out prior to termination, together with preliminary items, costs of materials that the contractor is legally liable to accept, and the reasonable costs of the removal of the contractor's equipment under clause 64(2). Clause 63(5), which will also be applicable through the operation of clause 64(3), provides that a further effect of deemed abandonment is that retention monies are released and, if the contractor allows, an allowance can be made against the retention monies for any costs of making good. It may suit the contractor to make such an allowance rather than run the risk of the employer undertaking such works itself and charging the costs against the contractor.

ICE Design & Construct   The termination provisions of clause 64 are largely similar to those in the ICE 7th Conditions. However there is one change that is worthy of note:

- Under clause 64(4) an additional ground for termination is if the employer's representative fails to certify, or the employer fails to pay the contractor the amount due, within 56 days of the time period set out in clause 60.

Contractor default

The provisions relating to contractor default are found in clause 65. Not surprisingly the grounds for terminating the employment of the contractor under the contract are more extensive than the employer default grounds. Some of the grounds for termination are the same as for the employer default provisions, noticeably where the contractor:

- becomes bankrupt or presents its petition in bankruptcy
- has a receiving order or administration order made against it
- makes an arrangement with or an assignment in favour of its creditors
- if it is a company, has a receiver or administrator appointed or goes into liquidation (other than voluntary liquidation for the purposes of amalgamation or reconstruction)
- agrees to carry out the contract under a committee of inspection of its creditors
- has an execution levied on its goods which is not stayed or discharged within 28 days

- assigns or attempts to assign the contract without the prior written consent of the employer.

A further ground for termination is added at clause 65(1)(b) which provides that the employer may terminate the contractor's employment under the contract if the contractor is in breach of clause 4(1) which is the prohibition on the contractor sub-contracting the 'whole of' the works, without the prior written consent of the employer. Clearly the clause attempts to guard against a situation where the employer may have carried out a thorough due diligence procedure against the contractor during the tender stages prior to contract, but then finds that instead of its preferred contractor carrying out the works the preferred contractor has sub-contracted the whole of the works to another contractor, possibly one which may have been rejected by the employer during the tender stage. This clause therefore ensures that should such a situation arise the employer is able to call upon this mechanism to rectify the situation. It is however very unusual for this provision to be exercised.

A second limb of the termination clause requires that the engineer has 'certified in writing' to the employer, with a copy being sent to the contractor, that certain specified events have occurred which can give rise to termination. Following issue of the certificate the employer may expel the contractor from the site after giving seven days notice in writing to the contractor. The period of seven days may, as in the Abandonment provisions in clause 63, be extended by the employer to give the contractor the opportunity to rectify the situation, as noted above however it is not clear how long such an extension may be extended for. After expiry of the seven-day period the employer may 'enter upon the Works . . . and expel the Contractor therefrom'. Exactly what will constitute entering upon the site and expelling the contractor is not clear. In practice it may simply require the employer to ensure equipment, machinery, plant and materials are secure and that the site is locked.

The second limb events that can give rise to termination include:

- Abandonment of the contract – since abandonment is also covered in clause 40, which deals with the suspension of the works, it is likely that abandonment in this context would constitute suspension under clause 40 together with an indication that the works were unlikely to proceed.
- Failure to commence the works in accordance with clause 41 – clause 41(2) requires the contractor to 'start the Works on or as soon as is reasonably practicable after the Works Commencement Date'. Therefore unless there are mitigating circumstances which prohibit starting the works and the engineer does not think that it is in fact reasonably practicable to start the works then the event will be caught by this sub-clause;
- Suspension of the progress of the works without due cause for 14 days after receiving the engineer's written notice to proceed – this event is unclear. The circumstances of the suspension should really be clarified in the drafting of this clause, but they are not, and it is difficult to construe which notice is being referred to in this event;

- Failure to remove goods or materials from site or to replace work for 14 days after receiving the engineer's written notice that the said goods or materials have been condemned and rejected – at clause 39 the engineer has power to: (a) instruct the removal from site of materials not in accordance with the contract; (b) to substitute materials which are in accordance with the contract; and (c) remove and replace work whose workmanship, material or design is not in accordance with the contract. It follows that there is a clear link between the two provisions, however case law has demonstrated that prior notice under clause 39 is not necessary for the operation of this termination clause;[21]

- Despite previous warnings by the engineer in writing the contractor is failing to proceed with the works with due diligence or is otherwise persistently or fundamentally in breach of its obligations under the contract – it is submitted that this is intended to cover a situation where the contractor is not, for example, resourcing or committing staff to the project to enable it to proceed. The reference to 'previous warnings' implies that there must be at least two such warnings. Similarly the reference to 'persistently' also implies that more than one warning is required.

Once the employer has entered the site he has the option under clause 65(2) to either complete the works himself or employ another contractor to complete the works. In completing the works the employer or his chosen contractor reserves the right to use the 'Contractor's Equipment Temporary Works goods and materials'. In addition, if any money is due to the employer from the contractor whose employment was terminated the employer is entitled to set off against that amount any sums received from the sale of contractor's equipment, temporary works and unused goods and materials.

Once again it is worth noting that the procedure leading to the termination of the employment of the contractor should be followed to the letter. The contractor could treat a wrongful termination as a repudiatory breach. When the engineer is asked to certify one of the occurrences set out in clause 65(1)(e)–(j) then that is exactly what they should do. They should not go into detail as to why they are so certifying and on what evidential grounds they are doing so. It is submitted that merely referring to the relevant clause in the contract is all that is required.

Following termination of the contractor's employment under clause 65 there is likely to be a financial shortfall that the employer will seek to recover to make himself whole again. Accordingly clause 65(5) which covers payment after termination provides that there is no immediate payment to the contractor, rather payment will not occur until the engineer certifies that an amount is due to the contractor. In so certifying the engineer is required to ascertain the difference between: (a) the sum the contractor would have been entitled to had he completed the works in the normal way; and (b) the costs of completing the works, damages for delay and any other expenses properly incurred by the employer. If at any point prior to completing the works the engineer is satisfied that (b) will be more than (a), the engineer can issue an interim certificate and that certificate will be considered to be a debt due from the contractor to the employer.

Notes

[1] Wallace (1994), *Hudson's building and civil engineering contracts*, 11th edition.

[2] *Davis Contractors Ltd* v. *Fareham UDC* [1956] AC 696 at 729, HL.

[3] *Tsakiroglou & Co. Ltd* v. *Noblee Thorl Gmbh* [1960] 2 QB 318 at 370.

[4] *Amalgamated Investment Ltd* v. *John Walker Ltd* [1977] 1 WLR 164, CA.

[5] *Taylor* v. *Caldwell* [1863] 3 B&S 826.

[6] *Cricklewood Property & Investment Trust Ltd* v. *Leighton's Investment Trust Ltd* [1945] AC.

[7] *Baldwins Ltd* v. *Halifax Corporation* [1916].

[8] *Lebeaupin* v. *Richard Crispin and Co.* [1920].

[9] *D.R. Bradley (Cable Jointing) Ltd* v. *Jefco Mechanical Services* [1988].

[10] *Monklands DC* v. *Ravenstone Securities* [1980].

[11] *Photo Production Ltd* v. *Securicor Ltd* [1980].

[12] *Hoenig* v. *Isaacs* [1952].

[13] *Suisse Atlantique* v. *NV Rotterdamsche Kolen Centrale* [1966].

[14] *Felton* v. *Wharrie* [1906].

[15] *Swartz & Son* v. *Wolmaransteadt Town Council* [1960].

[16] *Heyman* v. *Darwins Ltd* [1942].

[17] *Muir Construction Ltd* v. *Hambly Ltd* [1990].

[18] *Architectural Installation Services* v. *James Gibbons* (1989) 46 BLR 91.

[19] *Modern Engineering (Bristol)* v. *Gilbert-Ash* [1974] AC 689, HL.

[20] *Arnott and Others* v. *Forbes* [1881].

[21] *Tara Civil Engineering Ltd* v. *Moorfield Developments Ltd* (1989) 46 BLR.

9. Claims

Introduction

In order to be able to pursue a claim successfully, it is not enough for the claiming party to point to some loss or damage that he has suffered. The first step in building a claim must be to establish some form of legal entitlement against the party from whom redress is sought.

Whilst that redress will often be directly financial, it can also include more time during the life of a contract, or, for example, the provision of additional drawings and documents to enable a contractor to progress works.

The basis for claims

The principal routes by which a party to an engineering contract can make a claim are as follows:

- In accordance with the **contract conditions** themselves, where those conditions set out a mechanism for a claim to be made. This is the most familiar type of claim that occurs on a day to day basis: a typical example would be a claim by a contractor for additional payment under clause 52 of the ICE 7th Conditions, made following a variation ordered by the engineer under clause 51. A detailed commentary on some of the claims which can arise under the ICE 7th Conditions follows below.
- A claim for **breach of contract** under general common law principles. A summary of this type of claim is set out below.
- A claim for what is known in Scots law as **delict** (the equivalent of tort under English law), which arises from the breach of a duty which one party may owe to another independently and irrespective of any contract between them.
- A claim for payment for work done in the absence of a contractual price mechanism, often known as a *quantum meruit* claim.[1]

Whilst the focus of commentary and debate is often on claims which a contractor may wish to make against an employer, these legal bases of claim (other than a *quantum meruit* basis) are equally available to the employer. Under the ICE 7th Conditions, for example, if the contractor is late in completing the works, the employer has available to him the mechanism for the recovery of liquidated damages set out in clause 47.[2]

The different types of claim are not necessarily mutually exclusive, and it is not uncommon for a party to present claims in the alternative to maximise the chances of recovery should one basis of claim fail.

Claims under ICE 7th Conditions

Clause 7 – further drawings

Clause 7 reads as follows:

Further Drawings, Specifications and instructions	7(1)	The Engineer shall from time to time during the progress of the Works supply to the Contractor such modified or further Drawings Specifications and instructions as shall in the Engineer's opinion be necessary for the purpose of the proper and adequate construction and completion of the Works and the Contractor shall carry out and be bound by the same. If such Drawings Specifications or instructions require any variation to any part of the Works the same shall be deemed to have been issued pursuant to Clause 51.
Contractor to provide further documents	7(2)	Where sub-clause (6) of this Clause applies the Engineer may require the Contractor to supply such further documents as shall in the Engineer's opinion be necessary for the purpose of the proper and adequate construction completion and maintenance of the Works and when accepted by the Engineer the Contractor shall be bound by the same.
Notice by Contractor	7(3)	The Contractor shall give adequate notice in writing to the Engineer of any further Drawing or Specification that the Contractor may require for the construction and completion of the Works or otherwise under the Contract.
Delay in issue	7(4)(a)	If by reason of any failure or inability of the Engineer to issue at a time reasonable in all the circumstances Drawings Specifications or instructions requested by the Contractor and considered necessary by the Engineer in accordance with sub-clause (1) of this Clause the Contractor suffers delay or incurs additional cost then the Engineer shall take such delay into account in determining any extension of time to which the Contractor is entitled under Clause 44 and the Contractor shall subject to Clause 53 be paid in accordance with Clause 60 the amount of such cost as may be reasonable.

(b)   If the failure of the Engineer to issue any Drawing Specification or instruction is caused in whole or in part by the failure of the Contractor after due notice in writing to submit drawings, specifications or other documents which he is required to submit under the Contract the Engineer shall take into account such failure by the Contractor in taking any action under sub-clause (4)(a) of this Clause.

One copy of documents   7(5)   One copy of the Drawings and Specifica-
to be kept on Site   tion furnished to the Contractor as aforesaid and of all Drawings Specifications and other documents required to be provided by the Contractor under sub-clause (6) of this Clause shall at all reasonable times be available on the Site for inspection and use by the Engineer and the Engineer's representative and by any other person authorised by the Engineer in writing.

Permanent Works   7(6)   Where the Contract expressly provides that
designed by Contractor   part of the Permanent Works shall be designed by the Contractor he shall submit to the Engineer for acceptance

(a)   such drawings specifications calculations and other information as shall be necessary to satisfy the Engineer that the Contractor's design generally complies with the requirements of the Contract and

(b)   operation and maintenance manuals together with as completed drawings of that part of the Permanent Works in sufficient detail to enable the Employer to operate maintain dismantle reassemble and adjust the Permanent Works incorporating that design. No certificate under Clause 48 covering any part of the Permanent Works designed by the Contractor shall be issued until manuals and drawings in such detail have been submitted to an accepted by the Engineer.

Responsibility   7(7)   Acceptance by the Engineer in accordance
unaffected by approval   with sub-clause (6) of this Clause shall not relieve the Contractor of any of his responsibilities under the Contract. The Engineer shall be responsible for the integration and co-ordination of the Contractor's design with the rest of the Works.

Clause 7 primarily provides a mechanism by which documents are to be supplied to the contractor by the employer or the engineer, so as to avoid delay to the contractor.[3] Under clause 7(1) the engineer is under a duty to issue further drawings and instructions where they are necessary for the adequate construction and completion of the works. The question as to what is 'necessary' may be construed by reference to clauses 8, 11, 13(2) and 14(9) which assist in demonstrating that 'necessary' effectively limits the engineer's 'duty' to those matters for which the engineer and/or the employer are responsible, i.e. the permanent and temporary works, rather than, for example, the method by which they are to be constructed.

If the engineer fails to issue the drawings and/or instructions referred to in clause 7(1) the contractor's entitlement to make a claim arises, provided the contractor has complied with clause 7(3), under which he must give 'adequate notice' to the engineer of what drawings or specifications are required for the construction and completion of the works. The entitlement to claim will, however, only arise if the drawings or specification have not been issued 'at a time reasonable in all the circumstances'. It is against the *actual* rate of the contractor's progress that this criteria will be measured – not the programmed rate.

The courts[4] considered this wording; amongst the circumstances to be taken into account are the views of the engineer and his staff. However, this case has been the subject of some criticism by commentators who have argued that further drawings should be issued to the contractor under clause 7 so that they are with the contractor in such time as to avoid delay. This view has found favour in further reported cases.[5]

Clause 11 – provision and interpretation of information

Clause 11 reads as follows:

Provision and interpretation of information	11(1)	As between the Employer and the Contractor and without prejudice to sub-clause (2) of this Clause information on the nature of the ground and subsoil and hydrological conditions and pipes and cables in, on or over the ground obtained by or on behalf of the Employer from investigations undertaken relevant to the Works shall only be taken into account to the extent that it was made available to the Contractor before the submission of his tender. The Contractor shall be responsible for the interpretation of all such information for the purposes of constructing the Works and for any design which is the Contractor's responsibility under the Contract.
Inspection of Site	11(2)	The Contractor shall be deemed to have inspected and examined the Site and its surroundings and information available in connection therewith and to have satisfied himself so far as is practicable and reasonable before submitting his tender as to the form and nature thereof including the

ground and sub-soil and hydrological conditions and the extent and nature of work and materials necessary for constructing and completing the Works and the means of communication with and access to the Site and the accommodation he may require and in general to have obtained for himself all necessary information as to risks, contingencies and all other circumstances which may influence or affect his tender.

Basis and sufficiency of tender   11(3)   The Contractor shall be deemed to have based his tender on his own inspection and examination as aforesaid and on all information whether obtainable by him or made available by the Employer and satisfied himself before submitting his tender as to the correctness and sufficiency of the rates and prices stated by him in the Bill of Quantities which shall (unless otherwise provided in the Contract) cover all his obligations under the Contract.

Clause 11 in itself cannot form the basis of a claim, and requires to be considered in conjunction with clause 12 in order to recognise its full significance. The extent to which a contractor will succeed in attempting to establish that physical conditions or artificial obstructions could not reasonably have been foreseen by an experienced contractor (in terms of clause 12), will be circumscribed by the extent of the information available (or deemed to have been available) in terms of clause 11. Typically, employers will seek to use the provisions of clause 11 as a means of defending themselves against a clause 12 claim: if a contractor could or should have foreseen physical conditions by a proper interpretation of site information, or an investigation of the site conditions, then his clause 12 claim will fail.

The contractor will have to overcome two initial hurdles encapsulated within clause 11 if he is to succeed in a clause 12 claim: he will need to establish that the existence of the physical conditions or artificial obstruction complained of in terms of clause 12 was not disclosed by:

- either the site information provided in terms of clause 11(1); or
- the investigations that the contractor is deemed to have carried out (whether or not he did actually carry them out) in terms of clause 11(2).

Clause 11(1) provides that the contractor is only required to take into account site information, to the extent that the site information was made available to him before he submitted his tender. This is a departure from the position under earlier conditions, whereby the employer was deemed to have made information available. Certainly, if an employer wishes to be protected as far as possible from future claims under clause 12, his approach must be to disclose all information at an early stage (this will not, however, transfer the risk of physical conditions which could not have been foreseen by an examination of the information, or the investigation of the site).[6] The corollary of this is that it may well prompt the contractor to adjust his price accordingly to take account of the potential risks which might be disclosed by the information.

The types of information envisaged by clause 11(1) appear to be wide-ranging: they extend to information not only obtained by the employer, but also to information obtained by third parties on his behalf. The requirement is that the information should be 'relevant to the Works': this will, by definition, vary from project to project. However, it would seem to be the case that information relating to other projects might well be relevant.

Clause 11(2) places an onus on the contractor to satisfy himself about ground conditions and anything else which might constitute a risk to his tender; in other words, the contractor is not entitled to simply sit back and rely on the information that emanates from the employer and his team. The practical implications in terms of time and money of a contractor carrying out ground investigations in a competitive tender are such that contractors rarely carry out these investigations in such a way as to satisfy fully the requirements of clause 11(2). At the very least, however, the prudent contractor should consider seeking to have the reports commissioned on behalf of the engineer assigned to him once the contract is awarded, or obtaining a collateral warranty from the ground investigation consultant.

Clause 12 – adverse physical conditions

The provisions of clause 12 are important, and are perhaps most usefully viewed by the use of a summary flowchart (Figure 9.1).

As has already been observed, clause 12 provides the contractor with a route to making a claim against the employer for both time and money, where he encounters physical conditions which could not, in the contractor's opinion, have reasonably been foreseen by an experienced contractor, and which the contractor did not, as a consequence, have the opportunity to price for in his tender. Where physical conditions fall into the definition in clause 12(1), they are at the employer's risk: in other words, the employer must bear the financial and time related costs.

Clause 12(1) is framed as an obligation on the part of the contractor to give written notice to the engineer *as early as practicable* once the conditions have been encountered. In terms of clause 12(3), the contractor should also provide the engineer with details of the anticipated effects of the conditions and what is to be done about them – this is to be either at the time of the clause 12(1) notice, or *as soon as practicable thereafter*. From the point of view of the engineer and the employer, this information is clearly crucial for cost and time management, and to allow the engineer, for example, to instruct a variation so that the conditions or obstruction can be avoided.

However, failure by the contractor to submit these written notices would not appear to be fatal to his claim. The right to payment, for example, is not dependent upon timeous notices having been given. Clause 12(2) provides that at the same time as the clause 12(1) notice, *or as soon thereafter as may be reasonable*, the contractor should inform the engineer of his intention to make

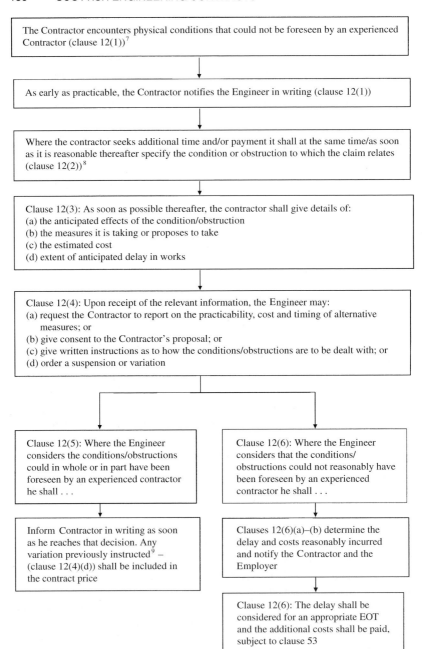

Figure 9.1.   Clause 12 provisions, ICE 7th Conditions.

a claim for additional time and/or payment: it does not make the submission of these notices a condition precedent.[10] Indeed, clause 53(5) gives the contractor some leeway in this respect, and this constitutes a substantial relaxation of the position from the earliest ICE conditions. This is all subject to the proviso that a late notice has not operated to the substantial prejudice of the engineer, or prevented him from investigating the situation. That might be the case where the measures taken by the contractor have obliterated the physical conditions, meaning that the engineer cannot make any assessment of them. It would also present the contractor with evidential problems in trying to pursue his claim at a later stage.

The scope of clause 12 is physical conditions or artificial obstructions, expressly excluding weather conditions or conditions caused by weather conditions. An occurrence such as a landslide caused by severe storms would therefore be excluded from the ambit of clause 12. This particular definition within clause 12 is identical to the 5th and 6th editions, and much of the consideration given by the courts to this topic has been under those earlier editions. For example, in *Humber Oil Terminals Trustee Ltd* v. *Harbour and General Works (Stevin) Ltd*,[11] the Court of Appeal was asked to look at the decision of an arbitrator in respect of the collapse of a jack-up barge, one of the legs of which punched through the ground on which it was resting. The Court decided that, whilst the general soil conditions were known, foreseeable and foreseen, their liability to sheer at a much lower loading condition than had originally been understood was an unforeseeable condition. The physical condition encountered by the contractor was therefore that the soil behaved in an unforeseeable manner under the stress that was applied to it. The application of the stress could therefore be considered to be part of the physical condition, this despite the fact that the application of the stress was part of the contractor's own method. It would appear, therefore, that conditions need be neither pre-existing nor permanent to fall within the scope of clause 12.

The definition of artificial obstructions has been the subject of less commentary and debate in the courts; Keating suggests buried services, statutory controls and obstructive members of the design team as examples.[12]

The issue of reasonable foreseeability is compounded by the difficulty in laying down general principles for application across all situations. Clause 12(1), for example, does not distinguish between the probable and the possible. In *Morgan Grenfell (Local Authority Finance) Ltd* v. *Seven Seas Dredging Limited*,[13] a contract made provision for rock to be pre-blasted, but otherwise anticipated that the rock would be dredgeable. When the works were carried out, rock had to be pre-blasted because it was undredgeable, and the contractor made a claim for additional time and payment. The arbitrator considered that some undredgeable rock could have been foreseen, but there was no reason why the contractor should reasonably have foreseen the existence of undredgeable rock in excess of the provisional quantities. The decision of the court turned on procedural matters relating to whether notice of various arguments had been given, and therefore does not provide any firm authority on the point, but nonetheless is illustrative of the types of issue that a tribunal might take into account.

Clause 13 – work to be to satisfaction of engineer

Clause 13 provides:

Work to be to satisfaction of Engineer	13(1)	Save insofar as it is legally or physically impossible the Contractor shall construct and complete the Works in strict accordance with the Contract to the satisfaction of the Engineer and shall comply with and adhere strictly to the Engineer's instructions on any matter connected therewith (whether mentioned in the Contract or not). The Contractor shall take instructions only from the Engineer or subject to Clause 2(4) from his duly appointed delegate.
Mode and Manner of Construction	13(2)	The whole of the materials Contractor's Equipment and labour to be provided by the Contractor under Clause 8 and the mode manner and speed of construction of the Works are to be of a kind and conducted in a manner acceptable to the Engineer.
Delay and extra cost	13(3)	If in pursuance of Clause 5 or sub-clause (1) of this Clause the Engineer shall issue instructions which involve the Contractor in delay or disrupt his arrangements or methods of construction so as to cause him to incur cost beyond that reasonably to have been foreseen by an experienced contractor at the time of tender then the Engineer shall take such delay into account in determining any extension of time to which the Contractor is entitled under Clause 44 and the Contractor shall subject to Clause 53 be paid in accordance with Clause 60 the amount of such cost as may be reasonable except to the extent that such delay and extra cost result from the Contractor's default. Profit shall be added thereto in respect of any additional permanent or temporary work. If such instructions require any variation to any part of the Works the same shall be deemed to have been given pursuant to Clause 51.

Clause 13(1) compresses into one sub-clause a number of provisions, the most important of which, in the context of claims, is in respect of work which is legally or physically impossible.

The contractor is not obliged to carry out works where it would be unlawful for him to do so, for example by rendering him in breach of statutory provisions. That extends to acts which would infringe the rights of an individual. In *Havant*

Borough Council v. *South Coast Shipping Limited*,[14] it was held that the engineer had a duty to issue a variation where temporary works had been stopped by an injunction obtained by local residents. The consequence of this was, of course, that the contractor became entitled to additional time and payment for the variation in the usual way; in other words, the employer bears the risk that carrying out of the works may become unlawful. This is, of course, dependent upon the unlawful activity having been *required* by the contract. There was some discussion in the *Havant Borough Council* case as to whether the method statement was a contract document to which the contractor was contractually bound to adhere. If it had not formed part of the contract, it appears that the contractor would have been free to adopt an alternative method at his own risk (and cost).

Physical impossibility is perhaps more difficult to define. There is a starting point in the decision of *Turriff Ltd* v. *Welsh National Water Development Authority*,[15] where the court came to the conclusion that physical impossibility must be considered 'in accordance with the precise limits of the specification and drawings, which are expressly made part of the contract'. In other words, where the work is only physically possible by departing from the strict provisions of the contract, the contractor is entitled to a variation.

The question of what constitutes impossibility was considered by Stabb J in *Turriff*. In that case, it was contended for the employer that impossibility should mean 'absolute impossibility'; the Judge considered that this could have two possible meanings:

- from a material or physical point of view, the end result would not be achieved, whatever the steps taken to try and get round or over the difficulty which was said to render the performance physically impossible; or
- impossible to perform in compliance with the contract specification and drawings.

The Judge preferred the second of these approaches; to adopt the first, he said,[16] would be to require a contractor to breach the contract in order to overcome the impossibility. At page 132, Stabb J said:

> If absolute impossibility is to be the test, then equally a strict construction of the Contract must be applied, in the sense that what is physically impossible in accordance with the precise limits of the Specification and Drawings ... should not be considered possible, because it can be rendered such by a deviation from the Contract on the part of the Contractor ... This Contract was not absolute in that insofar as physical impossibility of performance supervened, the contractor was excused. I cannot accept that Turriff were under an obligation to depart from [the] Specification ... Drawings, when performance in accordance with them became impossible.

In his findings in fact, the Judge concluded that it was impossible for the contractor to carry out the work *on an ordinary commercial competitive basis as the parties intended*. Most commentators conclude, however, that commercial impossibility is not sufficient to fall within the scope of clause 13(1).

This point was taken up in *Yorkshire Water Authority* v. *Sir Alfred McAlpine & Son (Northern) Ltd*[17] (a decision reached on the basis of the ICE 5th

Conditions). In that case, the Court was not required to decided whether work was physically impossible or not, but concluded (at page 126):

> If the variation which took place was necessary for the completion of the works because of impossibility within clause 13(1), then, in my judgment, the [contractor] was entitled to a variation order with the consequent entitlement to payment of the value of such variation as is provided in clause 51(2) and clause 52.

In other words, where carrying out the works is impossible within the meaning of clause 13(1), the contractor is entitled to have this treated as a variation, and also is therefore entitled to the benefit of the appropriate consequences in time and money.

The contractor is required to construct and complete the works to the satisfaction of the engineer. As the engineer has no power to amend the contract,[18] the practical effect of this clause is to require the contractor to construct and complete the works in accordance with the contract.

In the Scottish case of *Shanks & McEwan (Contractors) Limited* v. *Strathclyde Regional Council*,[19] the specification for the construction of an underground sewer provided for prefabricated tunnel segments to be capable of withstanding various forces without cracking. In fact, cracks did occur in the segments, and the contractor asked the engineer to meet the costs arising out of the cracking. The engineer responded by telling the contractor that the cracked segments were acceptable, provided that they were reasonably watertight. That letter was held to be an instruction or direction within the meaning of clause 13(3) and to constitute a variation in terms of clause 51.

Shanks & McEwan was cited in of *Norwest Holst Construction Ltd* v. *Renfrewshire Council*,[20] Norwest Holst had contracted to construct a railway underbridge in terms of the ICE 5th Conditions. The impossibility in that case related to the bearing piles; it was found that the design of these was not part of the Temporary or the Permanent Works, and as a consequence the construction difficulties were not part of Norwest Holst's design responsibilities. In the circumstances, the engineer was required to devise a solution to resolve the issue of impossibility, and to issue the appropriate instructions.

Clause 14 – Method/Programme

Clause 14 provides:

Design criteria	14(5)	The Engineer shall provide to the Contractor such design criteria relevant to the Permanent Works or any Temporary Works design supplied by the Engineer as may be necessary to enable the Contractor to comply with sub-clauses (6) and (7) of this clause.

Methods of construction	14(6)	If requested by the Engineer the Contractor shall submit at such times and in such further detail as the Engineer may reasonably require information pertaining to the methods of construction (including Temporary Works and the use of Contractor's Equipment) which the Contractor proposes to adopt or use and calculations of stresses strains and deflections that will arise in the Permanent Works or any parts thereof during construction so as to enable the Engineer to decide whether if these methods are adhered to the Works can be constructed and completed in accordance with the Contract and without detriment to the Permanent Works when completed.
Engineer's consent	14(7)	The Engineer shall inform the Contractor in writing within 21 days after receipt of the information submitted in accordance with sub-clauses (1)(b) and (6) of this Clause either
	(a)	that the Contractor's proposed methods have the consent of the Engineer or
	(b)	in what respects in the opinion of the Engineer they fail to meet the requirements of the Contract or will be detrimental to the Permanent Works.
		In the latter event the Contractor shall take such steps or make such changes in the said methods as may be necessary to meet the Engineer's requirements and to obtain his consent. The Contractor shall not change the methods which have received the Engineer's consent without the further consent in writing of the Engineer which shall not be unreasonably withheld.
Delay and extra cost	14(8)	If the Contractor unavoidably incurs delay or extra cost because
	(a)	the Engineer's consent to the proposed methods of construction is unreasonably delayed or
	(b)	the Engineer's requirements pursuant to sub-clause (7) of this Clause or any limitations imposed by any of the design criteria supplied by the Engineer pursuant to sub-clause (5) of this Clause could not reasonably have been foreseen by an experienced contractor at the time of tender.

Then the engineer shall take such delay into account in determining any extension of time to which the Contractor is entitled under Clause 44 and the Contractor shall subject to Clause 53 be paid in accordance with Clause 60 the amount of such cost as may be reasonable except to the extent that such delay and extra cost result from the Contractor's default. Profit shall be added thereto in respect of any additional permanent or temporary work.'

The contractor is only entitled to make a claim under clause 14(8) if he has *unavoidably* incurred delay or extra cost; to succeed in a claim, the contractor will have to show that he took all possible steps to avoid the delay and cost occurring. The delay and cost must have actually been incurred as a result of the engineer's actions under one of the categories set out below.

The first ground of claim to which these sub-clauses gives rise is in the situation where the engineer takes an unreasonably long period of time in which to give his consent to a method of working which has been proposed by the contractor.

The second ground of claim arises if the engineer imposes limitations and requirements on the contractor in respect of his method of working which could not have reasonably been foreseen by an experienced contractor at the time of the submission of tender. If the limitations and requirements were unforeseeable, the contractor has not had the opportunity to price for them.

It should be noted that any limitations or requirements in respect of the method are not variations: the method is the responsibility of the contractor, and therefore changes to it are at his risk, unless unforeseeable in the manner provided for in clause 14(8). Even if the limitations or requirements were not foreseeable, they are not treated in the same way as variations for valuation purposes. Clause 14(8) provides that the contractor is to be paid his 'reasonable' costs, which can include an element of profit, to the extent that they relate to additional works (whether permanent or temporary). Any delay is to be ascertained in accordance with the usual principles of clause 44.

Clause 31 – facilities for other contractors

Clause 31 provides:

Facilities for other contractors   31(1)   The Contractor shall in accordance with the requirements of the Engineer or Engineer's Representative afford all reasonable facilities for any other contractors employed by the Employer and their workmen and for the workmen of the Employer and of any other properly authorised authorities or statutory bodies who may be employed in the carrying out on or near the Site of any work not in the

		Contract or of any contract which the Employer may enter into in connection with or ancillary to the Works.
Delay and extra cost	31(2)	If compliance with sub-clause (1) of this Clause involves the Contractor in delay or cost beyond that reasonably to have been foreseen by an experienced contractor at the time of tender then the Engineer shall take such delay into account in determining any extension of time to which the Contractor is entitled under Clause 44 and the Contractor shall subject to Clause 53 be paid in accordance with Clause 60 the amount of such cost as may be reasonable. Profit shall be added thereto in respect of any additional permanent or temporary work.

If the contractor suffers actual cost and delay as a consequence of the activities of the employer's other contractors, workmen or other authorities, and that cost and delay could not reasonably have been foreseen by an experienced contractor at the time of tender, then he may be entitled to make a claim. Any claim for additional time will be dealt with in the usual way under clause 44. Additional money is not recoverable under the valuation principles of clause 52, but rather the contractor is entitled to his 'reasonable' costs (plus an element of profit so far as the costs relate to additional permanent or temporary works).

The facts which give rise to a contractor's claim under clause 31(2) may also entitle the contractor to make a claim arising from the employer's failure to give him possession of the site in terms of clause 42(3). In order to maximise his potential recovery, however, the contractor may choose to focus upon the clause 42(3) claim, which does not restrict costs to those that were not reasonably foreseeable at the time of tender.

Clause 40 – suspension of work

Clause 40 provides:

Suspension of work	40(1)	The Contractor shall on the written order of the Engineer suspend the progress of the Works or any part thereof for such time or times and in such manner as the Engineer may consider necessary and shall during such suspension properly protect and secure the work so far as is necessary in the opinion of the Engineer. Except to the extent that such suspension is
	40(1)(a) (b)	otherwise provided for in the Contract or necessary by reason of weather conditions or by some default on the part of the Contractor or

(c)   necessary for the proper construction and completion or for the safety of the Works or any part thereof in as much as such necessity does not arise from any act or default of the Engineer or the Employer or from any of the Excepted Risks defined in Clause 20(2) then if compliance with the Engineer's instructions under this clause involves the Contractor in delay or extra cost the Engineer shall take such delay into account in determining any extension of time to which the Contractor is entitled under Clause 44 and the Contractor shall subject to Clause 53 be paid in accordance with Clause 60 the amount of such extra cost as may be reasonable. Profit shall be added thereto in respect of any additional or permanent or temporary work.

Suspension lasting more than three months   40(2)   If the progress of the Works or any part thereof is suspended on the written order of the Engineer and if permission to resume work is not given by the Engineer within a period of 3 months from the date of suspension then the Contractor may unless such suspension is otherwise provided for in the Contract or continues to be necessary by reason of some default on the part of the Contractor serve a written notice on the Engineer requiring permission within 28 days from the receipt of such notice to proceed with the Works or that part thereof in regard to which progress is suspended. If within the said 28 days the Engineer does not grant such permission the Contractor by a further written notice so served may (but is not bound to) elect to treat the suspension where it affects part only of the Works as an omission of such part under Clause 51 or where it affects the whole Works as an abandonment of the Contract by the Employer.

The contractor may be entitled to make a claim where the engineer has suspended the works. The engineer is entitled to suspend the works without incurring any financial or time consequences on the part of the employer if:

- the conditions specifically entitle him to do so in particular circumstances
- weather conditions make it necessary to suspend the works
- the suspension is made necessary by the contractor's own default[21]

- the suspension is necessary for safety reasons – provided that the safety issue was not caused by some action of the engineer or the employer. If the engineer or employer is responsible for the safety issue having arisen, he is likely to be liable to the contractor for the time and money consequences of the delay
- the suspension is necessary for the proper construction and completion of the works (i.e. in accordance with the contract). Again if the suspension has become necessary through some action of the employer or the engineer, the employer will, in those circumstances, be liable for the contractor's associated costs and delay.

The costs that the contractor is entitled to recover under clause 40(1) are restricted to reasonable costs, again with the additional element of profit as provided for in terms of clauses 31(2) and 14(8). Delay is to be dealt with under the usual extension of time provisions in clause 44.

The contractor has further remedies available to him if the suspension carries on for more than three months, where that suspension is not specifically provided for in the contract or is not caused by the contractor's own default. Other than in those situations, the contractor is entitled to serve notice on the engineer seeking permission to be allowed back to continue work. If the permission is not forthcoming within 28 days, the contractor is entitled to treat the contract as having been abandoned (provided that the suspension related to the whole of the works). The contractor's remedies upon abandonment are not specified; he may well be entitled to argue that the works had been abandoned in breach of contract by the employer.[22] If the suspension relates only to part of the works, the contractor is not entitled to treat the whole of the works as having been abandoned: instead, his entitlement is to treat the suspended section as having been omitted as a variation in terms of clause 51. The relevant section would therefore no longer form part of the works, and the contractor would have no obligation to construct and complete that section, or to comply with any directions of the engineer in respect of it.

Clause 42(3) – failure to give possession

Clause 42(3) provides:

Failure to give possession	42(3)	If the Contractor suffers delay and/or incurs extra cost from failure on the part of the Employer to give possession or access in accordance with the terms of this Clause the Engineer shall take such delay into account in determining any extension of time to which the Contractor is entitled under Clause 44 and the Contractor shall subject to Clause 53 be paid in accordance with Clause 60 the amount of any extra cost to which he may be entitled. Profit shall be added thereto in respect of any additional permanent or temporary work.

This clause deals with the situation where the contractor suffers delay and extra cost from a failure by the employer to give possession or access to the site. Profit may be added to the claim in relation to any additional permanent or temporary work.

The 'site' is defined in clause 1(v) as 'the lands and other places on under in or through which the Works are to be constructed and any other lands or places provided by the Employer for the purposes of the Contract together with such other places as may be designated in the Contract or subsequently agreed by the Engineer as forming part of the Site'. Ideally, a plan of the site should be annexed to the contract although this is not provided for in the ICE 7th Conditions. If areas of the site are not to be made available on the commencement date then that should be explicitly stated. A failure to do so may give the contractor grounds for an extension of time or a claim for cost and profit if the site turns out not to be available.

Clause 44 – extension of time for completion

This topic is dealt with in Chapter 6.

Clause 46 – rate of progress

Clause 46 provides:

Rate of progress	46(1)	If for any reason which does not entitle the Contractor to an extension of time the rate of progress of the Works or any Section is at any time in the opinion of the Engineer too slow to ensure substantial completion by the time or extended time for completion prescribed by Clause 43 and 44 as appropriate or the revised time for completion agreed under sub-clause (3) of this Clause the Engineer shall notify the Contractor in writing and the Contractor shall thereupon take such steps as are necessary and to which the Engineer may consent to expedite the progress so as substantially to complete the Works or such Section by that prescribed time or extended time. The Contractor shall not be entitled to any additional payment for taking such steps.

Provision for **accelerated completion**	46(3)	If the Contractor is requested by the Employer to complete the Works or any Section within a revised time being less than the time or extended time for completion prescribed by Clauses 43 and 44 as appropriate and the Contractor agrees so to do then any special terms and conditions of payment shall be agreed between the Contractor and the Employer before any such action is taken.

This clause effectively provides an acceleration mechanism for the engineer to instruct the contractor to 'take such steps as are necessary' to expedite progress. Two conditions precedent must be met before such an instruction may be issued:

- in the engineer's opinion progress must be too slow to ensure substantial completion at the prescribed time (as that may have been amended)
- the reasons for the slow progress must be such that they do not already entitle the contractor to an extension of time elsewhere in the contract.

Expediting progress will almost certainly involve the contractor in additional cost. That cost is likely to be irrecoverable even if it later transpires that the clause 46 notice had been invalidly given, for example because the contractor was actually entitled to an extension of time which would render the notice redundant. Courts in other jurisdictions, particularly in the United States, have embraced the principle of recovery for constructive acceleration; this trend has not so far been followed in the UK courts.

Clause 47 – liquidated damages for delay

This topic is dealt with in Chapter 6.

Clause 51 – alterations, additions and omissions

This topic is dealt with in Chapters 5 and 6.

Clause 52 – valuation of ordered variations

This topic is dealt with in Chapter 5.

Breach of contract at common law

Common law claims

Whilst the standard forms deal extensively with the rights of the parties in various situations, and set out procedures for claims to be made, the position at common law (i.e. aside from the conditions of contract) must also be considered. This may be because the parties have not entered into a formal contract, and there are no standard form conditions which apply. It may be because the conditions of contract do not cover the specific situation in which the claiming party finds himself, or because he wishes to explore other remedies. If a claimant has failed to observe a condition precedent which must be complied with before a claim can be made, he may find his route to recovery under the contract conditions barred, and will wish to seek an alternative common law remedy. In any event, a claiming party is not restricted to pursuing the remedies available to him under the standard form conditions of contract.[23]

In order to succeed in a claim for breach of contract, the claiming party must establish that there is an express or implied term that has been breached, and as a result of that breach he has suffered some loss. The most usual common-law claims in this category are in respect of implied terms, and these are dealt with in more detail below.

Claims for common-law breach of contract do not fall within the remit of the engineer in the ICE 7th conditions, and he is not entitled to make a ruling on the entitlement of either the employer or the contract in such a claim, unless the parties expressly give him that power.

Remedies at common law for breach of contract

The common law has a scale of penalties, which can be exacted against the party in breach. However, the appropriate remedy will depend upon the type of breach. It would not be in the interests of commerce for the courts to allow parties to walk away from the contract over a trivial or immaterial breach. We have already seen in Chapter 8 that it is open to the innocent party to terminate the contract if he thinks the breach is serious enough. This begs the question of how serious such a breach would need to be.

Whether a breach is deemed to be fundamental will depend, to a large extent, upon how important the breached clause is within the contract. Any breach of a clause fundamental to the contract is deemed to be a material breach. A material breach attracts the severest penalty, allowing the innocent party the choice of insisting on proper performance of or otherwise enforcing the contract, accepting the breach and thereby ending the contract completely. It may be the case that the parties do not wish such an important decision to be left to the courts. In such situations, the parties should themselves expressly indicate which clauses are fundamental to the contract[24] and therefore, if one party does breach one of these clauses the other party can take decisive action without fear. After the contract has been terminated the innocent party is free to sue for damages in respect of any loss caused. It should be noted that where a party terminates the contract in respect of a breach which is non-material, their termination of the contract will in itself be treated as a material breach leaving them open to possible claims by the other party.[25]

Where a breach is deemed non-material there are various remedies open to the innocent party:

- **Damages** – he may continue to perform the contract but sue for damages for the loss caused by the breach.
- **Suspension** – he may refuse to perform his part of the bargain in return.

- **Interdict** – he may raise an action against the party in breach to prohibit him carrying out the any action which will breach the contract.
- **Specific implement** – he can raise an action against the party in breach to compel him to perform his contractual obligations.

Damages

This is the most familiar and commonly claimed common-law remedy for breach of contract. It gives the claiming party the opportunity to carry on with the contract, whilst being able to claim for any loss he has sustained as a result of the breach.

The purpose of damages is to compensate for any loss sustained and to put the innocent party in the same position as he would have been in had the contract been performed properly.[26] The actual loss which a party has sustained as a result of the breach is not directly relevant to a calculation of common law damages for breach of contract.[27]

Conversely, the claiming party will not necessarily therefore be entitled to claim all the loss that he has sustained. The amount recoverable will be limited to:[28]

- Either, the loss which could fairly and reasonably be said to have arisen from the particular breach of contract in the usual course of things (but not to loss caused by some special characteristics or circumstances of the claiming party); or
- the loss that might reasonably be supposed to have been in the contemplation of both the parties at the time that the contract was entered into as having been the probable result of the breach. Under this limb, if it was in the contemplation of the parties that some particular or special loss might occur, then this loss might be recoverable. However, if the contract between the parties excludes recovery for 'consequential' loss, that could act as a bar to the success of this type of claim.

The claiming party must also act positively to mitigate the extent of his loss. Damages will be reduced or even lost completely if no steps are taken to seek to limit the loss as soon as the breach is first discovered.[29]

The approach to damages can be illustrated by various examples:

- Where a contractor breaches the contract by failing to complete the works, the employer may be entitled to damages. The measure of those damages will be what it costs the employer to engage another contractor to complete the works, less what the employer would have had to pay the contractor for the work (the contract price). If the contractor has carried out some work, he is entitled to be paid for that. If the employer has paid him for work not actually carried out, then the employer is entitled to the return of that money.
- Where the contractor carries out work that is defective or shoddy, the measure of damages would be the cost to the employer of putting that work right. If it can be established that the employer has no intention of putting the work right,[30] or it would cost a disproportionate amount to do so,[31] the measure of damages might instead be the difference between the

value of what the employer contracted to have, and what he actually ended up with.

- Where a contractor is late in completing work, and there is no liquidated damages provision, common law damages may apply. This topic is dealt with in Chapter 6.
- Where a contractor has work removed from him that he had contracted to carry out, he will be entitled to be paid for the work that he has done, together with the element of profit that he might have expected to earn on the remainder of the removed work.
- For common law claims relating to delay and disruption, see below.

Suspension

The concept of suspension is already familiar from the standard form conditions. As discussed above, clause 40 of the ICE 7th Conditions provides for suspension and Section 112 of the Act gives a party to a contract to which the Act applies the right to suspend performance for non-payment. The right is only to be exercised if the sum due under the construction contract is not paid in full by the final date of payment. That statutory right is far more limited than the right at common law. The common law remedy operates on the premise that where one party does not fulfil his obligations, the other party can withhold the performance of his own obligations.

Suspension is clearly a powerful remedy, which will almost certainly have significant financial consequences for the project as a whole. The risks inherent in a wrongful suspension are such that parties will rarely consider this as an option, other than as a last, and extreme, resort.

Interdict

Interdict, by its very nature, must be used before the behaviour inducing breach of contract is completed. If the court grants such a petition for interdict or interim interdict the effect is to prohibit the party from acting in breach of the contract in the specific way ordered,[32] or to require a party to refrain from doing something.

Interdicts are only available from the courts, and the courts do not approach this remedy lightly; indeed, as a last resort, breach of interdict can be punishable by imprisonment.[33] Any application for the remedy must be precise, and only go so far as is absolutely necessary to prevent the wrong in question; the courts will not award it where it restricts the actions of a party too widely.

Specific implement

Specific implement is the positive flip-side to interdict. Where an interdict forbids someone from doing something, specific implement compels them to do something. The courts have used this remedy to force a party to construct buildings,[34] or to rebuild them,[35] where the contract has required this to be done.

The remedy of specific implement is not available where the claiming party could be compensated sufficiently financially, or it would be legally or physically impossible to comply.

Common law claims for prolongation and disruption

As has already been discussed, if standard conditions of contract are not imported into a contract, a contractor will not be able to rely on specific contractual machinery to prosecute a claim for costs arising from delay or disruption to the contract works. In such circumstances, it will be far more difficult for a contractor to make such claims, although not impossible. The contractor will, in the absence of any established contractual procedure, require to rely on breaches of implied terms of contract and a damages claim founded on such breaches.

The Scottish and English courts have considered which terms can be implied into construction contracts. It should be noted that a court will only be prepared to accept the implication of a term into a contract if it is necessary to do so on the basis of, for example, business efficacy (see Chapter 2).

The leading case in Scotland on implied terms for recovery of delay and disruption costs is *Scottish Power plc* v. *Kvaerner Construction (Regions) Limited*.[36] In the circumstances of that case Lord McFadyen was prepared to accept that the following terms could be implied into the contract:

- The employer should not hinder or prevent a contractor from carrying out its obligations in accordance with the terms of the contract and executing and completing the contract works in a regular and orderly manner.
- The employer should take all steps in its power which are reasonably necessary to enable the contractor to discharge its obligations and to execute the contract works in a regular and orderly manner.
- The employer should provide the contractor with full and correct information concerning the contract works in such a manner and at such times as is reasonably necessary for the contractor to fulfil its obligations under the contract.

Lord MacFadyen also held that there could be no implied term in a contract that was contradicted by an express term, but if an express term of the contract merely touched upon the subject matter of an implied term it would not necessarily exclude it. In other words, a contractual mechanism for recovery of costs related to delay or disruption of works will not necessarily preclude a claim for loss as a result of a breach of an implied term, although the availability of such a claim will depend on the precise wording of the contract. Claims based on implied terms will, however, be difficult to establish if a contract provides for specific procedures to recover delay or disruption costs.[37]

The question as to whether or not particular terms can be implied into a contract will fall to be determined in the factual context of each separate case. Evidence will be required to support the proposition that a particular term should be implied into a contract, and claimants should beware of assuming that a court will automatically fill any gaps that the parties have left in their contractual arrangements.

Claims in delict

The law of delict

Delictual obligations differ substantially from contractual ones, and a detailed examination of the law of delict is outwith the scope of this book. The essence of delict is that a party may be obliged to compensate another who has suffered loss as a result of their wrongful actions. The measure of loss in a delictual claim also differs from that in contractual claims for damages: the purpose of damages in a delictual context is to put the claiming party into the position they would have been in had the delict never happened.

For a party to make a delictual claim against another, they must be able to show:

- that the other party owed them a duty of care
- that the other party breached the duty of care
- that the breach caused the loss complained of
- that the type of loss sustained is of a type in respect of which the law will allow recovery.

Duty of care

What will determine the existence of a duty of care will turn on the precise relationship between the parties, and whether that has involved an assumption of responsibilities on which the other party has placed reliance. Thus, even where there might be no contract between a contractor and an employer, the contractor who commences work will almost certainly owe a duty of care to the employer.

Conversely, where there is a contract between the parties, this does not in itself exclude the possibility of a claim being made in delict, and a contractor may owe a delictual duty of care to an employer even though there is a contract between them. There has been some debate about concurrent liabilities in delict and contract; the position would now appear to be as set out in the decision of the House of Lords in *Henderson* v. *Merrett Syndicates Ltd*,[38] namely that what is relevant is whether there has been an assumption of responsibility coupled with the concomitant reliance, irrespective of whether there is also a contract between the parties. Where there is a contract, this gives the claiming party the opportunity to choose which approach to take: contractual or delictual. In practice, where a party wishes to pursue a delictual claim, he will do so in addition to the contractual claim but on an alternative. He will not, however, be entitled to do this where the contract expressly excludes such a delictual claim being pursued. Furthermore, where there is a contract between the parties, a court or arbiter should have reference to its terms, which are likely to be determinative of the delictual duty of care.[39]

Breach of the duty of care

The claiming party must establish that there has been a breach of the duty owed to him, and not simply an involuntary action on the part of the other party.[40] In the context of a claim relating to professional services, a breach will be constituted by a failure to exercise the degree of skill and care which would have been shown by any member of that profession with ordinary skill at the time that the breach is alleged to have happened, who was exercising ordinary skill in carrying out his duties.

Causation

A legal and factual connection must be established between the breach that took place and the loss that it is alleged to have caused. In establishing factual causation, a simple 'but for' test will often be adopted.[41] For example, but for an architect failing to note an unstable wall, the resulting structure would not have collapsed.[42] This is the test in its simplest form; the situation becomes increasingly complex depending on the type of loss incurred and the number of duties of care owed. Even where the factual test is satisfied, however, legal causation may not be present. For example, where there has been an intervening cause, this may be held to have broken the chain of causation. To return to the example of the architect and the wall, where the cause of the wall collapsing was a supplier's van backing into it, the architect's act will no longer be deemed to be the cause of the harm. However, where the supervening act is reasonably foreseeable it will not break the chain of causation.[43] The chain can also be broken by the injured party's actions.

Where the injured party has voluntarily undertaken to risk the harm caused by the other party's behaviour he will not be able to claim for any loss, and he may well be held to have accepted a reduced standard of care. For example, a foreman will not be held liable for a labourer refusing to take adequate safety precautions even where the site is unsafe. Damages will also be reduced if the party claiming has in any way contributed to its own loss.[44]

Pure economic loss

As has already been noted[45] the area of pure economic loss, as opposed to injury to persons or other property, has proved a difficult one for the construction industry. The departure from the clear test presented in *Anns* v. *Merton Borough Council*[46] has left this area in some confusion.

In the Scottish case of *Junior Books Ltd* v. *Veitchi Co. Ltd*,[47] the House of Lords was divided as to whether recovery should be allowed for 'pure economic loss', or whether the loss in question could actually be classified as damage to property, in which case it would be recoverable under the usual principles in any event.

The employer (Junior Books) entered into a building contract for the construction of a new factory; Veitchi were a nominated sub-contractor, who laid a new floor in part of the factory. The flooring was found to be defective, allegedly due to poor workmanship, or use of poor materials, on the part of Veitchi. As a consequence, Junior Books claimed against Veitchi for the cost of replacing the floor, which they said was necessary to avoid ongoing and increased maintenance costs. This claim, which was essentially one for economic loss, had to be brought as a delictual claim, because there was no contract between Junior Books and Veitchi.

On a majority decision (4:1), the House of Lords decided that Veitchi were liable for the economic loss that Junior Books had sustained, although only on the basis of the specific circumstances which prevailed, and particularly the very close degree of proximity between the parties, arising from:

- Veitchi's knowledge of Junior Books' requirements
- Junior Books' reliance on Veitchi's expertise
- Veitchi's status as a nominated sub-contractor, meaning that Veitchi were aware that Junior Books were relying on their particular expertise in this area
- the relationship between the parties which was as close as it could possibly be without there actually being a contract – they were actually connected by a series of contracts (the main and nominated sub-contractor).

This very close relationship was distinguished from 'ordinary' consumer contracts where a manufacturer produces goods for ultimate sale to the general public. Because of the particular circumstances giving rise to the duty of care in the Junior Books case, the Court was prepared to find that the duty extended to economic loss. However, the case should not be read as providing any general endorsement of an extension of the principles relating to economic loss.

In *Murphy* v. *Brentwood District Council*,[48] it was held that a builder who had constructed the foundations to local authority approved plans could not be held to owe a duty of care to the subsequent owner of the house if those foundations proved to be defective, effectively restricting what might otherwise have been an indeterminate liability on the part of the builder.

The current position in respect of economic loss would therefore appear to be that pure economic loss is only recoverable where there is a 'special relationship of proximity imposing on the tortfeasor a duty of care to safeguard the [claiming party] from economic loss',[49] in other words where there has been an assumption of responsibility which has been relied upon.[50]

Assessment and evaluation of financial claims

Terminology

The terms 'cost', 'additional cost', 'extra cost', 'expense' and 'profit' are all used in the ICE 7th Conditions. Cost itself is defined at clause 1(5) as meaning '. . . all expenditure properly incurred or to be incurred whether on or off the Site including overhead finance and other charges properly allocated thereto but does not include any allowance for profit'. The remainder of the terms used are not so defined. The most noteworthy exclusion from the definition is the element of 'profit'. It follows that where any claim under the ICE 7th Conditions refers to 'cost' and there is no express reference to 'profit', there is no scope to claim any element of profit on that claim. The remainder of the terms, 'additional cost', 'extra cost', 'expense' and 'profit' fall to be construed in accordance with the facts and circumstances applicable to the clause to which they apply, although 'expense' has been held[51] to have a wider meaning than 'cost' and arguably may include elements for both profit and interest.

Overheads

Claims arising under engineering contracts frequently make reference to elements for head office and site overheads. Such overheads may include:

- travelling costs
- security costs
- on-site facilities costs
- insurance and ancillary financial security costs
- on-site storage and staff facility costs
- office accommodation.

The basis for recovering a contribution for either head office or site overheads is the inability of the site-based resources to earn head office contributions on other contracts because the site-based resources are tied up by the prolonged contract. It follows, therefore, that in making a claim for such elements it is essential that the contractor has been unable to take on other work that he would have won and on which he would have made a profit. Proof of these matters is of course potentially complex and involves consideration of the contractor's private commercial arrangements. The pragmatic course therefore grew up of using one of a number of formulae to calculate the lost head office overheads and profit.

Formulae

The Hudson, Emden and Eichleay formulae enable the contractor to calculate the loss of contribution to its head office overheads as a result of the delay and are often used by contractors when submitting claims. As the contractor will have been unable to release its resources to earn the contribution to overheads on another project, it must earn a similar contribution by making a claim on the delayed project. However, formulae do not amount to proof of the validity of the contractor's claim. They should be supported where possible by hard data and vouching. It is imperative to the success of overhead claims that full and accurate records are maintained.

Whether head office overheads are recovered will always depend on the availability of work and success in tendering for that work. This is where the use of a formula is generally accepted by the courts, although it has been a feature in the Scottish courts for far less time than in the courts of England and Wales. The courts have wrestled with the formulae approach in cases such as *Ellis-Don* v. *The Parking Authority of Toronto*[52] (where the formulae approach was deemed acceptable though the percentage had to be shown to be reasonable and market conditions required evidence); and *Tate & Lyle* v. *The GLC*,[53] where the contractor claimed 2 per cent on prime costs for managerial time – here the court accepted that such a claim was recoverable but refused to award any sum as it considered that there was inadequate documentary evidence and that a formula quantum analysis was speculation.

The high water mark of such contractors' claims came in the case of *Alfred McAlpine* v. *Property and Land Contractors* (1999).[54] Again, the formula approach to the assessment of quantum was accepted and it was confirmed that the reimbursement of head office overheads would be permissible where under-recovery was occasioned by the delay and the contractor had no means of reducing these costs, as a result of the events giving rise to the delay. A distinguishing feature of this case is that *Property and Land* was a contractor that generally worked on one project at a time and did not undertake another until the project was complete. Its dedicated approach to its client meant that it was not in a position to replace its turnover during a stoppage or delay in its current activity. Such a position would have been relatively easy to prove. A more conventional contractor may require to produce documentary evidence that it was, effectively, denied the opportunity to take on other work by reason of a delays, something which may not always be easy to do. As many commentators have observed, contractors do not tender for works simply to arm them with the relevant paperwork for a future claim.

That logic was followed in the recent Scottish case of *Beechwood Development Company (Scotland)* v. *Stuart Mitchell t/a Discovery Land Surveys*[55] in which Lord Hamilton approved the use of the Hudson formula in calculating a contractor's claim for head office overheads and profit. The court addressed the fundamental difficulty of such claims, namely whether there is sufficient evidence to support a claim being made on the basis of a formula. However the case did present unusual circumstances in that the contractor worked for one client only, and in general on one contract at a time.

A formula approach might be more likely to be accepted by the courts if, at the material time the construction market was buoyant (e.g. *St Modwen Developments* v. *Bowmer & Kirkland*[56]). It may be more difficult for a very large contractor to show that delay on one project hindered its ability to win other work, as in *AMEC Building Limited* v. *Cadmus*.[57]

The question of how these various cases may be reconciled must now be considered. The case of *Norwest Holst Construction* v. *Co-operative Wholesale Society*[58] reviewed the necessary foundations for assessing loss and expense upon a formula geared to the sub-contractor's overhead recovery. Judge Thornton considered that these foundations were as follows:

- The loss in question must be proved to have occurred.
- The delay in question must be shown to have caused the contractor to decline to take on other work which was available and which would have contributed to its overhead recovery. Alternatively, it must have caused a reduction in the overhead recovery in the relevant financial year or years which would have been earned but for that delay.
- The delay must not have associated with it a commensurate increase in turnover and recovery towards overheads.
- The overheads must not have been ones that would have been incurred in any event without the contractor achieving turnover to pay for them.
- There must have been no change in the market affecting the possibility of earning profit elsewhere and an alternative market must have been available.

These criteria generally capture the matters to which the contractor ought to have regard in promoting a claim on this basis.

Interest/finance charges

There are a number of routes by which a contractor may seek to recover interest as part of his claim:

- under an express condition of the contract relating to interest (this is dealt within Chapter 5)
- under the Late Payment of Commercial Debts (Interest) Act 1998 (this is dealt within Chapter 5)
- under a contractual condition which provides for the recovery of interest under a general claim, such as for 'costs'
- as part of damages at common law
- in terms of the award of an arbiter or court.

As has already been seen, there are various provisions throughout the ICE 7th Conditions which entitle a contractor to recover his 'cost' in the event of certain circumstances occurring (for example compliance with an engineer's direction relating to method which could not have been foreseen at the time of tender in accordance with clause 13(5)). Where the contractor is entitled to recover on this basis, his 'cost' may well include interest or finance charges.

The case of *F G Minter Ltd* v. *Welsh Health Technical Services Organisation*[59] related to a contract incorporating the 1963 edition of the RIBA conditions. The Court of Appeal referred to the distinction already discussed above between direct losses and consequential losses, direct losses essentially being those where the loss could fairly and reasonably be said to have arisen from the particular breach of contract in the usual course of things. The Court decided that, in the usual course of things, contractors require to fund operations; that will involve them either in borrowing (which will cost them interest) or using their own resources (which will lose them the interest which they might otherwise have earned). The ICE 7th Conditions do not, of course, make use of the term 'direct loss', and the reference is simply to 'cost'; nonetheless, it is submitted that the approach taken by the Court in *Minter* has applicability to contracts under ICE 7th Conditions.

An alternative route to interest is as special common law damages for breach of contract; in other words under the second limb of the rule in *Hadley* v. *Baxendale* referred to above. If it was within the contemplation of both the parties at the time when the contract was entered into that the contractor would incur particular interest or finance charges in the event of a particular breach of contract by the employer, then the charges may well be recoverable. The contractor must be able to prove the actual rates of interest involved, and the actual costs that he has sustained.

The final route to interest is as part of a dispute resolution procedure:

- An **adjudicator** has no general power to award interest in terms of the Act. He will only be able to do so where the claiming party has a contractual right to interest (for example, under clause 60(7) of the ICE 7th Conditions), or the parties have expressly agreed to confer on him the right to award interest.
- An **arbiter** only has power, at common law, to award interest from the date of his award together with contractual interest. The parties may

confer the power to award interest upon the arbiter, and most of the standard form sets of arbitration rules do provide for this power.

- In **court proceedings**, where the claim arises from sums due under a contract, interest is payable from the date on which the court proceedings are served on the defending party (the date of citation), unless the money can be shown to have been wrongfully withheld. Where the claim is for damages, the court does have the discretion to award interest prior to the date of citation, and may award it from the date on which the right to pursue the claim first arose.[60]

Claims under CECA Conditions

No form of sub-contract conditions specifically for use with the ICE 7th Conditions has been published at the date of writing. The most up to date successor to the FCEC 'Blue Form' is the CECA form of sub-contract conditions of July 1998, reprinted with amendments in April 2001, for use with ICE 6th Conditions.

Clauses 2 and 3 – obligations of the sub-contractor

The sub-contractor is required not only to carry out the sub-contract works in accordance with the sub-contract,[61] but also to carry them out such that in terms of clause 3(2)

> no act or omission of his in relation thereto shall constitute, cause or contribute to any breach by the Contractor of any of his obligations under the Main Contract . . .

In terms of clause 3(4), if the sub-contractor does commit an act or omission which constitutes a breach of the main contract, then the contractor is entitled to claim from him the loss that flows to the contractor as a result of the breach of the main contract. So, for example, if delay caused by the sub-contractor causes the main contract works not to have been completed by the contractual completion date, the liquidated damages which become due as a result are expressly stated to have been within the contemplation of the parties within the meaning of the second limb discussed in the section on Damages, and are therefore potentially recoverable by the contractor from the sub-contractor.

Clause 6 – delay

Clause 6(2) provides for the sub-contractor to be entitled to a 'fair and reasonable' extension of time for completion of the sub-contract works where the sub-contractor has been delayed *and*

- the delay was not caused by the sub-contractor; *and*
- the contractor is entitled to an extension of time under the main contract for the same reason; *or*
- the delay has been caused by a variation to the sub-contract works (see also below); *or*

- the delay was caused by the contractor in breach of the sub-contract.

The right to an extension of time only arises if the sub-contractor has first complied with the notice provisions of clause 6(2)(c), which require the sub-contractor to give written notice to the contractor of the delay within 14 days of the delay first occurring, together with 'full and detailed particulars' of the entitlement to an extension of time.

Clause 8 – variations

Variations can emanate from the contractor, the engineer, or the contractor and the employer in agreement together, but they are only valid (and hence give rise to an entitlement to time and money) if they are confirmed in writing by the contractor. The right to claim on the part of the sub-contractor only arises if the written procedure has been properly followed.

Clause 10 – adverse physical conditions

Clause 10(2) reflects the provisions of clause 12 of the ICE 6th and 7th Conditions, in that it requires the contractor to:

> take all reasonable steps to secure from the Employer such contractual benefits, if any, as may be claimable in accordance with the Main Contract on account of an adverse physical condition or artificial obstructions that may affect the execution of the Sub-Contract Works and the Sub-Contractor shall in sufficient time afford the Contractor all information and assistance that may be requisite to enable the Contractor to claim such benefits.

If the sub-contractor does not provide the information and assistance required and, as a result, the contractor fails to obtain sums which would have otherwise been due from the employer, the contractor is entitled to deduct those sums from money which he is due to pay to the sub-contractor.

To the extent that the contractor secures additional payment and/or an extension of time under the main contract in respect of conditions that affect the sub-contract works, the contractor is obliged to pass those on to the sub-contractor and to notify the sub-contractor of what is to be paid – see clause 10(2)(b). The contractor is under an obligation to ascertain the relevant sum to be paid and the appropriate extension of time. The contractor is obliged to ascertain payment to the sub-contractor in these circumstances regardless of whether he is actually paid under the main contract.

Prescription

The significance of prescription

Prescription is a legal mechanism which establishes or extinguishes certain rights or obligations by the passage of time. Prescription can also limit the methods of proving a particular right or obligation.

There are two types of prescription: negative and positive. Negative prescription is concerned with the extinction of rights by the lapse of time whereas positive prescription establishes rights by the same process. Negative prescription is focused on in this section as this is more likely to be of relevance to (and encountered by) those involved in the execution of conventional engineering contracts.

Negative prescription is important as it will end, for example, a party's right to pursue a claim for a payment under a contract or seek damages flowing from a breach of contract. It is not uncommon for claims raised in arbitration or court proceedings to be brought to a halt because the party making the claim did not take the necessary steps within the relevant 'prescriptive period' to formally prosecute the claim.

The key source of law on prescription in Scotland is the Prescription and Limitation (Scotland) Act 1973 ('the Prescription Act'). A number of decisions have also been reported which consider and interpret the provisions of the Prescription Act.[62]

Why does prescription exist? It is perhaps not difficult to see that it is in the interests of commerce and industry to have such a system in place. The problems which may arise in defending a claim for payment many years after an obligation to pay arose are obvious – for example, the paying party may have destroyed the paperwork relevant to a claim and may not be able to investigate whether it is legitimate; or personnel with a knowledge of the claim may have moved on or retired. A claim may become far more difficult to consider or defend simply because one party has been dilatory in pursuing it. Furthermore, businesses cannot be expected to make perpetual provisions in their accounts for liabilities which may or may not be pursued at some point in the future.

Short negative prescription: the five-year prescriptive period

The Prescription Act provides that certain obligations will prescribe (become extinguished) if:

- an obligation has subsisted for five years since the 'appropriate date' for that obligation. The appropriate date is different for different types of obligation and is discussed below; and
- the five-year prescriptive period has not been 'interrupted' by:
  - a relevant acknowledgement of the obligation; or
  - a relevant claim being made in relation to the obligation.[63]

Obligations

First, it is necessary to define the obligations which short negative prescription affects. These are defined in Schedule 1 of the Prescription Act. A number of obligations are set out in the Schedule, but only some of these are germane to the operation of engineering contracts. These are summarised below.

(a)   An obligation arising from, or by reason of any breach of, a contract, not being an obligation falling within any other provision of paragraph 1 of Schedule 1 – this obligation contemplates, for example, an obligation owed by an employer to make payment to a contractor for work carried out under a contract or an obligation upon a sub-contractor to compensate a contractor in relation to works carried out to rectify defective sub-contract works.[64]

(b) An obligation arising from liability to make reparation – this obligation contemplates an obligation to make payment to a party arising from the breach of a *delictual* duty of care. This is distinct from an obligation arising from a breach of contract.[65] For example, if repair work is carried out to a roadway adjacent to an office block the party carrying out such works may be held to owe a duty of care to (at least) the owners of the office block. If structural damage to the office block resulted directly from the road works the party carrying out these works may be obliged to meet a damages claim by the owner in respect of repairs to the office block.[66]

(c) An obligation based on the legal remedy of unjustified enrichment (which will include restitution, repetition or recompense) – an example of this obligation would arise where a party to a contract had been overpaid in error by the other party and was obliged to repay the overpaid amount (repetition).[67]

The appropriate date

The 'appropriate date' for an obligation determines *when* the five-year prescriptive period commences. The Prescription Act sets out specific provisions determining the 'appropriate date' for particular types of obligation. These provisions are to be found in Schedule 2 to the Prescription Act. For example, an obligation to pay money in respect of services rendered in a series of transactions between the same parties on the basis of a continuing account is referred to in Schedule 2. The commencement date for the prescriptive period for such services would be the date on which payment for the goods or services last supplied becomes due.[68]

If the obligation is not one to be found in Schedule 2, section 6(3) of the Prescription Act determines that the appropriate date in relation to such an obligation is 'the date when the obligation becomes enforceable'. For the obligations noted at (a)–(c) above, the appropriate date is the date when the obligation becomes enforceable.

When, then, does an obligation become enforceable?

The answer to this question is different for different types of obligation. In relation to obligations to make payment the position will differ according to the machinery set out in the contract for establishing when sums fall due. The Act of course requires that a contract subject to its provisions defines the date upon which an interim payment will fall due. An obligation to make payment under the ICE 7th Conditions will arise upon issue of a certificate by the engineer. The date of such certification will mark the beginning of the five-year prescriptive period in relation to the sum certified.

In the case of a performance bond the date an obligation would be held to become enforceable would be the date on which there was a default in performance which would allow the party holding the bond to insist on it. If the performance bond requires a demand for payment before it can be insisted upon, the bond will be held to be enforceable on the date the demand is made.[69]

What is the appropriate date for an obligation to pay damages for a breach of contract, or an obligation to make reparation for breach of a delictual duty? Section 11 of the Prescription Act is relevant to the types of obligation. The basic principle governing the identification of the appropriate date has two branches:

- There must have been an occurrence of **loss**, **injury** or **damage**. This has been described as 'a phrase of style commonly used to comprehend the various types of loss which may be sustained as a result of a breach of a legal duty or obligation';[70] and
- The loss, injury or damage identified as having occurred must have been *caused* by the **act**, **neglect or default** identified as creating it. These words are broad in scope and application, but do not apply to, for example, a failure to make payment under a contract, something which should be done *in accordance with* the contract. In other words, there must be a concurrence of the loss, injury or damage with the act, neglect or default. The act, neglect or default must either occur before or at the same time as the loss, injury or damage complained of. It has been held in the case of *Cole* v. *Lonie*[71] that a contractual obligation can give rise to more than one default leading to an obligation to make reparation for loss, injury or damages. Therefore – for the purposes of the Prescription Act – loss, injury or damage can occur at different times as a consequence of separate 'types' of breach of a contractual obligation.[72]

It was held in the case of *Strathclyde Regional Council* v. *Border Engineering Contractors Ltd and Babtie Shaw & Morton* 1997 SCLR 100 that, in relation to the defective pipeline works carried out under the ICE Conditions of Contract, 4th edition, that the date of occurrence of the relevant neglect, act or default in respect of the relevant breach of contract was not the actual date the pipeline was laid but instead the date of substantial completion of the contract.[73]

Section 11(2)–(3) of the Prescription Act is also important. Section 11(2) states that where as a result of a *continuing* act, neglect or default, loss, injury or damage has occurred *before* the act, neglect or default *ceases*, the loss, injury or damage is deemed to have occurred on the date the act, neglect or default ceased. An example of a continuing act or default may be the failure of a builder to properly secure joists supporting a floor which in turn leads to continual movement of the floor.

Section 11(3) states that the prescriptive period does not start to run where the party entitled to seek reparation was not aware (and could not with reasonable diligence have become aware) that loss, injury or damage had occurred. The theory behind this provision is that prescription should not run while a creditor is under excusable ignorance of his rights. A proper and sound awareness of the state of completed works and a rigorous regime of inspection to detect defects in any works in therefore important. The meaning of reasonable diligence will vary according to different factual circumstances and may be addressed by evidence from an expert engineer, architect or surveyor as to whether the defect in question should have been detected at an earlier stage.

Interruption of prescriptive period – relevant claims and acknowledgements

Relevant claims   If a relevant claim is made in relation to an obligation the five year prescriptive period which commenced from the 'appropriate date' will be interrupted. A relevant claim is defined by section 9 of the Prescription Act as 'a claim made by or on behalf of the creditor [the party to whom the obligation is owed] for implement or part implement of the obligation in appropriate proceedings . . .'.[74]

A claim could be made in the form of, for example, an action for payment or for damages. A letter seeking payment or threatening formal proceedings will not constitute a relevant claim. Appropriate proceedings may be court proceedings in a court of competent jurisdiction (whether in Scotland or not), arbitration proceedings in Scotland or arbitration proceedings outwith Scotland which would produce an award enforceable in Scotland.[75] Adjudication proceedings would not constitute appropriate proceedings for the purposes of the Prescription Act.

In the case of an action raised in court, the date of service of a Writ or Summons specifying the obligation relied upon will be the date a relevant claim will be held to have been made. In arbitration the claim will be held to have been made on the earlier of (i) the date the claim was actually made in the arbitration; or (ii) the date a preliminary notice was served (provided that the notice adequately specified the nature of the claim).

Relevant acknowledgement   Section 10 of the Prescription Act is applicable to relevant acknowledgements. Like a relevant claim, a relevant acknowledgement has the effect of interrupting the five-year prescriptive period. Section 10 states that the subsistence of an obligation shall be regarded as a relevant acknowledgement if:

- there has been such performance by or on behalf of the party under the obligation in question towards the implementation of the obligation which clearly indicates that the obligation still exists. An example of this would be the periodic reduction of a debt or payment of interest on a subsisting debt; or, alternatively
- there has been an unequivocal written admission made by and/or on behalf of the party under the obligation in question clearly acknowledging that the obligation still exists. Whether a document or letter amounts to such an admission will be a question of fact. Generally, absolute clarity will be required.

Long negative prescription: the 20-year prescriptive period

The period of long negative prescription is 20 years. The critical difference between short and long negative prescription relates to when the prescriptive period commences. The prescriptive period for long negative prescription does not commence on the 'appropriate date' but, instead, on the date the obligation in question became enforceable.

The real relevance of long negative prescription to engineering contracts is that it provides a 'long stop' date for claims relating to latent defects. Unlike short negative prescription, long negative prescription is not subject to the caveat that the prescriptive period cannot run where the party entitled to seek reparation was not (and could not with reasonable diligence have become) aware that loss, injury or damage resulting from an act, neglect or default had occurred. In other words the 'discoverability' principle set out in section 11(3) of the Prescription Act does not apply to long negative prescription.

Accordingly, if a latent defect which can be linked to, for example, defective workmanship during the original construction works of a bridge only becomes apparent 20 years after the works have been completed, *it will not matter* that it could not have been discovered before that time. The obligation upon the original contractor to make reparation may be held to have prescribed by an application of long negative prescription.

Like short negative prescription, the period of long negative prescription can be interrupted by a relevant claim or acknowledgement.

Notes

[1] See also Chapter 5, Treatment of variation in engineering contracts.

[2] See also Chapter 6, Liquidated damages.

[3] *Holland Hannen & Cubitt (Northern) Ltd* v. *Welsh Health Technical Services Organisation Ltd* (1981) 18 BLR 80.

[4] *Neodox* v. *Swinton & Pendlebury Borough Council* (1958) 5 BLR 34.

[5] *Holland Hannen & Cubitt (Northern) Ltd* v. *Welsh Health Technical Services Organisation Ltd, supra.*

[6] See para below.

[7] This is an objective test. See section on Suspension for discussion.

[8] Clause 12(2).

[9] Pursuant to clause 12(4)(d).

[10] In distinction to the position under, for example, clause 26 of JCT 1998 where failure to give timely notice of a claim for loss and expense is likely to be fatal to that claim.

[11] (1991) 59 BLR 1.

[12] Furst and Ramsey (2000), *Keating on building contracts*, 7th edition, at paras 20–76.

[13] (1989) BLR 31.

[14] (1998) 14 Const LJ 420.

[15] Reported in the *Construction Law Year Book* (1994), page 122, quoted at 32 BLR 117.

[16] Per Stabb J at page 131.

[17] 32 BLR 114.

[18] Clause 2(1)(c).

[19] 1995 SLT 172.

[20] 1996 GWD 40–2261.

[21] See clause 65.

[22] See below in respect of remedies for breach of contract.

[23] *London Borough of Merton* v. *Stanley Hugh Leach Ltd, supra* (1985) 32 BLR 31.

[24] *Dawsons Ltd* v. *Bonnin* 1922 SC (HL) 156, *EFT Commercial* v. *Security Change* 1993 SLT 128.

[25] *Wade* v. *Waldon* 1909 SC 571.

[26] *Spencer* v. *Macmillan's Trustees* 1958 SC 300 at 303, 315, *Haberstich* v. *McCormick & Nicholson* 1975 SC 1.

[27] *Brown* v. *Edinburgh Magistrates* 1907 SC 256.

[28] *Hadley* v. *Baxendale* [1854] 9 Ex. 341.

[29] *Daejan Developments* v. *Armia* 1981 SC 48.

[30] *C.R. Taylor* v. *Hepworths* [1977] 2 All ER 784, [1977] 1 WLR 959.

[31] *Ruxley Electronics* v. *Forsyth* [1996] AC 344.

[32] *Exchange Telegraph Co.* v. *Giullianotti* 1959 SC 19.

[33] *Maclay* v. *Macdonald* 1928 SC 776.

[34] *Stewart* v. *Kennedy* (1890) 17 R (HL) 47.

[35] *Middleton* v. *Leslie* (1892) 19 R 801.

[36] 1999 SLT 721.

[37] Further guidance on terms which the courts in England have been prepared to imply is given in the following cases: *London Borough of Merton* v. *Leach* (1985) 32 BLR 51, *Martin Grant & Co.* v. *Lindsay Parkinson* (1984) 29 BLR 31 and *J & J Fee* v. *The Express Lift Company* (1993) 34 Con LR 147. See also the Scottish case of *Ductform Ventilation (Fife)* v. *Andrews Weather Foil Limited* 1995 SLT 88.

[38] [1995] 2 AC 145.

[39] *William Hill Organisation* v. *Bernard Sunley & Sons* (1982) 22 BLR 1.

[40] *Waugh* v. *James K Allan Limited* 1964 SC (HL) 102.

[41] *Porter* v. *Strathclyde Regional Council* 1991 SLT 446.

[42] This example is based on the assumption that the architect is responsible for the works.

[43] *Sayers* v. *Harlow Urban District Council* [1958] 2 All ER 342.

[44] Section 1(1) Law Reform (Contributory Negligence) Act 1945.

[45] At page 17.

[46] [1978] AC 728.

[47] [1983] 1 AC 520.

[48] [1991] 1 AC 398.

[49] Lord Bridge in *Murphy* v. *Brentwood District Council* [1991] 1 AC 398 at 475.

[50] *Hedley Byrne* v. *Heller & Partners* [1964] AC 465.

[51] *Chandris* v. *Union of India* [1956] 1 WLR 147, [1956] 1 All ER 358 (CA).

[52] (1978) 28 BLR 98.

[53] [1983] 2 AC 509.

[54] (1995) 76 BLR 59.

[55] (2001) SLT 1214.

[56] (1996) CILL 1203.

[57] (1996) 51 Con LR 105.

[58] (1998) unreported, but referred to in *Keating on building contracts* at para 8–63.

[59] (1980) 13 BLR 1.

[60] Interest on Damages (Scotland) Act 1971.

[61] Clause 2(1) of the CECA Sub-contract.

[62] For those readers wishing a comprehensive commentary on the Prescription Act, reference should be made to *Walker on prescription and limitation of actions*, 5th edition, W. Green, 1996 or *Prescription and limitation*, Johnston, D. Greens (1999). The term 'limitation' should be distinguished from prescription. Limitation prevents formal proceedings from being raised to pursue a particular right after a defined period of time but does not, strictly speaking, extinguish a right (although the effect is often, for practical purposes, exactly the same). The term is more commonly used in England.

[63] Section 6(1) of the Prescription Act.

[64] See para 1(g) of Schedule 1. It should also be noted that an obligation to refer any dispute arising under a contract to an arbiter will be categorised as an obligation arising *under* a contract.

[65] At least for the purposes of Schedule 1 – compare with Section 11 of the Prescription Act which covers both contractual and delictual obligations to make reparation.

[66] See para 1(d) of Schedule 1.

[67] See para 1(b) of Schedule 1.

[68] Schedule 2 of the Prescription Act, para 1.

[69] See the case of *City of Glasgow DC* (No. 2) v. *Excess Insurance Co. Limited* 1990 SLT 225 for discussion in relation to the date a performance bond becomes enforceable.

[70] *Dunlop* v. *McGowans*, 1979 SC 22, at page 23.

[71] 2001 SC 610.

[72] A number of cases deal with these issues. See, for example, *Renfrew Golf Club* v. *Ravenstone Securities Limited* 1984 SC 22 where it was held that defects in design or workmanship would not give rise to loss, injury or damage until *actual* damage was sustained. See also *Scott Lithgow* v. *Secretary of State for Defence* 1989 SLT 236 (HL) and *Dunlop* v. *McGowans* 1979 *supra cit.*

[73] 1997 SCLR 100.

[74] Section 9(1) of the Prescription Act.

[75] Section 4(2) of the Prescription Act.

10. Dispute resolution

Introduction

The engineering contract captures the precise balance of the parties' various commercial risks.

The efficacy of the engineering contract depends upon the parties' ability to enforce the rights and obligations under it. However, the perception of both parties of their respective rights and obligations does not always coincide. For the engineering contract to work, each party must have some mechanism by which they can compel the other to adhere to the terms of the contract, or to compensate them in the event of their failure to do so.

Disputes can be resolved in, for example, the following:

- court
- adjudication
- arbitration
- conciliation
- mediation.

The advent of statutory adjudication has undoubtedly altered the nature of dispute resolution in most areas of the construction and engineering industry.

The decision of an adjudicator is not, however, finally binding upon parties to a dispute (unless they agree that it should be). The decision of a court, or, in many contracts, an arbiter, will be. Litigation and arbitration are therefore still very relevant to the industry as methods of resolving disputes. Some claims (such as claims arising from contracts excluded from the ambit of the Act) cannot be resolved by adjudication. The Scottish courts have on a number of occasions (as is explored further below) also had to deal with the enforcement of adjudicators' decisions, and challenges to these decisions.

This chapter is not intended to be an exhaustive guide to the different forms of dispute resolution procedures available to the engineering industry, but, instead, a practical guide to the key features of some of these procedures and the issues which are most frequently encountered in everyday industry life.

Litigation

Dispute resolution in the courts is commonly known as litigation. In the absence of an agreement by parties that disputes be referred to arbitration (or if the parties have decided to waive their right to arbitrate) the final determination of engineering contract disputes will be carried out by the courts.

In Scotland, civil litigation is conducted in the Sheriff Courts and in the Court of Session.

Jargon and terminology

Terminology used by lawyers to describe the various stages in the life of a court action can often be confusing. A simplified guide to the most commonly encountered terminology is provided in Appendix 7. Reference will be made to some of these terms in this chapter.

The Sheriff Courts   The Sheriff Courts are Scotland's local courts. Scotland is divided into six Sheriffdoms by reference to local government areas. The Sheriffdoms are in turn split into Sheriff Court Districts. In each District is a town or city where the local Sheriff Court is located.

Small to medium value claims are generally, but not exclusively, pursued in the Sheriff Court. Claims of a value up to £1500 must be pursued in the Sheriff Court.[1] The selection of the Sheriff Court in which to commence proceedings is governed by statutory rules of jurisdiction but turns largely on what is most convenient for the party pursuing a claim.[2]

Busier Sheriff Courts (e.g. Glasgow Sheriff Court) now allow certain disputes to be designated as 'Commercial Causes'. Commercial Causes are defined as actions arising out of or concerned with any transaction or dispute of a 'commercial or business nature' and include, for example, actions relating to building, engineering or construction contracts or to the sale or hire purchase of goods.

The Sheriff Court Rules contain separate provisions for Commercial Causes which allow such actions to be progressed more rapidly than other Sheriff Court actions.[3] The court will aim to focus quickly the issues of controversy in Commercial Causes and ensure that there is no unnecessary delay in proceedings. It will very often be in a pursuer's interest to elect to have an action proceed as a Commercial Cause.

Court of Session   The Court of Session is Scotland's superior civil court and is located in Edinburgh and in certain circumstances in London. Parties are generally represented by counsel (Advocates or Queens Counsel) in Court of Session actions, although some solicitors (Solicitor Advocates) also have rights of audience in the Court of Session.

The Commercial Court   As is the case with certain Sheriff Courts, pursuers in the Court of Session can elect to commence proceedings in the Commercial Court rather than under ordinary Court of Session procedure.[4] It is likely that virtually all disputes emerging from engineering contracts would fall within the wide definition of a Court of Session Commercial Action and would therefore be referable to the Commercial Court.[5] The procedure in Commercial Actions in the Court of Session (as with the Sheriff Court equivalent) is designed to be swifter and more flexible, and to place less emphasis on formal written pleadings than conventional Court of Session procedure.

A number of full-time commercial judges have been appointed. Commercial Actions are generally dealt with by the same judge throughout their duration, thus creating continuity and consistency of case management.

Scotland does not, as yet, have the equivalent of the English Technology and Construction Court. It is arguable that the Commercial Court fulfils a very similar role as many building and engineering disputes are referred to it. It does not, however, deal exclusively with these types of dispute.

Appeals   Appeals from the decision of a Sheriff can be made to the Sheriff Principal of the relevant Sheriffdom or to the Inner House of the Court of Session. The decision of an Outer House judge can be appealed to the Inner House. Certain matters can also be appealed from the Court of Session to the House of Lords.

The Administration of Justice (Scotland) Act 1972   This Act provides that in certain circumstances the court may be asked to provide an opinion on points of law dealt with by an arbiter in an arbitral decision, and that the arbiter can be asked to 'state a case' to the court for this purpose. This procedure, which is akin to an appeal to the court on a point of law, is more fully covered in the section of this chapter which explores arbitration.

Litigation tools: arrestment and inhibition

One of the most commonly encountered features of an action raised in court in Scotland (and often one of the most concerning for a defender of an action) is an arrestment. The inhibition is a close relative of an arrestment, but is less commonly encountered.

Arrestments and inhibitions can create acute and immediate financial difficulties for a defender. Their impact on a party can be commercially significant.

Exactly what is an arrestment?   An arrestment is a protective measure which gives the pursuer in a court action a preference over other ordinary creditors of a defender. In simple terms, it can be used to gain a measure of security for a claim. Arrestment can be used either:

(i)   before a court decides on the merits of an action – 'arrestment on the dependence'; or
(ii)   after a court has decided on the merits of an action and granted decree in favour of a pursuer – 'arrestment in execution'.

Arrestments on the dependence of actions are often used by pursuers at the outset of actions, and can be effected even before a writ or summons is served on a defender. The questions posed below mainly contemplate arrestments on the dependence of an action.

Arrestment allows a pursuer to prevent a third party which holds moveable (as opposed to heritable) property for a defender, or which owes money to a defender, from passing that property or money to the defender. This includes money held by a bank in a defender's bank account. An arrestment can therefore block a party's 'cash flow'.

An arrestment is only competent in an action for payment of a sum of money, including a claim for damages.

What is an inhibition?   Inhibition, like arrestment, is a protective measure. Inhibition allows a pursuer to prevent a defender from selling or granting security over his heritable property (e.g. land and buildings). The section below focuses specifically on arrestments as these are more commonly encountered in the day-to-day operation of engineering contracts. Advice should be sought on the execution and effects of an inhibition, albeit many of the principles applicable to arrestments are also relevant to inhibition.

How is an arrestment effected?

(i) Warrant for arrestment   A pursuer may obtain a warrant for arrestment on the dependence by including an application for warrant to arrest in the Initial Writ or Summons.

The court's warrant to arrest the Initial Writ or Summons (or a copy of it) is passed to Sheriff Officers (if the action has been raised in the Sheriff Court) or Messengers at Arms (if the action has been raised in the Court of Session), together with instructions as to the parties ('arrestees') in whose hands arrestments should be served.

(ii) Arrestments: a new regime?   The case of *Karl Construction Limited* v. *Palisade Properties plc*[6] has had a fundamental impact on the way in which Scottish courts deal with applications for warrants to arrest.

The case dealt with an attack on an inhibition on the dependence of an action. A number of bases for removal of the inhibition were advanced on behalf of the defender, but the most novel was that the system for granting warrants to inhibit on the dependence contravened the European Convention on Human Rights.[7] In particular, it was argued that the restraint on the sale of property presented by inhibition was struck at by the Convention's requirement that every natural or legal person (which would include a limited company) should be entitled to the peaceful enjoyment of their possessions.

The court considered whether the availability of inhibition was, on balance, justified – as permitted by the Convention – to allow the State to 'control the use of property in accordance with the *general interest*'. After considering not only the present Scottish system of inhibition, but also similar devices available in other jurisdictions such as France and Germany, the Court formed the view that in order for a measure such as inhibition to be compatible with the Convention four requirements require to be satisfied:

(i)   a pursuer must establish a *prima facie* case on the merits of the action;

(ii)   a pursuer must establish that there is a significant risk of the defender's insolvency or that the defender is likely to take steps to conceal or dissipate assets;[8]

(iii)   a hearing must take place where (i) and (ii) can be considered;

(iv)   if inhibition is eventually found to have been used without any objective justification, or if a pursuer is unsuccessful in an action, a defender may be entitled to damages for loss suffered as a consequence of the use of the inhibition.

The court in *Karl Construction* found that the present Scottish system of inhibiting on the dependence failed to meet these requirements and recalled the inhibition.

The presiding judge was careful to say that his decision did not extend to the system of arrestments on the dependence. In addition, the decision (which was one of the Outer House of the Court of Session), while being persuasive, does not bind other Court of Session judges or sheriffs.[9]

Notwithstanding this, it does seem at the time of writing that virtually all of Scotland's Sheriff Courts are now insisting that solicitors acting for a pursuer appear before a Sheriff in order to provide grounds for warrant to *arrest* on the dependence of an action to be granted. The reason for this significant change in procedure appears to be the *Karl Construction Limited* v. *Palisade Properties plc* decision. Before *Karl Construction*, obtaining warrant to arrest on the dependence of an action was a straightforward 'rubber-stamping' process carried out by the Sheriff Clerk.

It is not known, at the time of writing, whether this approach will eventually be extended to the Court of Session, but this seems likely. It is to be hoped that clarity and consistency in Scotland's courts as to the correct approach in obtaining a warrant to arrest on the dependence of an action will be achieved.

Following the decision in *Karl Construction*, a Sheriff Court has in fact held that the existing practice in the Sheriff Courts of automatically allowing a Pursuer in an action to arrest sums of money due to a Defender also contravenes the European Convention on Human Rights. In the case of *Fab-Tek Engineering Limited* v. *Carillion Construction Limited*[10] Fab-Tek raised proceedings in the Sheriff Court seeking payment under the terms of the contract. In common with normal practice, the Initial Writ sought a warrant to arrest on the dependence of the action, which was granted. Arrestments were served. Carillion applied to the court to have the arrestments recalled on the basis that, in light of the Court of Session decision in *Karl Construction*, the warrant had been granted in contravention of the Convention.

The Sheriff's decision is not as detailed as that of the court in *Karl Construction*, but it is clear that he has fully adopted the reasoning in the *Karl* decision. Although the *Karl Construction* decision expressly stated that the position with regard to arrestments did not have '. . . any direct bearing on arrestment on the dependence' the Sheriff nevertheless held that arrestments on the dependence were vulnerable to a similar attack. It remains to be seen whether other Sheriffs, or Judges in the Court of Session, will take a similar view in considering warrants to arrest granted prior to the *Karl Construction* decision.[11]

It will also be interesting to see the approach taken by other courts in granting new warrants to arrest and the criteria they will apply in doing so. Evidence of a party's financial position revealed by, for instance, accounts lodged with the Registrar of Companies may be required to obtain a warrant to arrest.

If it appears that there is no stateable defence to a claim, it may be that in these circumstances a court would be prepared to grant warrants to arrest, notwithstanding the financial status of a company. If, however, a party apparently has a stateable defence (subject of course to the defence being tested and proved in court) and is seemingly solvent, obtaining warrant to arrest may be very difficult. It can be said with reasonable confidence that arrestments will become more difficult to effect and, in all probability, less common.

When can an arrestment be used?   Arrestment is generally only competent where the action is for payment of a sum of money (including damages) and where the sum sued for is presently due, such as a sum which is certified as payable to a contractor by an employer.[12]

The leading case on this point is the case of *Costain Building & Civil Engineering Limited* v. *The Scottish Rugby Union plc*.[13] Costain was the contractor for the redevelopment of Murrayfield Stadium. The contract was governed by the ICE 5th Conditions. In accordance with the conditions of contract, payments only fell due to Costain upon issue of payment certificates. Costain sued for payment of an interim valuation. No certificate had been issued in relation to the sum claimed but Costain nevertheless proceeded to instruct an arrestment on the dependence in the hands of the Royal Bank of Scotland.

The arrestment was challenged by the SRU. It was held that the Costain claim for payment was contingent upon the decision of the Engineer appointed under the contract and the issuing of a payment certificate reflecting the Engineer's decision as to what should be paid to Costain.[14] Costain's claim was a contingent claim which was not presently due to Costain. The court held that Costain had no right to demand security for a debt which would only fall due at some point in the future (if at all) and accordingly recalled the arrestment.[15]

Arbitration   If the parties' contract provides for arbitration the party seeking payment can nevertheless commence court proceedings and implement arrestments on the dependence of the action. It has been held that it is legitimate to do this notwithstanding the existence of an arbitration clause which could be relied upon to have the court proceedings 'sisted' (suspended). Arrestments served on the dependence of such an action remain in place until the resolution of arbitration proceedings and settlement of any arbitral award.[16]

In whose hands can an arrestment be served?   Arrestments can be served in the hands of any third party which is subject to the jurisdiction of the Scottish courts and which holds moveable property for, or owes money to, a defender (for example, an employer under an engineering contract or a contractor's bank).

What can be arrested?   An arrestment can attach debts, an obligation to account to a defender by a third party, or moveable (as opposed to heritable) property belonging to a defender.

The obligation to make payment under a building contract is arrestable even if payment has not yet fallen due to a contractor, or if the obligation to pay is conditional upon completion of the work to the employer's satisfaction. The price of work yet to be performed is arrestable as what is being arrested is the right to be paid for work, a right which is vested in a contractor as soon as a contract is entered into.[17] The import of this principle is that if an arrestment is served in the hands of an employer between the issuing of payment certificates it is not the case that the arrestment is automatically ineffective. The obligation to account to the contractor for works carried out (but for which no payment certificate had yet been issued) would be caught by the arrestment. The sum certified in the next certificate as payable to the contractor should not in these circumstances be paid to the contractor nor should any balance of the current price.

How can an arrestment be released?   Arrestments will normally be recalled upon alternative security (such as a bank guarantee or money in a joint deposit account) being provided by the defender. However, an arrestment may also be recalled or restricted with or without security:

(a)   where it is 'nimious' (i.e. where it can be seen to be a superfluous and vexatious precaution) or it is oppressive;

(b)   where it has been effected or made possible by the fraud or wrong of the pursuer;

(c)   where the subjects are not arrestable[18]; or

(d)   where there is an irregularity in the execution of the arrestment. The courts have taken a very strict line in considering errors in the description of the defender in the arrestment schedule (the document served on the arrestee) – a misdescription in the name of a limited company may be enough to invalidate the arrestment.[19]

The test for nimiety and oppression is essentially equitable, and therefore at the discretion of the court. As a result, firm rules as to when an arrestment may be recalled on this basis cannot be laid down.[20]

An arrestment can also be restricted by agreement of a pursuer if it has caught a sum in excess of the sum sued for, together with allowance for interest and expenses which may be incurred in pursuing the sum sued for.

How long can an arrestment remain in place?   An arrestment on the dependence will remain in place until the pursuer agrees to release the arrestment (for example, after an action has settled or after alternative security has been provided) or until three years after the final decree of a court.

There is no duty on an arrestee to invest the arrested funds, nor is there a liability to pay interest on the funds in the event of the arrestment being released.[21]

In the event of a decree eventually being granted in the pursuer's favour, the pursuer may follow up the arrestment by 'an action of furthcoming', a procedure which allows sums arrested to be released to a Pursuer in full or partial satisfaction of a court's decree. A decree of furthcoming ordains the third party arrestee to pay a pursuer sums caught by an arrestment. In practice, furthcoming is seldom necessary as the defender usually grants a mandate authorising the third-party arrestee to release the subject arrested to the pursuer.

What happens if payment is made notwithstanding the presence of an arrestment?   If payment is made in breach of an arrestment (and providing there was knowledge of the arrestment) to the prejudice of the party instructing the arrestment, the party releasing the funds becomes liable to the pursuer for the value of the funds up to the limit of the amount secured by the arrestment. Payment in breach of the arrestment may also amount to contempt of court.

Obtaining payment following successful litigation

After a decree has been granted a written demand for payment (following the expiry of the time limit for an appeal)[22] is the usual first step to obtaining payment. If a written demand for payment is unsuccessful the crucial document is the 'extract' or official copy of the court's decree. This acts as a certificate that the decree exists in the court records and is authority for taking formal steps to give effect to the decree. The extract decree is simply a piece of paper which records the name of the case and the order made by a court. The extract decree can be used to effect further arrestments or to serve a 'charge' for payment. A charge is a formal request for payment of the debt and warning that if the debt is not paid within a specified time, winding-up or sequestration proceedings can be commenced.[23] Frequently, service of a charge will provoke payment.

Adjudication

Introduction

The Act introduced a statutory right to adjudication in all construction contracts entered into on or after 1 May 1998.[24] Its introduction was anticipated by Sir Michael Latham's 1994 report 'Constructing the Team'.

The availability of adjudication has unquestionably had a fundamental impact on the culture of dispute resolution in the industry. According to one survey. In the two years since the start of statutory adjudication in May 1998 the number of disputes being referred to adjudication (and which were reported to the survey compilers) increased by 600 per cent (from 187 in year one to 1309 in year two).[25] The same survey showed a levelling off of the number of disputes referred to adjudicators between May 2000 and April 2001.

It is probable that the use of adjudication will continue to increase and that this process will become the predominant method of resolving disputes in many sectors of the construction and engineering industry (if it is not already).

This section of the chapter is intended to be a simplified guide to the key features of the adjudication process with particular emphasis on how adjudication is dealt with in ICE and CECA contracts.

The body of procedural rules for adjudications referred to in ICE and CECA contracts, the ICE Adjudication Procedure (1997), is also considered.

What is adjudication?

Adjudication is a procedure whereby an impartial 'person of skill' is appointed to reach a rapid decision in determination of a dispute between parties to a construction contract. The adjudicator's decision is binding upon the parties until the dispute is finally determined by legal proceedings, by arbitration (if the contract provides for arbitration or the parties otherwise agree to arbitration) or by agreement. If either party is dissatisfied with the decision, it can refer the dispute for final determination by a court or an arbiter. Implementation of the adjudicator's decision will not normally, however, be suspended pending the outcome of those proceedings.

The requirements of the Act

The Act states (s 108(1)) that 'A party to a construction contract has the right to refer a dispute arising under the contract for adjudication under a procedure complying with this section of the Act at any time. For this purpose "dispute" includes any difference'.

In order to satisfy this statutory right to have a dispute determined by adjudication a contract must:[26]

(i)   Enable the parties to give notice of intention to refer a dispute to adjudication at any time.

(ii)   Provide a timetable with the object of securing the appointment of the adjudicator and referral of the dispute to him within seven days of such notice.

(iii)   Require the adjudicator to reach a decision within 28 days of referral or such longer period as is agreed by the parties after the dispute has been referred.

(iv)   Allow the adjudicator to extend the period of 28 days by up to 14 days with the consent of the party by whom the dispute was referred.

(v)   Impose a duty on the adjudicator to act impartially.

(vi)   Enable the adjudicator to take the initiative in ascertaining the facts and the law.

(vii)   Provide that the decision of the adjudicator is binding until the dispute is finally determined by legal proceedings, by arbitration or by agreement.

(viii) Provide that the adjudicator is not liable for anything done or omitted in the discharge or purported discharge of his functions as adjudicator unless the act or omission is in bad faith, and that any employee or agent of the adjudicator is similarly protected from liability.

What happens if the contract does not meet the Act's requirements?

If any one of the eight requirements is missing from a construction contract, then Part I, the Scottish Scheme, will apply.[27] The purpose of the Scottish Scheme is to implement the provisions of the Act and provide a framework for adjudication if the parties fail to provide for its requirements in the contract.

What kind of disputes can be referred to adjudication?

The Act gives a party to a construction contract the right to refer at any time a dispute arising **under the contract** for adjudication. Precise guidance on the meaning of 'dispute' is in relatively short supply, although in most cases it will be obvious when a dispute has arisen. The court in the case of *Cruden Construction Limited* v. *Commission for the New Towns* offered the view that if a claim was made and ignored or attempts were made to postpone a definitive response to a claim, a dispute could be said to exist.[28]

The Court in the case of *Fastrack Contractors Limited* v. *Morrison Construction Limited*[29] held that a dispute could only arise '. . . once the subject matter of the claim, issue or other matter has been brought to the attention of the opposing party and that party has had an opportunity of considering and admitting, modifying or rejecting the claim or assertion'. The court also held that a dispute was '. . . whatever claims, heads of claim, issues, contentions or causes of action that are then in dispute which the referring party has chosen to crystallise into an adjudication reference'.

The case of *Edmund Nuttall Limited* v. *R. G. Carter Limited* provided further guidance on the meaning of a dispute.[30] The court in that case formed the view that for a dispute to have arisen there must have been an opportunity '. . . for the protagonists each to consider the position adopted by the other and to formulate arguments of a reasoned kind'. The court also said that it may be said that there is '. . . a "dispute" in a case in which a party which has been afforded an opportunity to evaluate rationally the position of an opposite party has either chosen not to avail himself of that opportunity or has refused to communicate the results of his evaluation'. Importantly, however, it was held that while a party was entitled to refine arguments previously put to the opposite party and to abandon points not thought to be meritorious, it could not abandon wholesale 'facts previously relied upon or arguments previously advanced' and contend that '. . . because the "claim" remains the same as that made previously, the dispute is the same'.

It may be thought that the judge in the *Edmund Nuttall Limited* case wished to strike a blow against 'ambush' by a Referring Party. He said:

> the whole concept underlying adjudication is that the parties during an adjudication should first themselves have attempted to resolve their differences by open exchange of views and, if they are unable to, they should submit to an independent third party for decision [on] the facts and arguments which they have previously rehearsed among themselves. If adjudication does not work in that way there is a risk of premature or unnecessary adjudications . . .[31]

Care should therefore be taken in presenting, for example, justification and bases for claims which cannot properly be said to have been encompassed within the dispute as previously presented to the opposing party. It is clear, however, from the court's judgment in the *Edmund Nuttall Limited* case that each case will require to be considered on its own facts. There will be some instances, for example, where a party adjusts the figures it had previously put to an opposing party in respect of a particular claim, but where it could not be said that the dispute referred to adjudication was a *different* dispute from the one which had arisen prior to the adjudication process.[32]

The Act also provides that a dispute includes 'any difference'. The word 'difference' contemplates a situation where a party has not explicitly rejected a claim, but, equally, has not acceded to it. If a party has not accepted a claim within a reasonable period of time a difference – at least – would exist between the parties.

Not every dispute can be referred to adjudication. Section 108(1) of the Act refers only to 'a dispute arising under the contract'. A claim that a contract has been repudiated does arise under a contract, while a dispute concerning an extra contractual settlement agreement or a collateral contract would not.[33]

The case of *Gillies Ramsay Diamond* v. *PJW Enterprises Ltd* confirmed that an adjudicator operating under the Scottish Scheme has the power to make an award of damages arising from a breach of contract.[34] It had previously been thought by some commentators that this was not the case, and that the adjudicator required express power to make such an award. The *Gillies Ramsay* case appears to have clarified the position.[35]

A wide variety of disputes are, however, referrable to adjudication. Such disputes range from a failure to pay money thought to be due under a contract to claims for extensions of time and losses arising from a breach of contract. Although it may be said that Parliament did not intend that adjudication be used to determine disputes in relation to, for example, professional negligence claims based on breaches of obligations set out in professional appointments, there is no legal impediment to such a dispute being referred to adjudication. It was also held in the *Gillies Ramsay* decision that an adjudicator was entitled, under the Scottish Scheme, to reach conclusions and a decision on allegations of professional negligence (providing such a claim was founded on a breach of contract and not on a purely delictual basis). Whether as a matter of practicality it is advisable to use the adjudication process in this way is another question entirely. The more complex a dispute, the less suited the adjudication process may be to determining that dispute.

When can a dispute be referred to adjudication?

The Act provides that a dispute can be referred to adjudication 'at any time'. An adjudication can be started before or after completion of the works. Similarly, the right to refer a dispute to adjudication survives the determination of a contractor's employment under a contract or the repudiation of the contract by one party.[36]

Any attempt to limit or restrict a party's right to commence an adjudication will not satisfy the requirements of the Act and will invoke the application of the Scottish Scheme.

Adjudication at any time? The ICE and CECA position

Clause 66 of the ICE 7th Conditions appears to impose a restriction on the right (s 108(1) of the Act) to refer a dispute to adjudication at any time. Clause 66(3) of the ICE 7th Conditions states that no matter shall constitute a dispute until a 'Notice of Dispute' has been served. Such a notice can only be served after the Engineer has reviewed the issue in question, or a party to the contract has failed to give effect to a previous adjudicator's decision.

Clause 66 (3) states *inter alia*:

> The Employer and the Contractor agree that no matter shall constitute nor be said to give rise to a dispute unless and until in respect of that matter
>
> (a)   The time for the giving of a decision by the Engineer on a matter of dissatisfaction under Clause 66(2) has expired or the decision given is

unacceptable or has not been implemented and in consequence the Employer or the Contractor has served on the other and on the Engineer a notice in writing (hereinafter called the Notice of Dispute)

> . . . and the dispute shall be stated in the Notice of Dispute.

The ICE 7th Conditions state that until one of those conditions is satisfied there is no dispute but merely a 'matter of dissatisfaction'.

The inclusion of such a restriction on adjudication arguably renders the adjudication procedure set out in the ICE 7th Conditions vulnerable to substitution by the adjudication provisions of the Scottish Scheme.

The CECA Sub-contract contains a similar restriction. Clause 18(2)(a) states:

> Where the Sub-Contractor seeks to make a submission that payment is due of any amount exceeding the amount determined by the Contractor as due to the Sub-Contractor, or that any act, decision, opinion, instruction or direction of the Contractor or any other matter arising under the Sub-Contract is unsatisfactory, the Sub-Contractor shall so notify the Contractor in writing, stating the grounds for such submission in sufficient detail for the Contractor to understand and consider the Sub-Contractor's submission.

If the Contractor believes that the submission gives rise to a matter of dissatisfaction under the main contract, he must inform the Sub-Contractor of this and pursue the matter of dissatisfaction under the main contract, keeping the Sub-Contractor fully informed in writing of progress.[37] Clause 18(2)(b) goes on to provide that no such submission by a sub-contractor shall constitute or give rise to a dispute until:

(i)   the Contractor has had the time and opportunity to refer the matter of dissatisfaction to the Engineer under the Main Contract; and
(ii) the time for the giving of a decision by the Engineer has expired.

Once again, it seems that this approach conflicts with the requirements of the Act and may result in the application of the adjudication provisions of the Scottish Scheme. There is no reported authority on the compatibility of the ICE and CECA adjudication provisions with the Act, but the possibility that the Scottish Scheme may apply should not be discounted when the need arises to rely on the relevant adjudication clause.

Appointment of an adjudicator

Perhaps the simplest way to illustrate the procedure in having an adjudicator appointed, at least under (a) the Scottish Scheme and (b) the ICE 7th Conditions and the ICE adjudication procedure, is to refer to flowcharts of key events and timescales. These are shown in Figures 10.1 and 10.2.

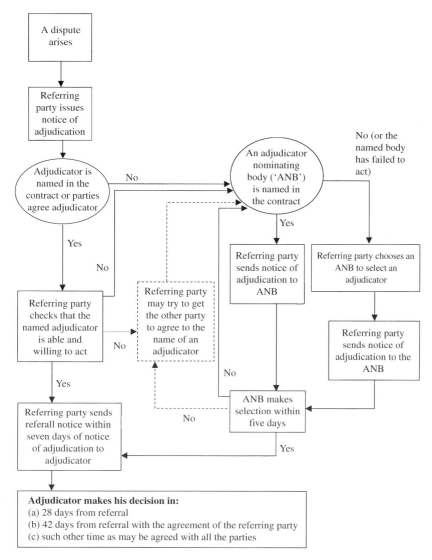

Figure 10.1.   Appointment of the adjudicator under the Scottish Scheme.[38]

If an adjudicator cannot be agreed, which bodies can be asked to appoint adjudicators?

There are a number of adjudicator nominating bodies. Many of the nominating bodies relevant to the Scottish engineering industry are listed in Appendix 3.

The most suitable bodies for appointing adjudicators for disputes arising under engineering contracts are often the ICE and the Chartered Institute of Arbitrators.[39] ICE contracts specify appointment of adjudicators by the ICE. The

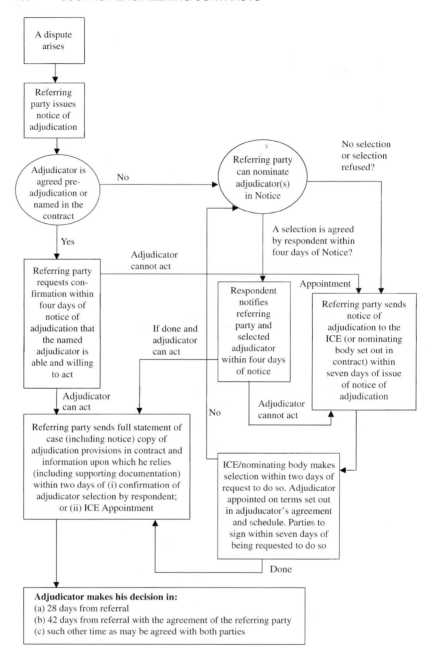

Figure 10.2.   Appointment of the adjudicator under the ICE Adjudication Procedure 1997.

ICE has a published list of adjudicators. If the contract does not provide for a nominating body (and depending on the precise nature of the dispute), many of the adjudicator nominating bodies listed in the appendix may be appropriate for engineering contract disputes.

Is there always an opportunity to reply to the referral notice and how long do I have to do this?

There is no specific provision to this effect in the Scottish Scheme. However, in practice, time is always given to reply to the referral notice. If not, it is arguable that the proceedings will have breached the rules of natural justice and as such any decision will be unenforceable. The adjudicator will normally set the timetable and procedure. Typically, the respondent is given seven to ten days to respond to the referral notice. It is not unusual for adjudicators – and often necessary – for adjudicators to allow a reply by the referring party to the response document.

The adjudicator must make his decision 28 days from the date of referral. If he considers that he will require more time he can approach the referring party for a 14-day extension or, if a longer one is necessary, make a request to this effect to both parties.

The ICE Adjudication Procedure (1997) states that the respondent may submit his response to the referral notice within 14 days of referral of the dispute[40] and that the period of response may be extended by agreement between the parties and the adjudicator.

What can the adjudicator do?

Under the Scottish Scheme the adjudicator may take the initiative in ascertaining the facts and the law necessary to determine the dispute, and can decide on the procedure to be followed in the adjudication. He can, for example, request parties to supply him with documents and written statements; meet and question any of the parties to the contract and their representatives; make site visits and inspections; carry out tests or experiments and appoint experts, assessors or legal advisors.

The wide-ranging powers of the adjudicator highlight the differences between the inquisitorial system of adjudication and other more traditional adversarial means of dispute resolution such as litigation and arbitration.[41] An adjudicator will take the initiative in ascertaining the facts and the law necessary to determine the dispute while judges, sheriffs and arbiters will rely on information submitted and pleaded by the parties. An adjudicator should nevertheless confine himself to taking the initiative to determine the facts and law in order to decide upon the dispute and should be wary of trying to ascertain facts and law which do not relate to the dispute as described in the Notice of Adjudication and referral notice.

It is not uncommon for adjudicators to appoint expert advisers such as lawyers or other professionals to provide advice on issues outwith their immediate expertise. Most procedural rules allow for this (as does the Scottish Scheme).

What exactly must the adjudicator decide upon?

The Scottish Scheme sets out the requirements for the notice of adjudication. Paragraph 1(3) of the Scottish Scheme provides that the notice of adjudication shall set out the nature and a brief description of the dispute and of the parties involved, details of where and when the dispute has arisen, the nature of the redress which is sought, and the names and addresses of the parties to the contract.

The notice of adjudication is of fundamental significance because it defines the 'dispute' that is being referred. If the adjudicator attempts to decide other matters, his decision will be of no effect.[42] Care must be taken to ensure that the 'nature . . . of the dispute' is accurately described in the Notice at least insofar as those matters upon which he had no jurisdiction to adjudicate are concerned. The ICE adjudication procedure states that the Notice of Adjudication should include the details and date of the relevant contract, the issues that the adjudicator is being asked to decide and the details of the nature and extent of the redress sought.

The referral notice will set out in more detail the referring party's case. The Scottish Scheme says little about the referral notice other than it should be accompanied by copies of all relevant extracts from the construction contract and such other documents as the referring party intends to rely upon. It should be remembered that the adjudicator has 28 days from receipt of the referral notice in which to reach his decision. Therefore, the issues should be well defined and clearly focused in the referral notice. The adjudicator needs to have all of the relevant facts presented to him in as concise and coherent a form as possible. Any relevant points of law should be also explained and, if necessary, supported by authority.

Must the adjudicator always decide the dispute within 28 days?

An extension of 14 days can be introduced with the agreement of the referring party. A longer period may be allowed if both parties agree.

Extensions are not infrequently given to the adjudicators. However, they do not tend to be much beyond two or three weeks from the end of the 28-day period. Extensions are sought, in particular, in complex and factually dense disputes.

The Scottish Scheme (see paragraph 8(2) of Part II) allows the adjudicator to 'adjudicate at the same time' on a different, but 'related', dispute under a different contract, provided that the parties to the original adjudication consent to this.

Am I stuck with the adjudicator's decision?

As has been noted previously, an adjudicator's decision is binding (unless the contract states otherwise) on parties until the dispute is finally determined by an arbiter or a court, or by agreement. The courts have in the last few years endorsed this basic principle on a number of occasions, starting with the seminal decision in *Macob Civil Engineering Limited* v. *Morrison Construction Limited*.[43]

Careful attention should also be paid to clause 18.7 of the CECA Sub-contract and clause 66(9)(b) of the ICE 7th Conditions which state that if a dispute which has been the subject of an adjudicator's decision is not referred to arbitration within three months of the adjudicator's decision, the adjudicator's decision becomes final as well as binding upon the parties. It will therefore be important to carefully consider within a short time after the adjudicator's decision whether arbitration is appropriate.

When can an adjudicator's decision be challenged?

(i) General principles A decision of an adjudicator which is open to criticism as to its factual or legal conclusions remains a decision that is enforceable. Therefore, a decision that is erroneous, even if the error is disclosed by the reasons, will not normally be capable of being challenged on that basis, and should, ordinarily, still be adhered to. Adjudication is intended to be a speedy process. In such a process it is not unlikely that such mistakes will occur, although every effort should obviously be made to avoid this. The English courts have guarded against characterising a mistaken answer to an issue within an adjudicator's jurisdiction as being an excess of jurisdiction. (See the case of *Sherwood & Carson Limited* v. *MacKenzie.*)[44]

In the case of *Barr Limited* v. *Law Mining Limited*,[45] Lord MacFadyen distinguished between a decision that is unsound but valid, and a decision that is invalid because it was not one that the adjudicator had the power to make. In addition, he did not rule out the possibility that a procedural error may result in the adjudicator making a decision that is beyond his jurisdiction. This is in slight contrast to the treatment of the 'procedural error' by Mr Justice Dyson in *Macob*.[46]

The courts (and in particular the English courts) have tended to the view that an adjudicator's decision, given properly within his jurisdiction, will be enforced whether that decision is right or wrong. However, in the case of *Ballast plc* v. *The Burrell Company (Construction Management) Limited*,[47] Lord Reed commented that it did not necessarily follow that adjudicators' decisions were intended to be *entirely immune* from challenge. He noted that he would be slow to attribute to the parties an intention that the adjudicator's decision should always be binding, notwithstanding errors of law, procedural unfairness or lack of consideration of relevant materials submitted to him by the parties, no matter how fundamental such a breach of the adjudicator's obligation might be.

In the case of *C & B Scene Concept Design Limited* v. *Isobars Limited*,[48] it was held that an error in law made by the adjudicator constituted an excess of jurisdiction with the result that the court refused enforcement. In that case no election had been made between payment alternatives A and B of Appendix 2 of the JCT Design & Build Contract Payment Provisions. It was therefore held by the court that the entirety of clause 30 of the contract fell away and the Scottish Scheme should be applied. The adjudicator was held to have had erred in law in basing his decision upon the provisions of clause 30.3.5. The case is an example of an adjudicator answering the wrong question and acting in excess of his jurisdiction.

The adjudicator must only address the question he is asked, but he must also *answer* the question which is posed. In the *Ballast* v. *Burrell* case Lord Reed was asked to declare that a decision by an adjudicator was to be set aside as a nullity. The adjudicator appeared to have decided that he could not carry out any valuation or find any payment due because the parties had departed from the terms of JCT conditions of contract in a number of respects. Lord Reed held that such an approach was wrong in law. As a result of that error, the adjudicator was held to have misconstrued his powers and to have failed to exercise his jurisdiction to determine the dispute. His decision was therefore a nullity, leaving the parties free to commence a further adjudication in respect of part or all of the dispute referred to the adjudicator.

(ii) Jurisdictional challenges   The courts have made it clear that if the adjudicator did not have jurisdiction to decide the dispute, the decision will not be enforced. Jurisdictional challenges have been upheld in various ways:

- Absence of a contract in writing, as defined by Section 107 of the Act[49] – in *Grovedeck* v. *Capital Demolition Limited*, G had carried out work for C under oral contracts. G claimed that C had not paid them in accordance with the contract and commenced an adjudication. C argued that the dispute was not susceptible to adjudication as the contracts were not in writing. The adjudicator held that the contracts were in writing as G had asserted this as part of the adjudication proceedings and C had not denied their existence. The court dismissed the action and held that the adjudicator did not have jurisdiction as the contracts were not in writing. It was not the case that a contract could be given the retrospective status of being 'in writing' merely by one party asserting that fact as part of proceedings in which the other party contested that assertion.

  In the case of *RJT Consulting Engineers Limited* v. *DM Engineering (NI) Limited*[50] it was held that the whole of the parties' agreement required to be evidenced in writing, and not just part of that agreement. The party challenging the adjudicator's decision had argued that the adjudicator had no jurisdiction as the parties' contract was not an agreement in writing. The Claimant in the adjudication had argued that there were documents such as minutes of meeting, programmes and invoices which evidenced the agreement in writing. The Court of Appeal distinguished between looking for evidence of the *existence* of a contract and, on the other hand, evidence of the terms of the contract. It is evidence of the terms of the contract – and the agreement reached between the parties – that a court will look for. One of the Appeal Court judges stated, however, that not *every* term of the contract need be recorded in writing, but only those that are material to the issue or issues giving rise to the reference to adjudication.[51]

- Contract not for construction operations[52] – in the case of *Palmers Limited* v. *ABB Power Construction Limited*, ABB sought to withhold payments due to P in relation to P's alleged breach of contract in failing to provide scaffolding services to be used in the erection of an industrial boiler. Palmer sought a declarator that the contract was a construction contract for the purposes of the Act. The court granted the declarator and held that the erection of the boiler was a 'construction operation', since, once in place, the boiler would form part of the land pursuant to s 105(1)(b) of the Act.

- Contract formed prior to 1 May 1998 – the adjudicator would have no jurisdiction if there was no construction contract for the purposes of the Act or if the contract was formed before the material date (1 May 1998).[53]
- Dispute not covered by adjudication agreement[54] – in the case of *A & D Maintenance & Construction Limited* v. *Pagehurst Construction Services Limited* it was held that as the Act was applicable to the construction contract, it followed that any disputes arising out of the contract could still be referred to adjudication notwithstanding the termination of the contract.
- Decision outside the terms of reference in the Notice of Adjudication – in the *F W Cook Limited* v. *Shimizu (UK) Limited*[55] case, the notice of adjudication highlighted four main issues. The adjudicator found that Cook was entitled to recover certain sums. The adjudicator considered that he had not been asked to give a decision as to how much the next interim payment between the parties should be. Instead he approached his task on the basis that he had been asked to look at a number of items in the overall final account. The referring letter issued by C expressed the view that it wished to have decisions on certain disputed matters only, with the intention of advancing the process of agreement on the final account as a whole. The referring letter did not ask for a revision of what had been paid so far, nor did the adjudicator have the necessary material which would have allowed him to determine any balance due from either party as a consequence of his decisions. The adjudicator's direction that 'all sums payable pursuant to this decision shall be paid . . .' was to be taken to mean payable pursuant to the sub-contract.
- The adjudicator should have resigned under paragraph 9(2) of the Scottish Scheme[56] – the adjudicator has jurisdiction to decide whether the disputes before him are the same, or substantially the same as those dealt with in a previous adjudication. If they are, he is bound (under the Scottish Scheme) to resign.

(iii) Failure to act in accordance with natural justice or the Human Rights Act 1998 The adjudicator has to conduct the proceedings in accordance with the rules of natural justice. Whilst he may, for example, due to time constraints, speak to the parties separately, he should advise the other party of what he has learnt that may be relevant to his decision and not leave it to the party he spoke to to inform that other party of what he told the adjudicator.[57] It is nearly always safer, however, for an adjudicator to speak to both parties at the same time in relation to any substantive matters.

The adjudicator may not take evidence from third parties and then not give the parties an opportunity to comment on it.[58] An adjudicator should also take care, where possible, to give a party an adequate opportunity to respond to any material submissions by the other party. This consideration, however, must be weighed up against the very tight timescale within which the adjudicator must operate.

The courts will refuse to enforce an adjudicator's decision where an adjudicator acts in a way which appears not to be impartial, notwithstanding the attitudes of the parties to the adjudication proceedings. This approach was reflected in the judgment of the court in the case of *Balfour Beatty Construction Limited* v. *The London Borough of Lambeth.*[59] In this case the court held that an adjudicator had to act in a way which would not lead an outsider to conclude that there was any element of bias or that one party had been treated unfairly. Actual bias need not be established. The adjudicator in the *Balfour Beatty* case had made the mistake of carrying out, in the absence of the contractor providing this information, a full critical path delay analysis. Such an approach was held to be capable of being construed as unfair to the other party, especially as the other party was not given an opportunity to respond to what the adjudicator had done.

The judgment also makes clear that the court would not ordinarily entertain challenges based on procedural breaches of lesser consequence and that it was accepted that the standards of procedural fairness to be adopted by a court or arbiter could not, given the timescales involved, be fully expected from adjudicators.

It has been held in England that Article 6 of the European Convention of Human Rights, and in particular the right of a party to have a reasonable opportunity of presenting its case, does not apply to adjudication proceedings under the Act, since they do not involve a final determination of the rights of the parties.[60]

(iv) Insolvency   It has been held in England that if it could be established that a referring party in an adjudication may, following subsequent litigation which effectively 'reversed' an adjudicator's decision, be unable (at the time the court's decision became enforceable) to repay a sum awarded in its favour in the adjudication, a court may then grant a 'stay'[61] of proceedings raised to enforce an adjudicator's decision.[62] This decision should, however, be treated with caution in Scotland as it is not binding on the Scottish courts and was linked to an English rule of court procedure.

What can be done to enforce an adjudicator's decision?

The conventional way to enforce an adjudicator's decision is to raise a court action for payment and seek summary decree. An application for summary decree can be made when there is no defence to a claim and, if successful, gives a pursuer decree without the need to prove his claim. In Scotland, the Commercial Court has been willing to shorten the normal timetable for such applications in order to deal quickly with the enforcement of adjudicators' decisions.[63]

The Scottish Scheme allows an adjudicator's decision to be registered per execution in the 'Books of Council and Session' if the adjudicator so orders.[64] Registration in this way enables diligence to be carried out pursuant to the adjudicator's decision. The problem with this method of enforcement is that it cannot be utilised without both parties signing the decision to this effect. If one party declines to do so, it becomes extremely difficult to have the decision registered so that it can be enforced.

Can the adjudicator ask that I pay his fees or the other side's costs?

Paragraph 25 of Part I of the Scottish Scheme provides that the adjudicator shall be entitled to payment of fees and expenses reasonably incurred by him, and that the parties shall be jointly and severally liable for payment of these fees. In other words, if one party refuses to pay its share of the adjudicator's fees, the adjudicator could ask the other party to pay that share of the fee **as well** as its own share. The Scottish Scheme allows the adjudicator to determine the apportionment of payment of his fees by the parties. Adjudicators often ask that the party which has to make payment of a sum awarded in an adjudication to bear their fees and outlays. Adjudicators will also normally outline their hourly charge-out rates and arrangements for payment of fees at the outset of an adjudication, even if there is no adjudication agreement to complete.[65]

The schedule to the ICE Adjudicator's Agreement will specify the hourly rate which he is to be paid and provides for payment of all disbursements properly made by the adjudicator. It also states that the fee will be due seven days after delivery of an invoice and allows interest at 5 per cent above base rate on overdue accounts. The expenses of the adjudicator will of course include the fees of any experts and advisers appointed by the adjudicator.

The Scottish Scheme does not give the adjudicator the power to award payment of a party's legal expenses incurred in the adjudication. It is not unusual, however, for parties to include a claim for such expenses in their referral notice. The question of expenses was raised in *Northern Developments (Cumbria) Limited* v. *J & J Nichol*.[66] It was held in that case that there was no implied statutory power granted to the adjudicator to award legal expenses, but the parties were able to widen the power given to the adjudicator by the English Scheme if they wished to do so. It is therefore possible to give the adjudicator power to award legal expenses by including a claim for such costs in the referral notice. If a respondent does not wish the adjudicator to have such a power (which will often be the case if a respondent believes it may have to pay something), the respondent should make it clear that it does not accept the adjudicator has this power.

It is now widely accepted that adjudicators are not permitted to award legal expenses unless expressly given the power to do so by the parties. The DETR have proposed clarification of this point.[67]

Guidance for adjudicators

The Construction Umbrella Bodies Adjudication Task Group have published a document entitled *Guidance for Adjudicators*. The Guidance was published in July 2002. Copies of the document are available to download for free from www.cic.org.uk

The document is a readable and practical summary of suggested 'best practice' for adjudicators in conducting adjudications, and deals with a number of issues such as natural justice, procedural fairness, challenges to jurisdiction, unmanageable documentation, accidental errors or omissions in decisions and the parties' costs in adjudications. It also provides references to the case law which is relevant to these topics.

The document has no binding legal effect, nor is it formally linked to either the Act or the Scottish Scheme. It may even be that some adjudicators and lawyers would disagree with certain aspects of what is set out in the document. It does, however, represent an instructive source of information and commentary not only for adjudicators, but also for parties and their advisers.

ICE Adjudication Procedure 1997 and the Scottish Scheme – a comparison

The major differences between the Scottish Scheme and the ICE Adjudication Procedure are highlighted in Table 10.1. The ICE Adjudication Procedure 1997 governs contractors under the ICE 7th Conditions and the CECA Sub-contract. As has been noted above, the Scottish Scheme would apply if the contract did not meet the requirements of s 108 of the Act.

Table 10.1.   Comparison between the Scottish Scheme and the ICE Adjudication Procedure 1997.

Scottish Scheme	ICE Adjudication Procedure
Notice of Intention to refer a dispute to adjudication	
• The Scottish Scheme does not specifically require any details of the contract itself to be given in the notice.	• ICE procedure requires the details and date of the contract between the parties; the issues which the adjudicator is being asked to decide; and details of the nature and extent of the redress sought to be given in the notice.
Adjudicator's Agreement	
• No form of adjudicator's agreement proposed.	• The ICE procedure provides for the execution of the standard form of adjudicator's agreement.
Referral Notice	
• Not later than seven days from the date of the notice of adjudication, the referring party shall refer the dispute in writing ('the referral notice') to the adjudicator. The referring party shall, at the same time as he sends to the adjudicator the referral notice and accompanying documents, send copies of those documents to every other party to the dispute.	• A full statement of the referring Party's case must be sent to the adjudicator and the other party within two days of receipt of the adjudicator's appointment.

Table 10.1.   Continued

Scottish Scheme	ICE Adjudication Procedure
Decision	
• The adjudicator shall reach his decision in accordance with the applicable law in relation to the contract.	• The ICE adjudication procedure does not explicitly state that the decision is to be in accordance with the law. 'The object of adjudication is to reach a fair, rapid and inexpensive determination of a dispute arising under the Contract and this Procedure shall be interpreted accordingly'.[68]
• The adjudicator does not require to give reasons unless so requested by one of the parties.	• The adjudicator shall not be required to give reason for his decision.
• As soon as possible after he has reached a decision, the adjudicator shall deliver a copy of that decision to each of the parties to the contract.	• At any time until seven days before the adjudicator is due to reach his decision, he may give notice to the parties that he will deliver it only on full payment of his fees and expenses. Any party may then pay these costs in order to obtain the decision and recover the other party's share of the costs.
Scope of adjudication	
• The adjudicator may take into account matters that are not the matters in dispute which the parties to the dispute agree should be within the scope of the adjudication or which are matters under the Contract which are necessarily connected with the dispute.	• The adjudicator shall determine the matter set out in the notice of adjudication, together with any other matters which the parties and the adjudicator agree should be within the scope of the adjudication.[69]
Mistakes in decision	
• Silent about what is to happen if the adjudicator makes a mistake in his decision.	• The adjudicator may on his own initiative, or at the request of either party, correct a decision so as to remove any clerical mistake, error or ambiguity provided that the initiative is taken, or the request is made within 14 days of the notification of the decision to the parties. The adjudicator shall make his correction within seven days of any request by a party.

Table 10.1.   Continued

Scottish Scheme	ICE Adjudication Procedure
Immunity	
• The adjudicator shall not be liable for anything done or omitted in the discharge or purported discharge of his functions as adjudicator unless the Act or omission is in bad faith, and any employee or agent of the adjudicator is similarly protected from liability.	• The ICE procedure provides the same, but also includes immunity for itself as nominating body.
Fees	
• The adjudicator shall be entitled to the payment of such reasonable amount as he may determine by way of fees and expenses reasonably incurred by him.	• The ICE adjudicator's agreement specifies the hourly rate to be paid and provides expressly for payment of all disbursements properly made. The adjudicator is to be paid a reasonable fee, together with his expenses.
• The parties shall be jointly and severally liable for any sum which remains outstanding in fees following the making of any determination on how payment shall be apportioned.	• Liability for the fees and expenses is joint and several. The adjudicator can direct that one party should pay all or part of those fees and expenses. If there is no such direction, they should be paid in equal shares. An adjudicator under the ICE procedure is entitled to be paid an appointment fee specified by him that is to be paid by the parties in equal amounts within 14 days of appointment.
Parties' costs and expenses	
• The Scottish Scheme does not give the adjudicator the power to award costs.	• The ICE procedure states that the parties should pay their own costs and expenses incurred in the adjudication.

Arbitration

Introduction

Conventionally in engineering contracts disputes have been resolved in arbitration. The perceived advantages of arbitration include:

- speed
- cost

- a sound decision on technical matters by a professional from a relevant technical background
- informality
- privacy.

The extent to which these advantages exist in practice will depend on, for example:

- the particular arbiter's characteristics[70]
- the arbitration rules adopted
- the parties
- the nature of the dispute.

The increase in popularity of adjudication has reduced the number of engineering disputes referred to arbitration. There is a further apparent trend towards court rather than arbitration as a means of resolving engineering disputes.

Generally, however, engineering contracts continue to provide for arbitration, rather than litigation, as the final forum for disputes that are not conclusively resolved by, for example, conciliation or adjudication. Arbitration is provided for by clauses 66 and 67 of the ICE 7th Conditions. The April 2001 amendment deals with arbitration and must be read with the Conditions as it makes certain important changes, including the application of the Scottish Arbitration Code 1999 (as supplemented by the ICE Appendix thereto) to arbitrations under those Conditions. Clause 18 of the CECA Sub-contract also provides for arbitration.

Arbitration is a process critically dependent upon agreement. The standard form engineering contracts go some way towards providing a comprehensive code by which to resolve disputes through arbitration. That is essential if arbitration is to capitalise upon its chief advantage – the involvement of a skilled person as decision maker. If the opportunity exists to consider the applicable rules, that should be carefully analysed, as – especially in Scotland – the outcome could significantly enhance or restrict the powers of the arbiter. Thereafter, the success of the process depends upon parties and the arbiter together adopting a commercial, non-legalistic approach to the procedure.

This section considers:

(a) the arbitration clause, as a procedure for resolving disputes
(b) the arbiter's jurisdiction
(c) the sources of arbitration law
(d) the potential expansion of those sources by arbitration reform
(e) the arbiter's powers
(f) the ICE arbitration
- when matters can be referred to arbitration
- what matters may be referred to arbitration
- how that arbitration is to be conducted
(g) arbitration under the CECA Sub-contract.

The arbitration clause

Arbitration is not available as a matter of right. Arbitration is born of agreement. The arbitration agreement may be:

- *Ad hoc* – that is to say, when a dispute arises on any contract, the parties may agree that it will be resolved by arbitration. That does not depend on any pre-existing agreement.
- In the *dispute resolution procedure* in the contract (as it is in the ICE suite of contracts). Such a clause will be triggered in the event of a dispute arising that falls within the ambit of the clause.

In either case, the arbitration agreement should provide for the class of disputes referable to arbitration, the appointment of an arbiter, the conduct of the arbitration, and so on.

These matters can be provided for in a bespoke agreement or, in the case of the ICE suite of contracts, by adoption of a particular standard procedure (for example, in the case of the ICE 7th Edition Conditions – the ICE Arbitration Procedure (Scotland) (1983)) or, in the 7th Edition print incorporating the April 2001 amendments, the Scottish Arbitration Code 1999.

It is therefore necessary to consider the precise arbitration clause in order to ascertain *what* disputes may be referred to arbitration, *when* they may be referred, *how* that reference can be commenced and progressed, and so on. These particular matters are addressed in more detail below by reference to ICE Conditions of Contract.

Jurisdiction   As is addressed in the section in this chapter on adjudication, the arbitration clause cannot exclude the statutory right to adjudication. That apart, the parties are free to agree the manner in which disputes between them are to be resolved. That agreement applies to arbitration as it does to, for example, alternative dispute resolution such as mediation.

If the arbitration clause is binding, and is insisted upon by either party in the event of a dispute, then the dispute must be referred to arbitration:

If the parties have contracted to arbitrate, to arbitration they must go.[71]

However, the jurisdiction of the courts is not avoided altogether. As mentioned earlier in this chapter, it is not uncommon for a court action to be raised in the first instance, but thereafter referred to arbitration for an arbiter to consider the substance of the dispute. Usually, the court action remains 'live' in tandem with the arbitration, though the court action will be sisted (i.e. frozen) while the arbitration proceeds.

Why raise a court action if there is an arbitration clause?   *Interim protective measures*   If the Claimant wishes to protect his position by arresting or inhibiting against the Respondent, he must raise a court action (though see earlier comments in this chapter in relation to the ongoing change in the law relating to diligence on the dependence, following the *Karl* case). An arbiter has no power to facilitate such diligence.

Remedies   The scope of an arbiter's power depends critically upon the arbitration agreement. This is addressed in more detail below. Certain remedies may not be available from the arbiter and litigation will therefore be necessary.

Enforcement   A court decree (i.e. judgment) is enforceable without further procedure. However, if a Respondent refuses to obey an arbiter's decree arbitral, it may be necessary to seek the court's support for such enforcement by, for example, raising an action for payment in terms of the decree arbitral.[72]

Third parties   Because arbitration is born of agreement, it can bind only those parties who have agreed to go to arbitration. So, an engineering contract between the employer and contractor, without a more sophisticated arbitration clause, does not allow either party to introduce into the arbitration, for example, the engineer or any of the contractors' sub-contractors or suppliers.

Sources of arbitration law

Arbitration remains largely governed by the common law. In other words, with certain limited exceptions detailed below, arbitration is governed by principle and convention as it has developed through the courts.

Sources of statutory intervention are as follows.

Arbitration (Scotland) Act 1894   Prior to this Act, the arbiter had to be named in the arbitration clause. This Act allows the more practical situation, adopted in the ICE suite of contracts, whereby the arbiter may be agreed by the parties following a reference to arbitration, failing which nominated by an independent third party such as (in the case of the ICE contracts) the President of the ICE.

Administration of Justice (Scotland) Act 1972   Section 3 of this Act created the 'Stated Case' procedure, by which decisions of an arbiter on a point of law may be put before the Inner House of the Court of Session for review. Thus, this Act effectively creates an appeal procedure against an arbiter's findings on points of law.

The Administration of Justice (Scotland) Act 1972 provides that either party may apply to the arbiter for a stated case on any point of law at any time during the arbitration (though see below in relation to the time constraints imposed by the Rules of Court). Accordingly the position is probably that for as long as the arbiter is seized with the dispute, the arbitration is live, and the parties may apply for a stated case. It is sometimes thought that if the arbiter reaches a decision on a point of law during the arbitration, the arbiter is *functus* in relation to that part of the arbitration (i.e. it has concluded and the arbiter has no further role). In practice, this is generally provided for by agreement that the arbiter will issue any such interim decision in draft form. If either party is inclined to apply for a stated case, he can therefore do so on the basis of the draft decision, thus avoiding the suggestion that the application is too late because the arbiter has already reached his concluded view on that part of the arbitration.[73]

If and when the arbiter issues his signed firm decision on any point, the Rules of the Court of Session provide that parties have only 14 days within which to apply to the arbiter for a stated case.[74]

The only circumstances in which an arbiter may refuse to state a case are:

(i)   the proposed question does not arise[75]
(ii)   the proposed question does not require to be answered for the purposes of the appeal[76]
(iii)   the proposed question is frivolous.[77,78]

(iv)   the question is not one of law, but of fact or procedure.[79]

Even if the arbiter refuses to state a case, a party may apply to the court to invite it to ordain the arbiter to state a case – thus, effectively, compelling the arbiter to state a case. The arbiter may defer a stated case pending hearing the facts.[80]

The safe view is that the Stated Case procedure allows only one 'appeal'. Accordingly, a decision of the Inner House of the Court of Session on a Stated Case cannot then be appealed to the House of Lords.

Clause 67(2)(e) of the amended ICE 7th Conditions preserves the stated case procedure, overriding the Scottish Arbitration Code, which does not allow an appeal from the arbiter.

Law Reform (Miscellaneous Provisions) (Scotland) Act 1999   This Act adopts in Scotland the provisions of the UNCITRAL model law on arbitration. The effects of that adoption are largely facilitative, rather than prescriptive. In other words, they deal with matters such as the arbiter's appointment, independence, removal, replacement, and so on. Certain of the rules improve materially on the jurisdiction and powers of the arbiter at common law. They provide greater certainty in relation to some aspects of arbitration practice and procedure.

The UNCITRAL provisions (recorded in a schedule to the Act) will apply if the arbitration is 'international'. Because the concept of internationality is determined by reference to states and, furthermore, because 'state' expressly includes Scotland, if a contract is entered into by, for example, the English office of an engineering contractor, and a Scottish employer, that will be deemed 'international'. In those circumstances, the UNCITRAL provisions would apply.

Probably the most important consequence of the application of the UNCITRAL provisions is that the Stated Case procedure is jeopardised. While the position is not beyond doubt, the annotated version of the 1990 Act suggests that, where the UNCITRAL provisions apply, a case may not be stated to the Court of Session. That is the safe view, though it is not decided whether the terms of clause 67(2)(e) of the amended ICE 7th Conditions (allowing a stated case) would prevail over the Model Law.

Arbitration reform?

The Scottish Law Committee on Arbitration is framing its draft arbitration bill. That bill seeks to rationalise Scottish arbitration law, to codify it and close the gaps in the arbiter's powers, and so on. Previous attempts to fulfil the same purposes included the Scottish Advisory Committee on Arbitration Law: Report – March 1996. This report was the subject of consultation in 1997. It proposed a draft arbitration bill, seeking to consolidate the various sources of Scottish Arbitration law and to rationalise the powers available to arbiters.

This bill was not debated in the Scottish Parliament or Westminster. Certain of its provisions are reflected in the Scottish Arbitration Code 1999.

Arbiter's powers

Because of the way in which arbitration law has developed, the following powers are not available to an arbiter unless they are expressly conferred upon him by the parties:

- *Damages* – the arbiter has no power to award damages in relation to, for example, a breach of contract. This gap is filled by article 16.3 of the Scottish Arbitration Code.
- *Interest* – at common law, the arbiter does not have power to award interest, other than from the date of his decree arbitral. Again, in the ICE conditions of contract, it is necessary to rely upon the adoption of the Scottish Arbitration Code, or in earlier prints, the 1983 arbitration procedure (or some other equivalent agreement or an express contractual provision) which do give the arbiter this power.
- *Third parties* – as noted above, the arbitration clause binds only the parties to it. Accordingly, unless there is a separate arbitration agreement among parties to different contracts (such as the employer and contractor under the main contract, the contractor and his sub-contractors under those sub-contracts, the employer and his engineer under the engineer's professional appointment, etc.) those third parties cannot be compelled to join the arbitration procedure.

  Similarly, the arbiter cannot – without the courts' support – compel third-party witnesses to attend any hearing or to produce documents relevant to the matters in dispute. In such instances, recourse must be had to the courts.

Limitations on the arbiter's powers such as those addressed above are of less practical importance standing the adoption by clauses 66 and 67 of the ICE 7th conditions of the Scottish Arbitration Code, or in earlier prints, the ICE Arbitration Procedure (Scotland) (1983). (That is not the case, though, with clause 18 of the CECA Sub-contract conditions, which leaves the arbitration procedure to be completed in the Second Schedule.) Generally, the 1983 procedure will give rise to an arbitration which is similar to litigation in the Court of Session. The Arbiter is given powers, as between the parties, considerably in excess of those available to him at common law.

By contrast, the Scottish Arbitration Code provides for a more innovative procedure than does the 1983 procedure. The code ought to allow a flexible and commercial arbitration framework and, if applied in spirit and word, should allow the arbitration to overcome the traditionally perceived criticisms of litigation. The following provisions of the Code are especially important:

- 1 – *Commencement* – new rules are laid down for the initial stages of referral of the dispute and defence.
- 1.3(h) – *Speed* – the Respondent's Notice of Defence is due within 30 days of the Arbitration Notice.
- 3 – *Appointment of Arbiter* – to ensure that the arbiter is validly appointed, it is necessary that this article, and clause 66(10) of the amended ICE 7th Conditions, are followed.

- 15 and 16.7 – *Discretionary Procedure* – the Arbiter has wide discretion to fix the procedure and real power (e.g. by dismissal) to enforce it.
- 16 – *Powers* – the Arbiter's powers include damages, interest (even compound), and rectification of contract terms.
- 17 – *Evidence, Hearings and Pleadings* – the thrust of the Code is to depart from traditional court procedure and pleadings, but fair notice is still required. This article sets out what is expected.
- 22.8 – *Stated Case* – this procedure is expressly excluded, so the parties' 'safety net' allowing an appeal on points of law, is withdrawn, were it not for clause 67(2)(e) of the amended ICE 7th Conditions, which preserves the stated case.

ICE arbitration

Entitlement to arbitration

What? When? How?   Perhaps the most distinguishing characteristic of the ICE arbitration procedure is the series of preliminary steps that must be taken before arbitration. These steps are most concisely illustrated by way of a flow-chart (see Figure 10.3).

That procedure begins the answer to the questions what, when and how matters can be referred to arbitration.

When can matters be referred to arbitration?

Before a dispute or difference can be referred to arbitration, clause 66 demands that it first be referred to the Engineer for his decision under that clause. This is described further below.

Debate continues as to whether the mandatory reference to the Engineer for a 'decision' is an unnecessarily cumbersome and inevitably futile exercise, or if it does reduce the volume of 'disputes' before they have to be formally resolved.

In relation to adjudication, and as commented upon in the section of this chapter dealing with adjudication, there is an argument that clause 66(3), which provides that there will be no 'dispute' until the clause 66 mechanism is exhausted, is ineffective, standing the mandatory right of a party to statutory adjudication. No such argument can be levelled at arbitration. That is because arbitration is a process critically dependent upon the existence and extent of agreement between the parties. Thus, if (as is the case in clause 66) the parties agree to defer arbitration until after the Engineer's clause 66 decision, then that is binding.

Clause 66 (11)(b) of the ICE 7th Conditions provides that arbitration may proceed 'notwithstanding that the Works are not then complete . . .'. That position is different to that in certain older editions of the conditions.

The procedure in clause 66 also has a number of important effects on the following.

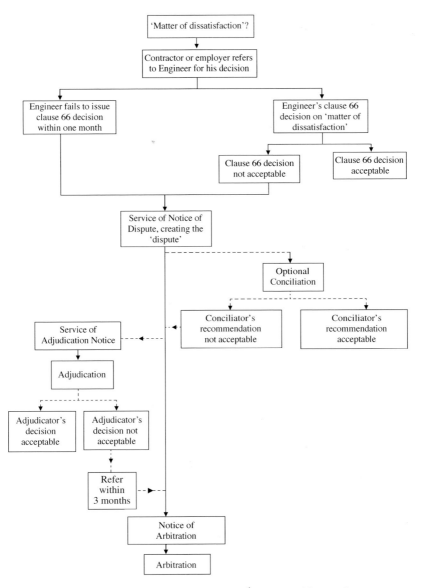

Figure 10.3.   Steps to arbitration, ICE 7th – clause 66 procedure.

What may be referred to arbitration?

This is a four-stage process.

Stage one   The starting point is the class of 'matters of dissatisfaction' that are described in clause 66(2)(a) as

> . . . any act or instruction of the Engineer's representative or any other person responsible to the Engineer

and in clause 66(2)(b) as

> . . . any decision opinion instruction direction certificate or valuation of the Engineer . . .

or

> . . . any other matter arising out of or in connection with the contract or the carrying out of the Works.

Stage two   These 'matters of dissatisfaction' may be referred to the Engineer for his clause 66 decision.

Stage three   The Engineer issues his decision to deal with those 'matters of dissatisfaction'.

Stage four   Part, or all, of the 'matters of dissatisfaction' that have been ruled upon by the engineer may then be captured in a 'notice of dispute' and then referred to the arbiter.

Accordingly, what can be referred to arbitration comprises only those issues which:

(a)   fall within clause 66(2)(a) or (b)
(b)   have been referred to the Engineer for his clause 66 decision
(c)   are the subject of an Engineer's clause 66 decision (or a failure to issue a decision at the correct time)
(d)   are recorded in the notice to refer to arbitration.

If an issue is raised that does not meet all of these criteria then (unless the parties agree to its inclusion) the Arbiter will have no jurisdiction over it.[81]

That rule is not so prescriptive as to limit the arguments that may be put to the arbiter. Provided those arguments have a bearing on an issue that fulfils these criteria, then it does not matter that the argument does not fall within the criteria (e.g. that argument may not have been advanced before the Engineer).

How are matters referred to arbitration?

The procedure provided for by clause 66 of the ICE 7th Conditions proceeds as in Figure 10.4.

Notice of arbitration   For this to interrupt the statutory time bar period, it must state the nature of the claim. Thus, it is good practice to err on the side of detail, perhaps by reference to the clause 66 reference and/or decision.[82] The 2001 ICE Appendix to the Scottish Arbitration Code provides a style notice of arbitration. Article 1.3 of the Scottish Arbitration Code sets out the necessary ingredients of the notice of arbitration, including a proposed arbiter if none has been identified in the contract.

Appointment by ICE   Form ArbICE is available on-line from www.ice.org.uk

Deed of appointment Although the arbitration agreement in the engineering contract is the parties' submission to arbitration (and therefore no deed of submission is required), it is good practice to enter into a deed of appointment of the arbiter. This should record:

- the parties' designations
- details of the parties' contract
- a brief description of the works
- a description of the disputes (in an ICE context in order to avoid the jurisdictional issues raised above, this should be by reference to the clause 66 decision(s) of the Engineer)
- the identity of the arbiter to whom the parties have agreed to refer the dispute

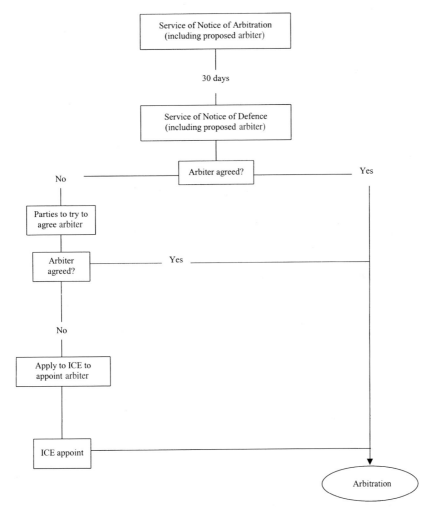

Figure 10.4.   How matters are referred to arbitration (ICE 7th – clause 66).

- the procedural rules governing the arbitration
- whether the stated case procedure is to apply
- that the arbiter's decrees arbitral (i.e. judgments) will be registrable in the Books of Council and Session (thus giving them equivalent status to a court decree)
- the arbiter's terms and conditions of appointment.

Arbitration procedure

Under the 1983 procedure arbitrations proceeded in a format close to traditional Scottish court actions. Parties submit written pleadings, adjust and amend them, debate their legal relevancy and go to proof on the evidence. Though generally less formal than litigation, the procedure was insufficiently flexible to achieve arbitration's aim as a more commercial and rapid alternative to court.

Under the 1999 Code, a much larger degree of discretion is afforded to the arbiter. There is less emphasis on written pleadings, which comprise the Notice of Arbitration, the Notice of Defence, perhaps a counterclaim in the Notice of Defence (in which case there will be a reply to that), whatever further written pleadings are ordered under Article 15.2, and a pre-hearing memorandum under Article 17. Provision is made for hearings, but the normal rules of evidence do not apply.

In both procedures, specific provision is made for the Arbiter to award the expenses of the arbitration (being both the Arbiter's fee as well as the parties' legal and other expenses) as he considers appropriate.

Sub-contract arbitration and the CECA Conditions

Clause 18 of the CECA Sub-contract provides for arbitration. Because the Engineer (as defined in the CECA Sub-contract) has no direct role to play in regulating affairs between the contractor and Sub-Contractor under the CECA Sub-contract, clause 18 does not involve the same procedure (as does clause 66 of the ICE 7th Conditions) of a preliminary reference to the Engineer.

However, clause 18 does give the Contractor the ability to have sub-contract disputes conclusively determined in the same way as the same dispute which exists under the Main Contract (i.e. 'back to back'). That in itself can re-introduce the reference to the Engineer as part of the dispute resolution procedure.

The clause 18 arbitration procedure is as shown in Figure 10.5. The dispute resolution procedure is relatively complex, and this diagram illustrates only its principal features. It omits the provisions which facilitate the combination of main and Sub-Contract disputes, differences and matters of dissatisfaction at e.g. adjudication and conciliation.

For the sake of clarity, Figure 10.5 omits the right to go to adjudication. Its reference to conciliation is included only for the sake of illustration – the stage at which conciliation is shown here is only one of the stages at which it can be sought.

The most obvious feature of this procedure is the degree of control afforded to the Contractor. It allows the Contractor to minimise the commercial risk of

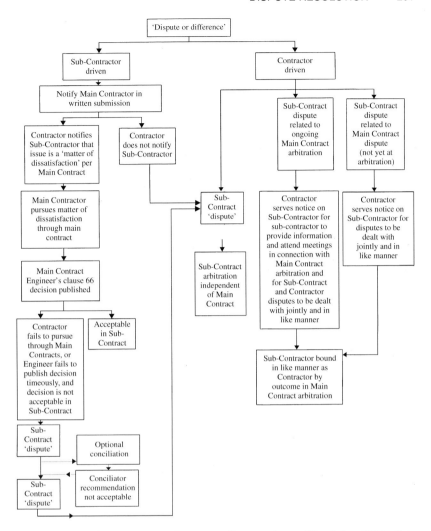

Figure 10.5.   Arbitration procedure according to clause 18 of the CECA Sub-contract.

inconsistent arbitration decisions up and down the contractual chain. It is the Contractor's opinion which governs whether a dispute or difference under the Sub-Contract is to be determined independently of any dispute or difference under the Contract.

Where the time limits on the Contractor are not defined prescriptively (e.g. he must pursue a related matter of dissatisfaction under the Main Contract 'promptly', or notify the Sub-Contractor 'as soon as possible' of his opinion that the Sub-Contractor' submission gives rise to a matter of dissatisfaction under the Main Contract)[83] there is a risk that the Contractor will use the Main Contract to stall resolution of sub-contract disputes.

The control available to the Contractor is limited in a number of ways:

- If he does not proceed with the Main Contract arbitration within a reasonable time, then the Sub-Contractor can go to arbitration under the sub-contract without reference to the Main Contract. In *Lafarge Redlands Aggregates Ltd (formerly Redland Aggregates Ltd)* v. *Shepherd Hill Civil Engineering Ltd*[84] it was held by the House of Lords that (in relation to the 1984 print of the FCEC sub-contract conditions) there was an implied obligation on the Contractor to progress the related Main Contract arbitration within 'a reasonable time' and that, if he did not do so, the Sub-Contractor could initiate a Sub-Contract arbitration unhindered.[85] What amounts to a 'reasonable time' is a question to be addressed in all the circumstances, but in that case, the Contractor's delay while it tried to settle the dispute was not thought by the court to be reasonable.[86]
- Although the intention behind the Sub-Contract dispute resolution procedure is to create a tri-partite arbitration, unless that is in the interests of the Employer (which is unlikely, as it will add to the cost and time involved) then he is unlikely to agree to it, and there will be a separate Sub-Contract arbitration.[87]

Conciliation and mediation

Conciliation

Conciliation is a quick, relatively cheap method of third-party assistance which resolves disputes without the full formality and expense of arbitration or litigation. The conciliator tries to help parties negotiate their own solution. If that fails, he provides a recommendation which can be challenged if either party wishes to do so.

Clause 66(5) of the ICE 7th Conditions and clause 18(3) of the CECA Sub-contract allow for disputes to be referred to conciliation under the Institution of Civil Engineers Conciliation Procedure 1999. Conciliation is optional, and must be commenced before a Notice to Refer a dispute to arbitration under clause 66(9) is served. Although conciliation is governed by detailed procedures, these are relatively flexible and the conciliator has scope to determine how best to conduct his task. The conciliator can be agreed in the contract, or agreed by the parties within 14 days after the notice of conciliation is given to the other party. If the parties cannot agree on a conciliator, an application can be made to the president of the ICE for an appointment.

The conciliator is given a wide scope to be 'inventive' in relation to procedure and to use an innovative approach to the dispute. He can call for the production of documents, request parties to speak to him; investigate facts, or obtain legal and/or technical advice. He can meet the parties together or separately. The conciliator is mandated to try to assist the parties to resolve the dispute in any way acceptable to them.

Prior to the conciliation meeting, written presentations can be given and documents delivered to the conciliator. Each party will present its own position and may lead expert evidence. The conciliator may then meet each party separately, exploring the strengths and weaknesses of each side's case and exploring areas of common ground. The conciliator may suggest ways of helping parties to find their own solution.

Unlike mediation, conciliation is not conducted on a 'without prejudice' basis. However, it is conducted on a confidential basis. This raises the question whether evidence from the conciliation could be lead at a later litigation or arbitration.

If parties are unable to reach agreement during the conciliation the conciliator prepares a recommendation setting out his solution to the dispute. The recommendation does not have to be based on principles of contract, law or equity. It could be a commercial approach. The conciliator does not have to give reasons for his decision.

Any recommendation of a conciliator will be regarded as finally determinative of a dispute unless the dispute is referred to either adjudication (under clause 66(6)) or arbitration within one month after receipt of the conciliator's recommendation by the dissenting party (clause 66((5)(b)).

Mediation

What is mediation?   Mediation has no formal basis in the ICE 7th Condition of the CECA Sub-contract. Mediation is a private and voluntary process of assisted negotiation. The mediator is a neutral, independent third party. The process is informal. Generally, mediations last about one or two days and are cheaper than litigation and other forms of dispute resolution. Mediation is a problem-solving procedure and its essence is finding a solution that satisfies everyone. Mediators are not responsible for taking sides, making judgments or giving guidance. Mediation is, therefore, different from processes like litigation and arbitration. The mediator is responsible solely for developing interaction between the parties. Mediations can be performed face to face or via a go-between (shuttle mediation). At the end of the process, the parties may agree on a settlement which is not legally binding, but which can be made so if the parties so wish. It is often useful to allow formal procedure to begin so that the parties focus their cases to an extent rather than to superimpose upon that a separate mediation.

Mediation has been described as an interest-based procedure where the future relationship of the parties can be brought to bear on the final agreement. In arbitration or litigation, only the past relationship of the parties is relevant and each side addresses their own arguments to the arbiter or judge in an attempt to convince him of the merits of their case. In mediation, since settlement must be by agreement between the parties, each side works with and through the mediator to reach an agreement. The process should not be adversarial. The mediator may facilitate communications between the parties in order to enable them to understand each other's perspectives and interests and may suggest a non-binding assessment of the dispute, which can be rejected or accepted by the parties as the basis for their settlement.

In England, mediation has grown substantially as a result of the recent reforms in civil procedure.[88] The civil procedure rules provide for the active management of cases by the court. Active management includes encouraging the parties to use an alternative dispute resolution procedure if the court considers it appropriate, and facilitating the use of such procedure.[89] A party which is perceived by the court to have unreasonably declined to engage in ADR may face indemnity costs and penal interest on both damages and costs.[90]

Is mediation useful? Mediation provides an alternative to pursuing litigation or arbitration and may offer parties more control over the way their dispute is dealt with. A resolution can be achieved in days or weeks rather than months or years.

Mediation can allow parties to rebuild relationships. This is in contrast to the more traditional processes of dispute resolution where often, at the end of the process, hostility may exist between the parties. A party can withdraw from mediation at any time and need not disclose anything it does not wish to disclose. Mediation may be of particular relevance in the construction and engineering industry where the relationship between parties is an ongoing one. The possibility of retaining communication between parties has a greater importance when their relationship could last for a number of years.

Mediation is not, however, always successful and can prove to be unattractive if a party believes that it would put itself at a tactical disadvantage explaining its position during a mediation only to find that the other side has no real interest in settling the dispute and that an additional layer of costs has been unnecessarily incurred. The success of the mediation will often depend on the receptiveness of the parties to the process, and the competence of the mediator.

Notes

[1] Small claims procedure, which allows simplified and cheaper litigation, is used for claims up to a value of £750 while 'summary cause' procedure should be used for claims above £750 and up to a value of £1500. The Scottish Executive intend to introduce changes to the financial limits in Summary Cause and Small Claim actions. However, at the time of writing, the orders by which these changes are to be made have not yet been approved by Parliament. The proposed changes are, in general terms, that an action where the sum sued for exceeds £1500 but does not exceed £5000 must be brought as a Summary Cause, and an action where the sum sued for is £1500 or less must be brought as a Small Claim.

[2] See the rules of jurisdiction contained in the Civil Jurisdiction and Judgments Act 1982 which set out the various grounds of jurisdiction. These include the defender's place of business and the place of performance of contractual obligations such as payment and delivery of goods.

[3] Chapter 40, Sheriff Court Ordinary Cause Rules 1993.

[4] If a defender wishes to have an ordinary action transferred to the Commercial Court, it could enrol a motion to that effect.

[5] Rules of the Court of Session 1994, Chapter 47.

[6] 2002 SLT 312.

[7] The European Convention of Human Rights is incorporated into UK Law by the Human Rights Act 1998.

[8] See the case of *Barry D Trentham Ltd* v. *Lawfield Investments Ltd* 2002 GWD 15-482, where the court refused to recall an inhibition and held that regard had

to be had to the likely financial position of a company at the conclusion of the action as well as at the time of the motion.

[9] See the case of *Advocate General for Scotland* v. *Taylor*, 2002 GWD 23-740, where Lord McEwan followed *Karl Construction* but referred to the implications of *Karl* on judicial, court and administrative time for consideration by the Inner House. As at the time of writing, the results of this analysis by the Inner House are awaited with interest.

[10] 2002 GWD 13-390.

[11] See the decision in *Irving's CB* v. *Skillen*, 2002 GWD 25-781, where a Sheriff at Glasgow Sheriff Court indicated that he did not necessarily agree that the reasoning in *Karl* extended to arrestments.

[12] Arrestment is also available in relation to debts which will not fall due until some time in the future or debts which are contingent on the occurrence of an event, but only if the debtor is 'verging on insolvency' or is 'considering absconding'.

[13] 1993 SC 650.

[14] Or, alternatively, the decision of an arbiter requested to determine what sum was due to Costain.

[15] The court's decision is of particular value as it was one of five Judges of the Inner House of the Court of Session. The courts decision was also referred to and relied upon in the case of *Karl Construction Limited* v. *Pallisade Properties plc, supra.*

[16] *Motodrift A/S* v. *Trachem Co. Ltd* 1982 SLT 127.

[17] In the case of *Park, Dobson & Co.* v. *William Taylor & Son* 1929 SC 571, the building contract provided for payment of work upon the issue of an architect's certificate. At the time the arrestment was served the architect had not issued any certificates, and no work had been carried out. Nevertheless it was held by the court that the arrestment had the affect of attaching the debt which was *conditionally* due at the date of the arrestment. The condition for payment of sums to the contractor would of course be performance of the work the contractor had undertaken to carry out.

[18] To this list might now be added '(e) if the warrant to arrest has been granted in contravention of the European Convention on Human Rights' (see the comments on *Karl Construction Ltd* v. *Palisade Properties plc, infra*).

[19] See *Richards* v. *Wallington (Earthmoving) Ltd* v. *Whatlings Ltd*, 1982 SLT 66. Great care should be taken to design the defender.

[20] Arrestment on the dependence will be recalled as oppressive if its main aim is to pressurise or embarrass the defender. *Conoco Speciality Products Inc.* v. *Merpro Montassa Limited* (Number 2) 1991 SLT 225.

[21] See *Glen Music Co. Ltd* v. *City of Glasgow District Council*, 1983 SLT (Sh Ct) 26.

[22] Fourteen days from the final interlocutor (court order) in an action.

[23] Or 'poinding' of a party's goods with a view to a warrant sale being held.

[24] Section 108 of the Act – see earlier commentary on the meaning of construction contract.

[25] Adjudication Reporting Centre, Glasgow Caledonian University, Reports Numbers 3 and 4, March 2001 and January 2002; P. Kennedy and J. Milligan. This survey only shows statistics for Adjudicator Nominating Body referral. The precise number of adjudicator referrals is not known. Further statistics are

produced in 'Adjudication: The First Forty Months' (August 2002, published by the CIC).

[26] Section 108(2) of the Act.

[27] Contracts for works performed in England and Wales are in these circumstances governed by the English Scheme.

[28] (1995) CILL 1035.

[29] (2000) BLR 168.

[30] (2002) BLR 312.

[31] See page 321 of BLR report, para 36.

[32] The *Edmund Nuttall Limited* case was later appealed but the dispute was settled before a judgment was issued by the Court of Appeal.

[33] *Northern Developments (Cumbria) Limited* v. *J & J Nichol* (2000) BLR 158.

[34] See 2002 GWD-742.

[35] An adjudicator is different from an arbiter in this respect: an arbiter, under Scots Law, requires express power to make an award of damages.

[36] *Northern Developments (Cumbria) Limited* v. *J & J Nichol* (2000) BLR 158.

[37] Clause 18(2)(b).

[38] Based on a flow chart in Guy Cottam (1998), *Adjudication under the scheme for construction contracts*, Thomas Telford.

[39] Or, in Scotland, the Chartered Institute of Arbitrators (Scottish Branch).

[40] The referral date under the ICE procedure is the date the adjudicator receives the document referred to in paragraph 4.1 of the ICE procedure.

[41] The fundamental differences between litigation and adjudication have been judicially recognised in Scotland in *Karl Construction (Scotland) Limited* v. *Sweeney Civil Engineering Limited* 2001 SCLR 95. In that case the Inner House commented that the rules of natural justice developed in the context of an adversarial system must adjust to and be viewed in the context of the structure of the adjudication process.

[42] See, for example, the court's opinion in *Fastrack Contractors Limited* v. *Morrison Construction Limited* (2000) BLR 168. In this case it was recognised that the referral notice may assist an adjudicator or a court in determining the precise dispute referred to adjudication in the notice of adjudication.

[43] (1999) BLR 93.

[44] (2000) 2 TCLR 418; *Bouygues (UK) Limited* v. *Dahl-Jensen (UK) Limited* (2000) 1 BLR 49.

[45] 2001 GWD 21-787.

[46] *Macob Civil Engineering Ltd* v. *Morrison Construction Ltd* (1999) BLR 93.

[47] 2001 SLT 1039.

[48] (2002) BLR 93.

[49] *Grovedeck* v. *Capital Demolition Limited* (2000) BLR 181; *Homer Burgess* v. *Chirex (Annan) Limited* (2000) SLT 277.

[50] (2002) BLR 217.

[51] It appears from the judgment that Lord Justice Auld did not agree entirely with the opinion of Lord Justice Ward. Many commentators prefer the reasoning of Lord Justice Auld. The case is, of course, not of binding authority in Scotland (albeit it is at least persuasive).

[52] *Palmers Limited* v. *ABB Power Construction Limited* (1999) BLR 426. See also *Homer Burgess* v. *Chirex (Annan) Limited, supra.*

[53] *The Project Consultancy Group* v. *The Trustees of the Gray Trust* (1999) BLR 377; *Christiani & Neilson Limited* v. *Lowry Centre Development Company Limited* 16 June 2000 (unreported).

[54] *Northern Developments (Cumbria) Limited* v. *J & J Nichol* (2000) BLR 158; *A & D Maintenance & Construction Limited* v. *Pagehurst Construction Services Limited* (2000) 16 Const LJ 199.

[55] *F W Cook Limited* v. *Shimizu (UK) Limited* (2000) BLR 199.

[56] *Sherwood & Casson Limited* v. *MacKenzie Engineering Limited* (2000) 2 TCLR 418, *Barr Ltd* v. *Law Mining, supra cit.*

[57] *Discain Project Services* v. *Opecprime Developments* (2000) 8 BLR 402.

[58] *Woods Hardwick Limited* v. *Chiltern Air Conditioning* (2001) BLR 23.

[59] (2002) BLR 288.

[60] *Elanay Contracts Limited* v. *The Vestry* (2001) BLR 33.

[61] In Scotland, a 'sist', or suspension of proceedings.

[62] *Herschel Engineering Limited* v. *Breen Property Limited* (2000) BLR 272.

[63] See the case of *The Construction Centre Group Limited* v. *Highland Council*, 2002 GWD 27-932 for an example of a successful application for summary decree, despite various challenges to the adjudicator's decision.

[64] See para 24 of Part I of the Scottish Scheme.

[65] Paragraph 26 of Part I of the Scottish Scheme.

[66] (2000) BLR 158.

[67] DETR Consultation Paper, 'Improving Adjudication in the Construction Industry', 27 April 2001.

[68] Paragraph 1.2.

[69] Paragraph 5.2.

[70] In Scotland, arbiters are conventionally referred to as 'arbiters'. Importantly, however, the new Scottish Arbitration Code 1999 and the 1997 Arbitration Bill of the Scottish Advisory Committee on Arbitration Law adopt the English term 'Arbitrators'.

[71] *A. Sanderson & Son* v. *Armour & Co. Ltd* 1922 9 SC(HL) 117.

[72] A good arbitration clause and, in any event, the arbitration rules adopted by the parties, should provide for the registration of the decree arbitral in the Books of Council and Session 'for preservation and execution'. Thus, the decree can be registered in those public registers, at minimal time and expense, and an extract obtained. That extract can then be enforced as if it were a court decree. See clause 67(2)(7) of the ICE 7th Conditions, introduced by the April 2001 amendments.

[73] See also *Fairlie Yacht Slip* v. *Lumsden* 1977 SLT (Notes) 41.

[74] Rule 41.5 of the Rules of the Court of Session 1994 (as amended) and *John L. Haley* v. *Dumfries and Galloway Regional Council* 1985 SLT 109.

[75] See Rule 41.7(1)(b) of the Rules of the Court of Session 1994 (as amended).

[76] *Op. cit.*

[77] *Op. cit.*

[78] *Pumpherston Oil Company Ltd* v. *John Cavaney* (1903) JF 663.

[79] See *ERDC* v. *HM Love & Co., supra.*

[80] Rule 41.7(1)(c) of the Rules of the Court of Session (as amended).

[81] See, for example, *Morgan Grenfell (Local Authority Finance) Ltd* v. *Seven Seas Dredging Ltd* and *Secretary of State for Transport* v. *Birse-Farr Joint Venture* (1993) 62 BLR 36. See also *J T Mackay & Co. Ltd* v. *Gosport Marina*

Ltd, as yet unreported, 3 July 2002, in which an attempt to refer to arbitration a dispute under the ICE 6th edition, following adjudication, failed as it did not follow (within 3 months) a clause 66 decision of the Engineer.

[82] See the Prescription and Limitation (Scotland) Act 1973 (as amended) and *Douglas Milne Ltd* v. *Borders Regional Council* 1990 SLT 558.

[83] Both clause 18(2)(b).

[84] [2001] 1 All ER 34.

[85] [2001] 1 All ER 34.

[86] In *Dredging and Construction Company Limited* v. *Delta Civil Engineering Co.* [2000] CLC 213; 68 Con LR 87 The Technology and Construction Court applied the same logic to a similar question under the FCEC 1991 form. The provisions of the latter part of clause 18(8) of that form are substantially the same as those of the relevant sub-clauses of 18(10) of the July 1998 (with April 2001 amendments) print of the CECA Sub-contract conditions. Accordingly, the current print is likely to be applied in the same way.

[87] In *Lafarge Redlands Aggregates Ltd (formerly Redland Aggregates Ltd)* v. *Shepherd Hill Civil Engineering Ltd, supra*, the minority view was that what was intended by the clause was that the Contractor would simply represent the interests of the sub-contractor before the Engineer at arbitration. The clause did not, in their view, envisage a true tri-partite arbitration in which the Employer, Contractor and Sub-Contractor would all feature. However, the majority view, was that the clause did intend such a tri-partite proce-dure. The ability of the contractor and Sub-Contractor to bring about such an arbitration would, however, depend upon the Employer's agreement.

[88] Lord Woolf's Civil Justice Reforms, April 1999.

[89] CPR Rule 1.4.

[90] *Dyson & Field* v. *Leeds City Council*, unreported, 22 November 1999. See also *Dunnett* v. *Railtrack* [2002] 1 WLR 2434 and *Hurst* v. *Leeming* [2002] EWHC 1051.

11. Insurance, indemnities, guarantees and bonds

Guarantees and bonds

Terminology

The terminology used in reported cases and textbooks in relation to this topic can be confusing, with more than one term commonly used to refer to the same concept. For example the words 'guarantee' and 'bond' as they are used in the construction industry are in effect synonymous since a bond is a type of guarantee. However, it is perhaps helpful to note that the word 'bond' is typically used in the case of a guarantee by an independent third party while the word 'guarantee' is typically used in the case of a guarantee given by a parent or group company in respect of another group company. This chapter uses the word 'guarantee' rather than 'bond' in most instances in the hope that this will limit confusion. Scottish cases also refer to the 'caution'[1] which is synonymous with the term 'guarantee'.[2]

The following terms are used to refer the parties generally interested in guarantees:

- **guarantor** – the party giving the guarantee
- **creditor** – the party benefiting from the guarantee
- **principal debtor** – the party whose obligation is guaranteed.

What is a guarantee?

A guarantee is a contract by which one party ('the guarantor') undertakes to be liable to the other party ('the creditor') for the debt, default or miscarriage for which another person ('the principal debtor') is primarily liable to the creditor.[3] There must be an independent principal contract to which the guarantee relates.[4]

The obligation undertaken by the guarantor will generally be either (i) to pay up to a specified sum of money to the creditor, or (ii) alternatively, to perform the obligations of the principal debtor; in the event of a failure by the principal debtor under a contract between the creditor and the principal debtor under the contract.[5] Guarantees operate as a protection against the insolvency of the principal debtor.

Where the principal debtor is a contractor the contractor will generally build the cost of providing the guarantee or bond into their contract sum.

The general principles which apply to guarantees in England are very similar to those which apply in Scotland. As a result, English court decisions in this area of the law are persuasive in Scotland.[6]

Types of guarantee

Conditional guarantee

The obligation of the guarantor in terms of a conditional guarantee is secondary (or accessory) to the principal obligation owed by the principal debtor to the creditor. The guarantor's liability under the guarantee does not arise until the principal debtor has defaulted in its obligation owed to the creditor[7] or possibly later if the guarantee so provides e.g. upon the issue of a demand following the default.[8] In principle, the guarantor's liability is co-extensive with and cannot exceed the principal debtor's liability to the creditor.[9] Due the accessory nature of the guarantor's obligations, the guarantor will generally be discharged upon the extinction of the principal obligation.[10] The guarantor will not be discharged in certain circumstances such as where the principal obligation is extinguished due to the bankruptcy of the principal debtor.[11]

To ascertain the guarantor's liability under the guarantee it is necessary for the creditor to prove: (i) that the principal debtor is in default under the principal contract; (ii) that damages have been sustained by the creditor; and (iii) the quantification of those damages subject to any limit in the guarantee.[12] The guarantor will be answerable to the creditor for damages suffered by the creditor due to the principal debtors default under the principal contract.

Unconditional/on demand 'guarantee'

It is important to distinguish between a guarantee in the traditional sense of being conditional to an underlying principal contract and an unconditional or on demand 'guarantee' which itself constitutes an independent primary obligation similar to an indemnity. The guarantor's liability under unconditional guarantees is not dependent on: (i) the principal debtor being in default under the principal contract; or (ii) damage having been sustained by the creditor. An unconditional 'guarantee' is then not in fact a guarantee in the proper sense of a liability arising on the default of another, but has been described as analogous to a bank's letter of credit or a promissory note payable on demand.[13]

The creditor's liability under an unconditional 'guarantee' depends only (subject to any limit in the guarantee) on some event, document or certificate being produced or a demand or call being made against the guarantor irrespective of its accuracy or justification.[14]

Such guarantees are occasionally referred to as 'unconditional performance guarantees' or 'on demand performance guarantees'. However, the reference to 'performance' is misleading and of no legal effect, since the guarantor's liability under such guarantees does not depend on any actual failure to perform or default by the principal debtor being established.[15]

Such 'performance' wording may be relevant in the relationship between the creditor and the principal debtor. If the creditor makes a call under an unconditional guarantee which contains performance wording then the principal debtor could attempt to interdict payment by the guarantor. However, to be successful the principal debtor would probably need to establish an implied term in the principal contract. It is perhaps difficult to identify grounds for such a term being implied.

If a creditor fails to provide finance which it is obliged to provide under the principal contract this may lead to some failure by the principal debtor under the principal contract. The Court of Appeal appears to be of the view that it should be entitled to take such circumstances into consideration if a creditor is seeking to enforce an unconditional bond.[16]

It would seem equitable to allow a principal debtor to recover from the creditor any sum paid under an unconditional guarantee which was paid out following a call which was not justified and which the guarantor has recovered from the principal debtor.

Obligations guaranteed

There are various types of obligations which are the subject of guarantees in the construction industry. We have identified below some of the more common ones, but almost any obligation can be guaranteed.

Payment guarantee

A guarantee of the payment obligations owed by one of the contracting parties in respect of the performance of the other party.

For example, if the financial covenant of the employer is weak, a contractor may require the employer to provide a payment guarantee in respect of its payment obligations under the engineering contract.

Advance payment guarantee

A guarantee in favour of the employer of a contractor's obligation to repay an advance payment made by the employer at the commencement of a contract in order to enable the contractor to start work.[17]

Retention guarantee

A guarantee in favour of the employer of a contractor's obligation to rectify defects within the defects liability period.[18]

Performance guarantee

A guarantee of performance by the contractor of his obligations under the principal contract. Performance guarantees are commonly demanded by the employer in an engineering project to secure the performance of the contractor's obligations under the contract.[19] In the UK they will typically be limited to 10 per cent of the contract sum.

Guarantors

Guarantees are commonly provided on a commercial basis by banks, insurance companies or specialist surety companies. However, guarantees may also be provided by a parent company in respect of the contractual obligations of one of its group companies.

Clearly the creditor should ensure that the covenant of the guarantor is satisfactory having regard to the obligations which are to be guaranteed.

Form of guarantee

Does a guarantee need to be in writing?

Generally the answer to this question, in relation to guarantees granted in connection with engineering contracts which are subject to Scots law, is 'no'. The position as regards engineering contracts governed by the law of England and Wales is different.

Section 1(2)(a)(ii) of the Requirements of Writing (Scotland) Act 1995 requires that 'a gratuitous unilateral obligation except an obligation undertaken in the course of business' must be constituted in a written document. While a guarantee is, it is submitted, a gratuitous[20] (as between the guarantor and the creditor) unilateral obligation the exception of 'an obligation undertaken in the course of business' will in most cases apply to guarantees granted in connection with engineering contracts. However, in practice all such guarantees will usually be set down in writing in any event.

Drafting a guarantee

While many traditional forms of guarantee are drafted in confusing and archaic language this is not necessary for them to have effect.

Traditional forms of guarantee purport on their face to create an immediate monetary debt binding on the guarantor, and then provide for future release of that debt and the end of the obligation under the guarantee either upon payment of the guarantee or upon full performance of the guaranteed obligations by the principal debtor.

In fact the following words are adequate to create a basic performance guarantee:

> We, A, hereby guarantee to you, B, the performance by C of his contract made with you dated [ ].

As a practical point the creditor, normally the employer, should stipulate the precise form of bond required (in the case of the employer in the tender documents). The employer should then ensure either: (i) that the form is incorporated within the engineering contract itself with an obligation on the contractor to deliver it to the creditor executed by the guarantor immediately upon execution of the engineering contract; or (ii) that the stipulated form executed by the guarantor is delivered to the creditor prior to execution of the engineering contract.

Standard forms

There are a number of standard form guarantees/bonds in existence produced by construction industry bodies such as the ICE, ABI, NJCC and FIDIC forms. These standard forms are used fairly commonly but it is also common for creditors and guarantors to have preferred amendments to these styles, or their own bespoke forms.

Interpretation of guarantees

Historically guarantees have been interpreted in a way which is favourable to the guarantor[21] and the courts have discharged guarantors from their obligations in situations where no real prejudice to the guarantor can have in reality occurred. It has been suggested that this favourable status of guarantors arose from the fact that historically guarantees were commonly granted gratuitously. However, in recent times it has become more common for guarantees to be granted by banks, insurance companies, specialist surety companies or by a parent or group company on a commercial basis. In Scotland at least the fact that a guarantee has been granted on a commercial basis does not appear to dilute significantly the favoured position of the guarantor.[22] The *contra proferentem* rule applies to the interpretation of guarantees. This means that if there is an ambiguity in the wording of the guarantee it will be construed against the party who seeks to rely upon it.

Liability of the guarantor

General

Perhaps it goes without saying, but the liability of the guarantor depends upon the particular wording of the guarantee in each case.[23]

Traditional forms of guarantee tend to provide that the whole sum guaranteed will become due upon breach. However, equity prevents the creditor claiming the whole sum guaranteed but rather up to the damage suffered by the creditor.[24]

The creditor's remedy against the guarantor is in damages. In general terms the level of damages which the creditor can seek to recover is the loss suffered by the creditor due to the principal debtor's failure to do what the guarantor guaranteed that he would do.[25]

In assessing the extent of the guarantor's liability under a conditional guarantee the state of the accounts between the creditor and the principal debtor will usually require to be examined, including any counterclaim.[26] Some guarantees preclude the guarantor setting off sums due by the creditor to the principal debtor against the amount guaranteed in terms or the guarantee.[27] However, in the absence of an express exclusion, set off will generally be permitted.[28]

Care must be taken where liability of the guarantor under a guarantee is conditional upon the principal debtor's breach of the principal contract. Depending upon how the termination provisions of the principal contract are drafted an event which allows termination may or may not be a breach of contract. If the event which allows termination of the principal contract is not strictly a breach then a guarantee which is conditional on breach will not respond.[29]

Unless it is otherwise agreed the guarantor will have an implied right of indemnification against the principal debtor whose obligations have been guaranteed.[30] The guarantor's right to be indemnified includes a right to interest on the amount paid and expenses incurred by the guarantor in defending an action against him by the creditor.[31] As a result the guarantor's only real risk is the insolvency of the principal debtor. If the principal debtor remains solvent, the guarantor should be able to recover from him any sums paid to the creditor in terms of the guarantee.

It is common for the principal debtor to be made a party to a performance guarantee and accept joint and several liability under the guarantee with the guarantor.[32] This facilitates the guarantor's pursuit of his indemnity against the principal debtor if necessary.

The guarantor is also entitled upon full satisfaction of his obligation to demand from the creditor an assignation of the debt under the principal contract, any security granted by the principal debtor held for that debt, and any diligence done upon it in order to enable him to enforce his right of indemnification against the principal debtor.[33] Any payment by the guarantor to the creditor should not be viewed as payment of the debt due by the principal debtor to the creditor but rather as payment for assignation of the right of the creditor against the principal debtor. Otherwise there will be no debt under the principal contract for the creditor to assign.

Guarantors can also seek from the creditor an assignation of any claims which the creditor may have against a third party other than the principal debtor. Such a situation arose in a Canadian case where the guarantor had paid out under a guarantee but then pursued the contract engineer in the creditor's name on the basis that the engineer failed to ensure that the principal debtor contractor complied with the engineer's instructions.[34]

When the debt which is guaranteed has become due, the guarantor has the right to insist that the sum is paid by the principal debtor. Indeed the guarantor may decide simply to pay the debt without a demand by the creditor and then seek relief from the principal debtor.[35]

Duration of liability

The period of time for which a guarantee will continue in force depends upon the terms of the guarantee[36] and the nature of the obligation guaranteed.

It is becoming more and more common for guarantees to contain specific timescales within which (or the happening of specific events upon which) the guarantor is to be discharged. However, generally the guarantee will be worded such that the guarantee will remain valid as regards claims which have arisen or been intimated prior to the end of the relevant timescale or by the happening of the relevant event.

Payment guarantee It is usually clear from the nature of the transaction whether a payment guarantee is a continuing one or will expire once the guaranteed payment takes place.[37]

Performance guarantee In the absence of any provision to the contrary the guarantor will not be released from liability for defects by a certificate of practical completion or notice of completion of making good defects or their equivalent. Where, as in most engineering contracts, a defects liability period is provided for, the contractor will remain liable for any defects discovered during that period and, thereafter will be liable for any latent defects for the duration of the prescriptive period.

Guarantors providing guarantees on a commercial basis generally insist upon their liability under the guarantee terminating on a specified date or the occurrence of a specified event[38] and therefore exclude liability extending to the full prescriptive period. This removes all liability of the guarantor for the contractor's defects undetected as at the expiry date or expiry event.[39]

It is not uncommon for a guarantee to provide that notice of any breach under the principal contract will be required to be given to the guarantor by the creditor within a set period after the breach.

Enforcing a guarantee[40]

Conditional guarantee

Default of principal debtor As stated above,[41] the obligation of the guarantor in terms of a conditional guarantee is secondary to the principal obligation owed by the principal debtor to the creditor. The guarantor's liability under the guarantee does not arise until the principal debtor has defaulted in its obligation owed to the creditor.

Compliance with requirements of guarantee The creditor should take care to comply with the precise requirements of the guarantee. In the absence of express provision in the guarantee, the creditor is not required to give notice of the principal debtor's default to the guarantor before the guarantor's liability can be enforced.[42]

Pursuit of claim against principal debtor in the first instance
Payment guarantee In the absence of express provision in the guarantee to the contrary, the creditor does not require to pursue his remedies against the principal debtor in the first instance, or even bring him in as a co-defender in an action against the guarantor.[43] The creditor will often prefer to proceed against the guarantor alone, leaving the guarantor to join the principal debtor as a third-party defender to the guarantor's claim for an indemnity.

Performance guarantee The lack of performance must be established (constituted) against the principal debtor before the guarantor can enforce the terms of the guarantee.[44]

Unconditional/on demand 'guarantee'

No default of principal debtor required   As noted above, the guarantor's liability under unconditional 'guarantees' is not dependent on: (i) the principal debtor being in default under the principal contract; or (ii) damages having been sustained by the creditor.

Compliance with requirements of guarantee   As with a conditional guarantee, the creditor should take care to comply with the precise requirements of the guarantee. In particular where the event that triggers liability under the guarantee is a written or other demand or call made by the creditor, the terms of that demand or call must conform to the requirements of the guarantee.[45]

Unjustified call   If the creditor unjustifiably makes a call on an on demand 'guarantee' the principal debtor may have a claim in damages against the creditor. The principal debtor can attempt to reduce the chances or effect of an unjustified call by having the 'guarantee' reduce in amount as the project progresses and/or insist upon an expiry date.

Discharge[46]

General

There are various circumstances (other than through the relevant guarantee's natural expiry) in which a guarantor may be discharged from the obligations which the guarantor has undertaken in terms of the guarantee.[47]

In Scotland, if a guarantor is to be discharged for a particular reason the practice has been to discharge the guarantor *in toto* (wholly) rather than *pro tanto* (to the extent that the guarantor can show loss). Discharge on a *pro tanto* basis has found favour in the United States particularly with regard to professional compensated guarantors, and was considered favourably in an English case.[48]

Conditional guarantees

Full performance of the obligations guaranteed *Performance guarantee*   One might think that it would be equitable to discharge a party guaranteeing performance of the contractor under an engineering contract upon the issue of the notice of completion of making good defects or its equivalent. However, the guarantor will not be discharged (unless the guarantee provides to the contrary) until the end of the prescriptive period.[49]

Payment guarantee   If a guarantor is guaranteeing a payment obligation then payment of the full amount will not discharge the guarantor where that payment is subsequently set aside by law on the grounds, for example, that it is an unfair preference in a bankruptcy situation.[50]

Repudiation *Repudiation of principal contract by principal debtor* A creditor who accepts the repudiation of the principal contract by the principal debtor does not thereby release the guarantor.[51]

Repudiation of principal contract by creditor Repudiation of the principal contract by the creditor of the guarantee will discharge the guarantor if the principal debtor accepts the repudiation.

However, the breach must be a repudiatory breach since discharge of the guarantor should depend on the importance of the breach in relation to the risk undertaken.[52] The guarantor will be discharged if the breach results in the creditor not being entitled to sue the principal debtor. A non-repudiatory breach by the creditor will not discharge the guarantor unless both the breach is 'not unsubstantial' **and** the term which has not been complied with can be regarded as having been embodied in the guarantee.[53]

Non-disclosure Guarantors have argued that a guarantee is a contract *uberrimae fidei* (of the utmost good faith) and that as a result if the creditor does not disclose to the guarantor any material facts the guarantor should be discharged. However, such arguments have not been accepted by the courts.[54] As a result there is no general duty upon a creditor to disclose to the guarantor material facts which might affect the guarantor.[55] However, where the guarantor puts specific questions to the creditor or the creditor decides to make a disclosure to the guarantor then the creditor has a duty to make full disclosure.[56]

There may, depending upon the particular circumstances of the transaction, be a duty upon the creditor to disclose to the guarantor 'anything that might not naturally be expected to take place between the parties' in the principal contract.[57] In such circumstances it may be possible to imply a warranty by the creditor that no unusual risks exist.[58] For example, a performance guarantee was released where the creditor (employer under the principal contract) had not disclosed to the guarantor that the works were to be carried out under the joint supervision of the creditor's surveyor and the surveyor of an undisclosed third party.[59]

If information comes to the attention of the creditor during the period the guarantee is in force which is material to the risk undertaken by the guarantor then the creditor should pass on that information to the guarantor.[60]

Failure to give notice In the absence of express provision in the guarantee, the creditor is not required to give notice of the principal debtor's default to the guarantor before the guarantor's liability can be enforced.[61]

If a notice provision is included in the guarantee, it is a matter of the interpretation of the guarantee as a whole whether or not the requirement for notice to be given constitutes a condition precedent of the guarantor's liability.[62]

Where the guarantee provides the guarantor with a right to step-in in the event of default by the principal debtor and complete the principal debtor's obligations under the engineering contract then a strict interpretation is likely be given to the notice provision.

Extinction of principal obligation   As stated above,[63] due to the accessory nature of the guarantor's obligations the guarantor will generally be discharged upon the extinction of the principal obligation.

Preservation of securities   The guarantor will generally be released where the creditor loses or abandons any security which it holds in respect of the principal debtor's obligations.[64] The guarantor will be released *pro tanto* (to the value of the lost security) rather than *in toto* unless there is an express provision between the guarantor and the creditor that the security is to be maintained. However, the creditor owes the guarantor a duty of care in realising such a security.[65]

Acts to the prejudice of the guarantor   *General*[66]   In the course of an engineering project situations will often arise where some form of compromise (e.g. the granting of an extension of time) would be the most expedient way of resolving a dispute with the contractor and allow the project to proceed smoothly. In the absence of a provision in the guarantee allowing such compromises[67] to be reached without the consent of the guarantor the striking of such a compromise may discharge the guarantor on the basis that it may be prejudicial to him. It will be a question of fact whether the acts of the creditor are sufficiently prejudicial to justify the discharge of the guarantor.[68]

If it is evident, without investigation, that the compromise is insubstantial or can only be beneficial to the guarantor then the guarantor will not be discharged. In all other circumstances United Kingdom case law tends to suggest that a guarantor should be discharged unless he has consented to the compromise.[69]

Generally no enquiry will be allowed to determine whether as a matter of fact prejudice to the guarantor has occurred.

Payment guarantees[70]   Failure by a creditor to take action against the principal debtor following late payment alone will not discharge the guarantor. In order for the guarantor to be discharged there must be a binding agreement between the creditor and the principal debtor deferring the time for payment without the consent of the guarantor.

A binding agreement to defer payment of one instalment of the contract sum will discharge the entire guarantee.[71] However, if a deferred payment instalment relates to a particular item of work it may be possible to treat that instalment as severable, in which case the guarantor's liability will remain unaffected in regard to the remaining work and instalments.

Performance guarantees[72]

(a)   **Overpayment** – while inadvertent overpayment will not discharge the guarantor, payment concessions willingly agreed by the creditor, usually the employer, may release the guarantor in full.[73] It is not uncommon for employers in engineering contacts to take a flexible approach to the payment provisions set out in the contract to assist a contractor who is in financial difficulty.

Where an overpayment is made, the creditor and the guarantor have lost an element of security against the principal debtor's failure to perform. Overpayment also increases the liability of the principal debtor and therefore the guarantor to the creditor. It also reduces the incentive on the principal debtor to complete its obligations under the principal contract, thus potentially increasing the guarantor's risk.

As stated above generally no enquiry will be allowed to determine whether as a matter of fact prejudice to the creditor has occurred. If such an enquiry was to be carried out then it would be necessary to consider what use the principal debtor actually made of the overpayment. If the overpayment was, for example, used to progress the works in the performance of an engineering contact then arguably the guarantor has not been prejudiced.

(b) **Extensions of time** – where a binding agreement is entered into between the creditor and the principal debtor, without the consent of the guarantor, giving the principal contract an extension of the time for performance of the principal contract the guarantor will, unless it is provided for in the principal contact, be discharged even if the guarantor has suffered no prejudice.[74] As with overpayment, under a performance guarantee an extension of time has the effect of reducing the incentive on the principal debtor to complete its obligations under the principal contract, thus potentially increasing the guarantor's risk.

(c) **Alteration of contract terms** – a binding agreement between the creditor and the principal debtor to an alteration of the principal contract will discharge the guarantor if it is capable of prejudicing the guarantor.[75] Generally an alteration will not discharge the guarantor if it was wholly trivial and inconsequential or self evidently could not in any conceivable circumstances prejudice the guarantor.[76] As above, mere acquiescence by the creditor to departures from the principal contract will not generally discharge the guarantor.

Parties to engineering contracts often agree that variations should be made to works to be carried out in terms of the contract. Unless the engineering contract provides for such variations or the guarantor consents the guarantor may be discharged by the creditor and the principal debtor agreeing the variation.[77] Occasionally performance guarantees contain an express exclusion of the power to vary the principal contract.[78]

Unconditional/on-demand 'guarantees'

Generally where there is an unconditional guarantee the guarantor will be obliged to pay the creditor without the need for investigating the contractual position between the creditor and the principal debtor.

However, a guarantor may refuse to honour a call on an unconditional guarantee where there has been an element of fraud[79] or where the demand or call was not made honestly and in good faith.[80]

If a guarantor has a reasonable prospect of establishing that the principal contract was a sham and that the guarantee had been obtained by fraud and misrepresentation as to the genuineness of the underlying deal, then a guarantor may be entitled to be discharged.[81]

Indemnities

Terminology

The following terms are used to refer to the parties generally interested in an indemnity:

- **Indemnifier** – the party giving the indemnity
- **Indemnitee** – the party benefiting from the indemnity.

What is an indemnity?

A distinction must be drawn between a guarantee and an indemnity. As stated above, a guarantee is secondary (or accessory) to a principal obligation owed by the principal debtor to the creditor. A guarantor assumes a secondary liability to answer for the default of the principal debtor who remains primarily liable.[82] However, an indemnity is an independent contract under which the indemnifier assumes a primary obligation to keep the indemnitee harmless against loss or damage.[83]

Rights of indemnity can arise from a contract (express or implied), from the relationship between two parties or by statute.[84] An employer will be obliged to indemnify a contractor, if as a necessary consequence of complying with its obligations in terms of the engineering contract, the contractor is exposed to a claim by a third party.[85]

Types of indemnity

A party to a contract may not only undertake simple contractual obligations but also give the other party an indemnity against its breach of those contractual obligations. However, it is not uncommon for one party to give to the other an indemnity in respect of matters which are not contractual responsibility and/or which are not within their control. One party may give to another party an indemnity against claims by a third party or third parties.[86]

Indemnifiers

In engineering contracts the contractor will normally be the party principally providing indemnities.[87] The indemnities will commonly be against the occurrence of certain losses and claims in respect of, for example, death of or injury to persons,[88] loss of or damage to property (other than the works being carried out in terms of the engineering contract),[89] infringement of intellectual property rights[90] and noise and other pollution.[91] In that scenario the contractor will be the indemnifier and the employer the indemnitee. Engineering contracts also provide for insurance to be maintained in respect of certain of the risks to which the indemnities relate.

Form of indemnity

Does an indemnity need to be in writing?

An indemnity does not require to be in writing.

Drafting of an indemnity

The express use of the word 'indemnity' or 'indemnify' in a contract is not essential to establish an obligation to indemnify. It is a matter of interpreting the contract to establish the intention of the parties. An indemnity may be implied into a contract in the absence of any specific contractual provision.

A contractual right of indemnity may arise by implication. There seems to be a general principle that if a person contracts with another to perform some action which is not itself delictual and that party duly performs without any negligence on its own part, there will be an implied indemnity in the event that the performance renders that party liable to a claim by a third person.[92] This principle has been recognised as being applicable in engineering contracts in Australia.[93]

Interpretation of indemnities

Indemnity clauses will usually be strictly construed and will be interpreted *contra proferentem* (if there is an ambiguity in the wording of the indemnity it will be construed against the party who seeks to rely upon it). This is particularly the case where the indemnitee party seeks to try and enforce the clause where the loss or damage is the consequence of the indemnitee's own negligence or breach of contract.[94]

In the *Alderslade* case in England the House of Lords held that an indemnity clause will not be enforceable by a negligent indemnitee unless it expressly so provides, or where negligence could be the only basis of liability under the clause, because to hold that it did not apply to negligence would strip the clause of any meaning.[95]

Following the *Alderslade* case, expressions such as 'all claims or demands whatsoever' or 'loss or damage arising from any cause whatsoever' began to appear in indemnity clauses aimed at covering indemnitee negligence. Initially the courts considered the use of such words as an indication of the party's intention that indemnitee negligence was to be covered.[96] However, in a later English case[97] the House of Lords considered a contractor's obligation to indemnify the employer against 'any liability, loss claim or proceedings whatsoever . . . arising out of, or in the course of, the execution of the order'. One of the contractor's employees was injured as a result of the employer's negligence. The employer sought to enforce the indemnity clause against the contractor to avoid liability. Applying the *Alderslade* case, the House of Lords held that such a clause could not exclude liability for the indemnitee's own negligence unless the word negligence or a synonym was expressly used.

Liability of the indemnifier

As stated above it is not uncommon for a party to contract to have not only simple contractual obligations but also to give the other party an indemnity against its breach of that contractual obligation. This can have implications not only as regards the sums that the party suffering the breach can recover from the party in breach but also as regards the commencement of the prescriptive period in respect of any claim.[98]

In general an indemnitee, if the indemnity relates to claims made against the indemnitee by a third party, is entitled to recover from the indemnifier sums that are payable by him to a third party in terms of any judgment made against him in any legal proceeding together with all costs, including his own, properly incurred in defending such legal proceedings or in terms of a compromise reached.[99] This position as regards compromises reached can even apply where a compromise has been reached but the third party claim has subsequently been shown to be unjustified.[100] While not essential it is advisable for the indemnitee to join the indemnifier as third party to or notify the indemnifier of any proceedings against the indemnitee to which the indemnity relates. This should limit the likelihood of the indemnifier questioning the defence of the proceedings or the terms of any compromise reached.

Enforcing an indemnity

The indemnitee is entitled to recover from the indemnifier as soon as it has a liability to the third party and before it has paid the third party unless the indemnity expressly excludes this.[101]

An express indemnity may be unenforceable for illegality.

There is no right of indemnity where either the indemnifier or the indemnitee knows at the time, or would have known had he not been grossly negligent, that the act in terms of which the indemnity is granted is illegal.[102]

'Secondary' indemnitee negligence

Contractors under the terms of the engineering contract commonly give the employer third-party liability indemnities. It is possible that even in cases where the third-party claim which is the subject of the indemnity arises as a result of the contractor's negligence, the employer (indemnitee in terms of the engineering contract) may be liable to the third party for what may be regarded as their secondary forms of negligence, for example their failure to adequately supervise the contractor, or their failure to detect or prevent the contractor's negligence. In such cases the third party may bring an action against both the contractor and the employer, and the question will then arise whether the contractual indemnity in favour of the employer will be enforceable in light of the employer's secondary or incidental negligence.[103]

Insurance

The purpose of this section is to introduce the basic principles of insurance, to consider briefly the terms of the ICE 7th Conditions insurance provisions and then to look at some other forms of insurance available in the market. A detailed consideration of the nature and scope of insurance policies and the law relating to them is outside the scope of this chapter.

Insurance is undoubtedly one of the most significant areas in which both a contractor and employer may seek to preserve their positions under an engineering contract. Full knowledge of the scope of applicable insurance policies can also considerably shorten negotiations as very often parties will discuss the allocation of risk and the potential liability that can arise from it without considering whether or not the risk in question is covered by the relevant insurance policy. In all projects best practice dictates that insurance provisions are given consideration very early on in the project.

Insurance polices can be taken out to cover a wide variety of situations which arise in connection with engineering projects. However, the most usual forms of insurance to be taken out include liability insurance and property insurance covering the contract works. Policies can also be amended so that waiver of subrogation rights can be added (to ensure that the contractor cannot be sued separately by the insurer following a claim). Advanced loss of profits and business interruption extensions may also be added, as can extensions covering environmental risk and professional indemnity.

Definition of insurance

A contract of insurance is one whereby one party ('the insurer') promises in return for money consideration ('the premium') to pay the other party ('the assured') a sum of money or provide him with some corresponding benefit upon the occurrence of one or more specified events.[104] There will usually be some degree of uncertainty as to whether the specified events will or will not occur.

Types of insurance

Insurance under engineering contracts can generally be classified into two areas: (a) liability; and (b) property.

Liability insurance

An example of liability insurance can be found in ICE 7th Conditions at clauses 22 and 23. This type of insurance will cover the liability that the insured may have to a third party. At clause 22 the contractor undertakes to indemnify the employer against losses and claims in respect of death or injury to any person or loss of or damage to property other than the works, provided such losses and claims arise out of the works. At clause 23 the indemnity given by the contractor under clause 22 is effectively backed up by the requirement for the contractor to take out an insurance policy in the joint names of the employer and the contractor in respect of the liabilities under clause 22 (excluding items (a), (b) and (c) of the Exceptions to clause 22). The Employers' Liability (Compulsory Insurance) Act 1969 must be complied with in relation to the insurance policies (usually a public liability policy) which cover death or injury and such policies, and usually the Public Liability and Employer's Liability policies will have to comply with the Act's statutory minimum level of insurance cover.

Carved out from the general indemnity given under clause 22(1) are five areas, stated to be the responsibility of the employer and in respect of which the employer provides an indemnity (which is capped under clause 22(4)(b)) to the contract under clause 22(3), comprising:

- damage to crops on the site (except to the extent that possession has not been given to the contractor)
- use or occupation of land provided by the employer or interference whether temporary or permanent with any right of way, etc.
- right of the employer to construct the works on over in or through any land
- damage being the unavoidable result of construction of the works in accordance with the contract
- death or injury to persons or loss of or damage to property resulting from any act neglect or breach of statutory duty committed by the employer.

Clause 22(4) provides for a limit to the level of indemnification insofar as the level of indemnification required shall be reduced in proportion to the extent that the 'act or neglect of the Employer his agents servants or other contractors . . . may have contributed to the said death injury or loss'.

Clause 24 concludes the liability insurance and provides an indemnity from the contractor to the employer in respect of claims for damages and compensation arising out of any accident or injury to anybody employed by the contractor, except to the extent that the accident was caused by or contributed to by the employer.

Property insurance

The main property indemnity and corresponding insurance clauses in ICE 7th Conditions are clauses 20 and 21. These cover responsibilities for the works, materials, equipment and plant.

The clauses are similar in layout to the liability clauses at clauses 22 and 23 in that at clause 20, sub-clause (1) the extent of the contractor's responsibility is set out in terms of both scope and time.

Clause 20(1)(a) provides that the contractor takes 'full responsibility for the care of the works' from 'Works Commencement Date' until 'issue of a Certificate of Substantial Completion' after which responsibility passes to the employer.

Clause 20(1)(b) provides that if the works are divided into sections for the purposes of sectional completion then the same principle as outlined in relation to clause 20(1)(a) applies such that the contractor's responsibility for that section ceases on issue of the certificate of substantial completion for that section. It is interesting to note that there is some doubt as to how the reference to 'part' in this clause is construed. Whilst 'Section' is a defined term under the contract, 'part' is not, and it is not clear how the courts would construe this reference.

As noted above, the contractor is not responsible for loss or damage to the extent that it arises due to the 'Excepted Risks', which are summarised as follows:

- use or occupation by the employer of the permanent works
- any fault defect error or omission in design (note that this is qualified in the ICE Design and Construct Conditions such that it reads 'any fault defect error or omission in the design of the Works for which the Contractor is not responsible under the Contract')
- riot, war or invasion act of foreign enemies or hostilities
- civil war, rebellion, revolution, insurrection or military or usurped power
- ionizing radiations or contamination by radioactivity from any nuclear fuel or from any nuclear waste from the combustion of nuclear fuel radioactive toxic explosive or other hazardous properties of any explosive nuclear assembly or nuclear component thereof
- pressure waves caused by aircraft or other aerial devices travelling at sonic or supersonic speeds.

This clause deals with the consequences of any loss or damage arising out of clause 20(1) and requires that if the contractor was responsible for the care of the works, materials, plant or equipment at the time of the loss or damage then without the need for any instructions the contractor shall at his own cost rectify the loss or damage. However, if the loss or damage occurs as a result of one of the excepted risks then the contractor is only required to rectify the damage or loss when instructed by the employer, and at the employer's cost.

Where there is a concurrent cause of loss or damage caused by a combination of the contractor and an excepted risk the engineer has the power under clause 20(3)(c) to apportion liability.

Clause 21 is the insurance clause that relates to the provisions of clause 20. The contractor is required to insure the works and materials, plant and equipment in the joint names of the contractor and the employer to the full replacement costs. An additional 10 per cent is required to be added to the level of insurance maintained to cover costs that may arise out of any rectification works; for example, legal costs, additional professional costs etc. The period for which the contractor is required to maintain the insurance is from works commencement date to issue of the certificate of substantial completion (clause 21(2)(a)).

ICE 7th Conditions also provide for the following provisions in relation to the insurance policies to be maintained by the contractor:

- The contractor must provide satisfactory evidence, usually in the form of a broker's letter, prior to works commencement date that the insurances required under the contract have been effected. Whilst there is a mechanism for calling for the insurance policy itself this is rarely done in practice. It should also be noted that the terms of the insurances are subject to the employer's approval, which cannot be unreasonably withheld or delayed.
- Excesses on the policy must not exceed those stated to apply in the contract.
- A failure to produce evidence that insurances are in place allows the employer to take out such policies and to recover the costs of doing so from the contractor.
- A failure by either the employer or the contractor to comply with the terms of the insurance policies shall result in each party indemnifying the other against losses and claims arising from failure to so comply.

Other forms of insurance

Latent defects/decennial insurance

This insurance is also known as 'inherent structural defects insurance'. It is aimed at the cost of putting right defects in the works on a no-fault basis to enable the owner or user of the works to get defects rectified without having to sue the construction team. This insurance attaches to the project under construction, not those constructing it. It usually lasts up to ten years with the client and other interested parties' names being noted on the policy. The insurance is best taken out before the works commence, but can be purchased after completion for a higher cost. Insurers will want to appoint their own monitoring engineers to perform a technical inspection service establishing the technical feasibility of the project and watching its progress.

The decision whether or not to obtain latent defects insurance will be based on a number of factors. There is initially its cost. The premium for this cover will be a percentage of the sum insured based upon the value put on the foundations, structure, roof and cladding of the building. Insurers may reserve the provision of or qualify the cover should the technical inspection reveal any matter that might give rise to a qualification on the terms of the cover. Typical exclusions include faults, defects, errors or omissions in the design, workmanship, materials used in fixtures and fittings and internal works and equipment.

Structural alterations or repairs or modifications to a building during the insurance period are excluded unless the insurers were notified of them beforehand, accepted them and endorsed the policy accordingly. An additional premium might also be required.[105]

Professional indemnity insurance

Professional indemnity insurance covers against legal liability arising through negligence in design. The ICE form of contract does not incorporate an obligation requiring the contractor or engineer to maintain professional indemnity insurance.

Professional indemnity insurance is normally taken out by construction professionals and design and build contractors to cover their liability for professional negligence. As with other liability policies, the insurer's obligation is to indemnify the insured, not the party claiming against the insured.

The amount of cover a professional buys will be governed by his professional body, the requirements of his clients and the depths of his pockets. Design and build contractors will have cover but it is not unusual for sub-contractors to go without even if they have some design input into the project. Professional indemnity insurance covers only professional negligence. This is usually enough for professional consultants, but contractors' liabilities extend beyond this into the realms of faulty workmanship and materials and a commitment to the works being 'fit for purpose'. With such clauses, the insured has to prove that the works are fit for purpose instead of the claimant proving that professional negligence has occurred. This shift in the onus of proof is not popular with insurers and, when they are persuaded to extend cover to include fitness for purpose clauses, it is usually on the basis that the insured has to prove to them that the claim would have succeeded under the pure negligence rule.

Professional indemnity policies are written on a 'claims made' basis. This provides cover for claims made during the period of insurance regardless of when the act of professional negligence took place. Because of this, policies have to provide retroactive cover to include work done before the policy started and cover has to continue even if professional work is no longer carried out.

All material facts have to be notified to insurers. Delays in notifying potential claims can lead to a claim not being covered, particularly if insurers have changed in the meantime.

Most professional indemnity policies are annual policies, issued on behalf of the individual professional firms and design and build contractors. However, there are some project specific policies which can last for up to six years and include all parties involved in the project.

Project insurance

Larger projects will often be covered by policies specifically written for the project and potentially embracing a wide variety of different types of insurance. They are often favoured by banks or institutional investors seeking to carefully and closely manage the interfaces between what would otherwise be a large number of separate and potentially conflicting and overlapping insurance polices.

Although based around the concept of the contractor's all-risks policy with joint names insurance and often other named parties, often bolted onto that core policy will be public and employer liability, product liability, existing structures insurance, advanced loss of profits and business interruption insurance.

Product liability insurance

Occasionally sub-contractors with design responsibility will not carry professional indemnity insurance but do offer product liability insurance.

Product liability insurance is a variant of public liability insurance in that it will indemnify the beneficiary against liability for death or injury or accidental loss or damage to property together with consequential loss arising from defects. However, it will not cover any cost of replacing the faulty part where the fault was a design defect. This means that there are clearly arguments both in favour of and against the use of product liability insurance. On the plus side is the fact that it is not restricted to simply liability arising from the sub-contractor/supplier failing to exercise a duty of care. Instead, it arises because of the provision of defective or dangerous goods. It does not however, as noted above, cover the beneficiary for the cost of replacing the defective part.

Notes

[1] Pronounced 'kayshun'.

[2] This was not always the case. See *Aitken's Trustees* v. *Bank of Scotland* 1944 SC 270 at 281.

[3] Bell's Commentaries I, 364, Bell's Principles s 245 and Erskine Institute III, 3, 61. Care must be taken to distinguish a guarantee from an undertaking to perform the principal contract should the principal debtor fail to so perform. Such an obligation is perhaps better described as a contingent principal obligation.

[4] cf. In relation to Unconditional/on demand 'guarantees' – see below.

[5] cf. In relation to Unconditional/on demand 'guarantees' – see below.

[6] *Aitken's Trustees* v. *Bank of Scotland* 1944 SC 270.

[7] *City of Glasgow District Council* v. *Excess Insurance Co. Ltd* 1986 SLT 585, OH; and *Nene Housing Society* v. *National Westminster Bank Ltd* (1980) 16 BLR 22.

[8] *Royal Bank of Scotland Ltd* v. *Brown* 1982 SC 89; and see clause 1(2) of the ICE Form of Default Bond found in the ICE Conditions of Contract – 7th edition which requires service upon the Surety (Guarantor) of a copy of the certificate issued by the engineer under clause 65(5) of the ICE Conditions of Contract – 7th edition and certified by the engineer as being a true copy.

[9] cf. Where the principal debtor has a natural but not a legal obligation (e.g. where the principal debtor did not have the legal capacity to contract) and the guarantor has guaranteed the principal debtor's obligations. In these circumstances the guarantor will be legally liable for the principal debtor's obligation even though the principal debtor is not. See Bells Principles s 251.

[10] It is interesting to note that a novation of the principal obligation will result in the extinction of the principal obligation and therefore the discharge of any guarantor of the principal obligation.

[11] Bell's Commentaries I, 360.

[12] *Royal Bank of Scotland Limited* v. *Dinwoodie* 1987 SLT 82; but see the ICE Form of Default Bond found in the ICE Conditions of Contract – 7th edition which has a very specific mechanism for establishing the circumstance in

which the surety (guarantor) is obliged to pay the employer (creditor) and the sums payable.

[13] See the Example Form of Performance Security–Demand Guarantee forming Annex C to the FIDIC Conditions of Contract for Construction as an example of an on demand 'guarantee' and *Edward Owen Engineering Ltd* v. *Barclays Bank International Ltd* [1978] QB 159 at 170.

[14] See *Howe Richardson Scale Co.* v. *Polimex-Cekop* [1978] 1 Lloyd's Rep. 161; *Esal (Commodities) Ltd and Reltor Ltd* v. *Oriental Credit Ltd and Wells Fargo Bank NA* [1985] 2 Lloyds Rep. 546.

[15] *IE Contractors Ltd (formerly GKN Contractors Ltd)* v. *Lloyds Bank plc and Rafidain Bank (a Body Corporate)* (1990) 51 BLR 1, CA.

[16] *Potton Homes Ltd* v. *Coleman Contractors (Overseas) Ltd* (1984) 28 BLR 19 per *Eveleigh* L J.

[17] See the Advance Payment Bond annexed to JCT Standard Form of Building Contract 1998 edition suite of contracts and *Wardens and Commonality of the Mystery of Mercers of the City of London* v. *New Hampshire Insurance Co. Ltd* (Sub Nom: *Mercers Co.* v. *New Hampshire Insurance Co. Ltd*) [1992] 2 Lloyd's Rep. 365.

[18] See the Bond in lieu of Retention annexed to JCT Standard Form of Building Contract 1998 Edition suite of contracts and the Form of Retention Repayment Guarantee annexed to the ICC General Conditions of Contract.

[19] See Clause 1 of the ABI Model Form of Guarantee Bond.

[20] See Thomson, J., *Promises and the requirements of writing*, 1997 SLT (News) 284, and Hogg, M., *A few tricky problems surrounding unilateral promises*, 1998 SLT (News) 25. But see also *Stair Memorial Encyclopaedia*, volume 3, para 880. However, if a guarantee is in fact a non-gratuitous unilateral obligation then it will not require to be in writing – section 1(1) of the Requirements of Writing (Scotland) Act 1995.

[21] *Baird* v. *Corbett* (1835) 14 S 41. But see comments of Parker L J in *Wardens and Commonality of the Mystery of Mercers of the City of London* v. *New Hampshire Insurance Co. Ltd* (Sub Nom: *Mercers Co.* v. *New Hampshire Insurance Co. Ltd*) [1992] 2 Lloyd's Rep. 365, 368. The form of guarantee that had been proposed by the guarantor was ambiguous. Parker L J expressed the view that in those circumstances the guarantee should be construed against the guarantor.

[22] But see *Watt* v. *National Bank of Scotland* (1839) 1 D 827.

[23] *Lewis* v. *Hoare* (1881) 44 LT 66 HL.

[24] As regards the extent to which the creditor can recover from the guarantor expenses incurred in pursuing the principal debtor, see *Stair Memorial Encyclopaedia*, volume 3, para 916.

[25] *Moschi* v. *Lep Air Services Ltd* [1973] AC 331.

[26] *Royal Bank of Scotland Ltd* v. *Dinwoodie* 1987 SLT 82, OH.

[27] See *Hyundai Heavy Industries Co. Ltd* v. *Papadoulous* [1980] 1 WLR 1129.

[28] But see *Cellulose Prods Pty* v. *Truda* (1970) 92 WN (NSW) 561.

[29] See *Perar B V* v. *General Surety & Guarantee Co. Ltd C A* (1994) 66 BLR 72.

[30] Erskine Institute III, 3, 65. In certain circumstances the guarantor will have a right of relief against the principal debtor even though the debt has not yet become due (see *Stair Memorial Encyclopaedia*, volume 3, para 936).

[31] *Stair Memorial Encyclopaedia*, volume 3, para 935.

[32] *Tins Industrial Co. Ltd* v. *Kono Insurance Ltd* (1987) 42 BLR 110.

[33] *Smithy's Place Ltd* v. *Blackadder and McMonagle* 1991 SLT 790, OH.

[34] *City of Prince Albert* v. *Underwood McLellan* (1968) 3 DLR (3d) 385.

[35] *Gray* v. *Thomson* (1847) 10 D 145.

[36] See clause 5 of the ICE Form of Default Bond found in the ICE Conditions of Contract – 7th edition.

[37] See *Construction contracts: principles and policies in tort and contract*, Wallace, D., 1986, para 19.17.

[38] See clause 5 of the ICE Form of Default Bond found in the ICE Conditions of Contract – 7th edition which provides expiry on the earlier of the dates stated in the certificate of substantial completion and the specified final expiry date.

[39] See further *Hudson's building and engineering contracts*, 11th edition, 1995, paras 17.021–17.022 and *Construction contracts: principles and policies in tort and contract*, D. Wallace (1986) para 19.17.

[40] See generally *Hudson's building and engineering contracts*, 11th edition, 1995, paras 17.012–17.016.

[41] See section on Conditional guarantee.

[42] See Clause 1(2) of the ICE Form of Default Bond found in the ICE Conditions of Contract – 7th edition which requires service upon the surety (guarantor) of a copy of the certificate issued by the engineer under clause 65(5) of the ICE 7th Conditions and certified by the engineer as being a true copy.

[43] Section 8, Mercantile Law Amendment Act (Scotland) 1856.

[44] *Johannesburg Municipal Council* v. *D. Stewart & Co.* (1902) Ltd 1909 SC 860 and 1909 SC (HL) 53.

[45] See *Howe Richardson Scale Co.* v. *Polimex-Cekop* [1978] 1 Lloyd's Rep. 161; *Esal (Commodities) Ltd and Reltor Ltd* v. *Oriental Credit Ltd and Wells Fargo Bank NA* [1985] 2 Lloyds Rep. 546.

[46] See further: *Keating on Building Contracts*, 7th edition, 2001, paras 10.31–10.39; *Hudson's building and engineering contracts*, 11th edition, 1995, paras 17.023–17.053 and 17.067–170.71; *Construction contracts: principles and policies in tort and contract*, Wallace, D., 1986, paras 19.08–19.15.

[47] This text does not attempt to identify the circumstances in which a guarantee will be void (rather than allowing the guarantor to be discharged) such as misrepresentation by the creditor to the guarantor. See *Smith* v. *Bank of Scotland* (1829) 7 S 244.

[48] *Wardens and Commonality of the Mystery of Mercers of the City of London* v. *New Hampshire Insurance Co. Ltd* (Sub Nom: *Mercers Co.* v. *New Hampshire Insurance Co. Ltd*) [1992] 365, 377.

[49] As regards the relevant prescriptive period and when it will commence see *Stair Memorial Encyclopaedia*, volume 3, para 984.

[50] *Petty* v. *Cooke* [1871] LR 6 QB 790.

[51] *Moschi* v. *Lep Air Services Ltd* [1973] AC 331 at 349.

[52] *National Westminster Bank plc* v. *Riley* [1986] BCLC 268 CA.

[53] *National Westminster Bank plc* v. *Riley* [1986] BCLC 268 CA.

[54] *London General Omnibus Co. Ltd* v. *Holloway* [1912] 2 KB 72; *Provident Accident & White Cross Insurance Co. Ltd* v. *Dahne and White* [1937] 2 All ER 255.

[55] *Royal Bank of Scotland* v. *Ranken* [1864] 6 D 1418.

[56] *Op. cit.*

[57] *Hamilton* v. *Watson* (1845) 12 Cl. & F 109 and 119.

[58] Generally there will be no duty of subsequent disclosure on the creditor but see *Stair Memorial Encyclopaedia*, volume 3, para 900.

[59] *Stiff* v. *Eastbourne Local Board* (1869) 20 LT 339.

[60] See *Stair Memorial Encyclopaedia*, volume 3, para 964.

[61] *Clydebank & District Water Trustees* v. *Fidelity & Deposit Co. of Maryland* 1915 SC 362. This judgment was affirmed in appeal case IL 44.

[62] Compare the judgment in *Clydebank & District Water Trustees* v. *Fidelity & Deposit Co. of Maryland 1916* SC 69, HL where notice was found to be a condition precedent to liability with the judgment in *Thomas Fuller Construction* v. *Continental Insurance* (1973) 36 DLR 3d 336, 350.

[63] See section on Conditional guarantee.

[64] *Hume* v. *Youngson* (1830) 8 S 295.

[65] *The Lord Advocate* v. *Maritime Fruit Carriers Ltd* 1983 SLT 357, OH.

[66] See further *Hudson's building and engineering contracts*, 11th edition, 1995, paras 17.034–17.040.

[67] See clause 6 of the ICE Form of Default Bond found in the ICE Conditions of Contract – 7th edition.

[68] *The Lord Advocate* v. *Maritime Fruit Carriers Ltd* 1983 SLT 357, OH.

[69] See *Holme* v. *Brunskill* (1877–78) LR 3 QB D 495, 505.

[70] See further *Construction contracts: principles and policies in tort and contract*, D. Wallace (1986) para 19.08 and *Hudson's building and engineering contracts*, 11th edition, 1995, paras 17.041 and 17.042.

[71] *Calder & Co.* v. *Cruickshank's Trustee* (1889) 17 R 74.

[72] See generally *Hudson's building and engineering contracts*, 11th edition, 1995, paras 17.043–17.053; *Construction contracts: principles and policies in tort and contract*, D. Wallace (1986) para 19.08.

[73] *Calvert* v. *London Dock Co.* (1838) 2 Keen 638 and *General Steam Navigation Co.* v. *Rolt* (1858) 6 CB, NS, 550.

[74] *C. and A. Johnstone* v. *Duthie* (1892) 19 R 624; *Polak* v. *Everett* [1876] I QB D 669; and see *Hudson's building and engineering contracts*, 11th edition, 1995, para 17.052.

[75] Bell's Principles s 259, *Holme* v. *Brunskill* [1877–78] LR 3 QB D 495, 505 and *Wilsons and Clyde Coal Co.* v. *McAuley* 1931 SLT (Sh Ct) 9.

[76] *Holme* v. *Brunskill* (1877–78) LR 3 QB D 495, 505.

[77] *Op. cit.*

[78] See further *Hudson's building and engineering contracts*, 11th edition, 1995, paras 17.049–17.051.

[79] *Royal Bank of Scotland Ltd* v. *Dinwoodie* [1987] SLT 82, OH; and *GKN Contractors Ltd* v. *Lloyds Bank plc* (1985) 48 BLR 53, CA.

[80] *Edward Owen Engineering Ltd* v. *Barclays Bank International Ltd* [1978] QB 159.

[81] *Solo Industries UK Ltd* v. *Canara Bank* [2001] 2 Lloyd's Rep. 578.

[82] *Yeoman Credit Ltd* v. *Latter* [1961] 2 All ER 294 at 296.

[83] *Laird* v. *Securities Insurance Co. Ltd* (1895) 22 R 452.

[84] *Boyle* v. *Morton* (1907) 5 F 416; *Aberdeen Harbour Board* v. *Heating Enterprises* 1988 SLT 762, *Scott Lithgow* v. *Secretary of State for Defence* 1989 SLT 236 (HL); and *Halsbury's Laws of England*, 4th edition, volume 20, 1993.

[85] *The Crown* v. *Henrickson & Knutson* (1911) 13 CLR 473 and this is dealt with to a degree expressly in clause 22(2)(d) of the ICE 7th Conditions.

[86] See clause 22 of the ICE 7th Conditions.

[87] See clauses 22, 24, 26(3), 27(1), 28(1), 29(1), 29(3) and 30(2) of the ICE 7th Conditions, which are examples of contractor indemnities in favour of the employer. But see also clauses 29(4) and 30(3) of the ICE 7th Conditions, which are examples of employer indemnities in favour of the contractor.

[88] See clauses 22(1)(a) and 24 of the ICE 7th Conditions.

[89] See clause 22(1)(b) of the ICE 7th Conditions.

[90] See clause 28 of the ICE 7th Conditions.

[91] See clause 29(3) of the ICE 7th Conditions.

[92] *Sheffield Corporation* v. *Barclay* [1905] AC 392.

[93] *The Crown* v. *Henrickson & Knutson* (1911) 13 CLR 473.

[94] *North of Scotland Hydro-Electric Board* v. *D. & R. Taylor* 1956 SC 1; and *Scottish Special Housing Association* v. *Wimpey Construction UK Limited* 1986 SLT 559, HL; and see *Hudson's building and engineering contracts*, 11th edition, 1995, para 15.040, *A guide to the indemnity and insurance aspects of building contracts*, P. Madge (1990), page 28 and clause 22(2)(e) which excludes indemnitee negligence from the indemnity in respect of death or injury to persons and loss of or damage to property.

[95] *Alderslade* v. *Hendon Laundry* [1945] KB 189.

[96] *Gillespie Brothers & Co.* v. *Roy Bowles Transport Ltd* [1973] QB 400, CA; *Joseph Travers & Sons Ltd* v. *Cooper* [1915] 1KB 73.

[97] *Smith* v. *South Wales Switchgear Ltd* [1978] 1All ER 18.

[98] See *Hudson's building and engineering contracts*, 11th edition, 1995, para 15.038.

[99] See further *Halsbury's Laws of England*, 4th edition, volume 20, 1993, para 354.

[100] *Comyn Ching Ltd* v. *Oriental Tube Ltd* (1979) 17 BLR 47, CA.

[101] Re *National Financial Co., ex p Oriental Commercial Bank* [1868] 3 Ch App 791.

[102] *Askey* v. *Golden Wine Co. Ltd* [1948] 2 All ER 35.

[103] See *Hudson's building and engineering contracts*, 11th edition, 1995, paras 15.047–15.054.

[104] *Prudential Insurance Company* v. *Inland Revenue Commissioners* [1904] 2KB 658 per Channell J.

[105] Tolleys, para D.30, 50–52.

12. Sub-contracts

Introduction

This chapter seeks to provide an overview of the engineering sub-contractor relationship with the main contractor. Elsewhere in this book specific reference has been made to specific clauses of the engineering sub-contract, and detailed guidance on the terms of the sub-contract is therefore beyond the scope of this chapter.

In an engineering project the employer will usually engage a contractor to carry out the works. With few exceptions the contractor will then engage one or more sub-contractors to carry out part of the works on the contractor's behalf. On a large engineering project, and depending on the type of procurement route chosen (see Chapter 1 for further information on procurement routes), the number of sub-contractors will often be very large, simply because a contractor cannot be an expert in all areas of the works and will frequently need to call upon the services of specialist cladding or air-conditioning sub-contractors. It follows therefore that the role of the sub-contractor and the interface between the sub-contract and the main contract is of significant importance to the engineering industry.

A variety of engineering sub-contract forms are available, the best known being as follows:

- Civil Engineering Contractors Association Form of Sub-contract for Civil Engineering, Building and Mechanical and Electrical Works (July 1999) for use with GC/Works/1 with Quantities (1998) or PC/Works/1 (1998) (including Without Quantities Supplement).
- Civil Engineering Contractors Association Without Quantities Supplement (July 1999) to Civil Engineering Contractors Association GC & PC/Works/1 With Quantities Sub-Contract for use with GC/Works/1 Without Quantities (1998) or PC/Works/1 Without Quantities (1998).
- Civil Engineering Contractors Association Form of Sub-Contract for Civil Engineering, Building and Mechanical & Electrical Works (July 1999) for use in conjunction with GC/Works/1 Single Stage Design & Build (1998) or PC/Works/1 Single Stage Design & Build (1998).
- Civil Engineering Contractors Association Form of Sub-Contract for use with the ICE Conditions of Contract 6th Edition (July 1998).
- Civil Engineering Contractors Association Form of Sub-Contract for use with the ICE Conditions of Contract 5th Edition (October 1998).
- Civil Engineering Contractors Association Form of Sub-Contract for use with the ICE Conditions of Contract Design and Construct (November 1998).

Privity of contract

When an employer contracts with a contractor for the carrying out of particular works, he does so in the knowledge that he has in all probability been through a tender process with that contractor and as such has come to know that contractor. Sub-contracting is a different process, however and, leaving aside nominated sub-contractors, the selection process, will be left to the contractor rather than the employer. However, as can be seen above, the contract does usually have built into it various control mechanisms to ensure that the employer has a degree of control over the sub-contractor.

The doctrine of privity of contract provides in essence that only the parties to a contract can enforce the obligations set out in that contract. The most commonly cited example of privity of contract is the English case of two relatives in the nineteenth century agreeing to provide money to a third relative. One of the parties to the contract died and the other refused to honour the contract. The beneficiary of the agreement sued the survivor. His action was unsuccessful, as he had not been a party to the contract.[1] It should be noted that had the case been under Scots law the outcome may have been different because of the operation of the doctrine of *jus quaesitum tertio*, and indeed in the law of England and Wales the Contracts (Rights of Third Parties) Act 1999 enables parties to circumvent the doctrine of privity of contract in certain circumstances.

Accordingly the employer can enforce its obligations under the contract with the contractor, and the contractor can enforce its obligations under the sub-contract against the sub-contract. However, the employer cannot enforce the sub-contractor's obligations under the sub-contract because there is no direct contractual relationship between the employer and the sub-contractor. In Scots law exceptions this rule is: if assurances or warranties relating to, among other things, fitness for purpose are given by a supplier of products.[2] An example of such a case is *Shanklin Pier Ltd* v. *Detel Products* in which the employers were refurbishing a pier. A paint manufacturer made certain representations as to its own product as a result of which the employer asked the contractor to engage the paint manufacturer. The product was defective and the employer sued the manufacturer, basing its claim on the representation given by the manufacturer to the employer. The court found that a contractual warranty existed and that the manufacturer was liable to the employer.

ICE 7th Conditions relating to sub-contracts

In setting the scene for the remainder of this chapter it is worth reminding ourselves of some of the control mechanisms introduced under the ICE 7th Conditions to ensure that the employer has a degree of control over the sub-contracting process. Other mechanisms, such as nominated sub-contracting, are dealt with later in this chapter:

- Contractor will not sub-contract the whole of the works without the prior written consent of the employer (clause 4(1)).
- Contractor entitled to sub-contract any part of the works or the design provided the name and address of the sub-contractor is notified to the

employer 14 days before any sub-contract is signed or the sub-contractor starts on site (clause 4(2)). This requirement does not apply to labour-only sub-contractors.

- The employer can give written reasons to the contractor as to why any sub-contractor to be engaged should not be so engaged and provided such reasons are good and are given not later than seven days after the employer has been told of the intention to engage the sub-contractor, then the sub-contractor will not be engaged (clause 4(2)).
- Contractor remains liable for all work carried out by the sub-contractor and for his acts, defaults and neglects (clause 4(4)).
- Sub-contractors can be removed from the works or their design if, following a written warning from the engineer to the contractor as to the conduct (whether incompetent or negligent or failing to conform with contractual health and safety provisions or engaged in conduct prejudicial to health and safety) of the sub-contractor, the sub-contractor fails to adhere to the required standards. In such circumstances the contract will be obliged to remove the sub-contractor from the works or their design (clause 4(5)).

To increase the measure of control exercised by employers over the sub-contracting procedure employers may require the right to approve the form of the sub-contractors contract and any collateral warranty documentation annexed to it. The purpose of this is two-fold in that: (a) the employer may wish to ensure that any collateral warranty documentation provides for appropriate step-in provisions for the employer, so that if the contractor should become insolvent during the project then the employer has the mechanism to ensure that it can step into the contractor's shoes, or procure an alternative contractor to do likewise to ensure that the project can be built out with as little additional disturbance to the contract programme as possible; and (b) once the project is complete, any requirement to provide collateral warranties to any third party purchaser or tenant can be completed expediently and with little time being lost through arguments and disagreements as to the required terms of such documents.

Nominated and domestic

General

Sometimes when an employer prepares the tender documents for a project, he may wish to name a particular sub-contractor who should be used on the project. This may be for a variety of reasons that may include the sub-contractor having worked closely with the employer on previous projects or because the sub-contractor has specialist knowledge that the employer feels may assist the project. Such sub-contractors are commonly referred to as 'nominated sub-contractors'. This contrasts with the more usual position by which the contractor invites various sub-contractors to tender for a particular sub-contract package. Sub-contractors appointed in this way are often referred to as 'domestic sub-contractors'.

Problems

Nominated sub-contractors are less common in the engineering sector. Although the employer would benefit from a potentially known quantity in the form of the sub-contractor without having to either administer the sub-contract itself directly (as the sub-contractor would be employed by the contractor). Lord Reid best expresses the problems with nominated sub-contractors:

> The scheme for nominated sub-contractors is an ingenious method of achieving two objects which at first sight might seem incompatible. The employer wants to choose who is to do the prime cost work and to settle the terms on which it is to be done, and at the same time to avoid the hazards and difficulties which might arise if he entered into a contract with the person whom he has chosen to do the work.[3]

A further problem with nomination has been the court's reluctance to make the contractor liable for the work carried out by a nominated sub-contractor[4] where the contractor had little or no control over the works being carried out. This potentially creates a problem for the employer in that it has in place its preferred (nominated) sub-contractor yet if the employer potentially has no recourse against either the contractor or the sub-contractor (because there is no privity of contract between the employer and sub-contractor) for the works carried out by the sub-contractor there is therefore a lacuna in the employer's ability to recover for the sub-contractors defective work. In practice this lacuna can be resolved by requiring the sub-contractor to enter into a direct contractual agreement with the employer.

ICE 7th Conditions

The main conditions relating to nominated sub-contractors are to be found in clause 59, the main provisions of which are summarised below.

- Contractor is not obliged to contract with a nominated sub-contractor if the contractor raises reasonable objections or if the nominated sub-contractor refuses to enter into a sub-contract containing provisions that: (a) in respect of the work goods materials or services the subject of the sub-contract the nominated sub-contractor will undertake towards the contractor such obligations and liabilities as will enable the contractor to discharge his own obligations and liabilities towards the employer under the contract; (b) the nominated sub-contractor will indemnify the contractor against claims demands and proceedings etc arising out of any failure by the sub-contractor to perform its duties and obligations; (c) the nominated sub-contractor will indemnify and keep indemnified the contractor from and against negligence by the nominated sub-contractor; (d) nominated sub-contractor will provide the contractor with security for the proper performance of the sub-contract; and (e) provisions relating to frustration set out in clause 63 (clause 59(1)).
- If the contractor either does not enter into a sub-contract with the nominated sub-contractor or if it does and the contractor terminates that sub-contract because of the default of the nominated sub-contractor the

engineer will: (a) nominate an alternative sub-contractor; (b) vary the works by order; (c) order the omission of works so that they can be carried out by people employed directly by the employer; (d) instruct the contractor to employ a domestic sub-contractor; and (e) invite the contractor to carry out the works itself (clause 59(2)).

- Contractor to be responsible for work carried out by a nominated sub-contractor (clause 59(3)).
- If the contractor believes an event has occurred which entitles it to terminate the employment of the nominated sub-contractor, the contractor shall notify the engineer in writing with reasons for such termination (clause 59(4)(a)).
- Provided the engineer has given his written permission the contractor can expel the nominated sub-contractor from the site (clause 59(4)(b)).
- If the nominated sub-contractor is expelled from the works the engineer shall immediately give effect to the re-nomination procedure set out under clause 59(2); (clause 59(4)(c)).
- Once the nominated sub-contractor is expelled from the site the contractor shall try to recover from the sub-contractor any additional costs and expenses incurred, including costs incurred because of the termination (clause 59(4)(d)), however if the contractor cannot recover all his reasonable expenses from the nominated sub-contractor the employer will reimburse any unrecovered expenses (clause 59(4)(e)).
- The engineer is to take any delay to the completion of the works arising out of the nominated sub-contractor's default into account in determining any extension of time to which the contractor is entitled under the contract (clause 59(4)(f)).
- For all work carried out or materials supplied by the nominated sub-contractor an appropriate amount is included in the contract price (clause 59(5)). If the contractor fails to pay the nominated sub-contractor without any reasonable cause for withholding payment, and the sums due have been certified by the engineer as being due, then the employer is entitled to make a direct payment to the nominated sub-contractor (clause 59(7)).

Sub-contract interface

A significant area for concern with any sub-contract is the nature of the interface between the sub-contract and the contract.

In drafting the sub-contract the contractor seeks to ensure that risk assumed under the contract is passed down into the sub-contract. In that way the contractor ensures that any risk which it assumes under the contract is mapped directly on to a risk assumed by the sub-contractor under the sub-contractor. Similarly where specified time periods are set out under the contract within which time the contractor needs to carry out a particular obligation, then in passing such time periods down to the sub-contractor the contractor will be concerned to ensure that they are either shortened or lengthened as is appropriate to ensure that the sub-contractor can complete the relevant obligation under the sub-contract without putting the contractor in breach of its corresponding obligation under the contract.

There are a variety of methods by which the contractor can ensure that the relevant obligations flow down from the contract into the sub-contract:

- **Bespoke sub-contract** – a bespoke sub-contract in which all the relevant clauses are passed down into the sub-contract is perhaps the safest method by which to ensure that the contract and sub-contract are 'back to back' in terms of liability and obligations. However, such a sub-contract is time-consuming and expensive to prepare and is appropriate in only large or complex projects.
- **Incorporating contract terms** – sometimes the contractor will try to incorporate by reference the contract terms directly into the sub-contract. This is a far from satisfactory way to proceed. The main problem with this approach is how the contract terms are to be construed when incorporated by reference into the sub-contract.[5] Whilst largely dependent on how the contract is incorporated by reference, the courts seem prepared to accept that parties have intended the main contract to apply to the sub-contract. However, the recurring theme seems to be that in each case the parties have either not made it explicitly clear which terms are to be incorporated or else have not specified to what extent each clause is to be incorporated.[6] The courts will not carry out 'major surgery' on main contract conditions in order to make them workable – this would come perilously close to rewriting the contract to suit the parties' apparent intentions. It may therefore be that without careful thought many forms of main contract conditions will not be capable of incorporation via a general and basic 'incorporation by reference' provision.

  The current position in Scotland is perhaps best summarised by Lord Jouncey in the case of *Parklea Limited* v. *W. & J R Watson Limited*.[7] 'If it appears from a consideration of [the Sub-contract] documents as a whole that the parties have not incorporated the whole of the main contract provisions then it matters not that some of those provisions had they been incorporated, would have fitted very neatly with the Sub-Contract'.
- **Hybrid** – the CECA Sub-contract follows the format of a hybrid sub-contract although it does steer rather more to the bespoke form, as one would expect. A hybrid form of sub-contract will often largely contain bespoke forms but will, to ensure that the interface between the contract and the sub-contract is managed effectively, contain some additional provisions, which may include:
  - relying on definitions set out in the contract rather than introducing 'stand alone' definitions into the sub-contract, for example, in the CECA Sub-contract the definition of main works relies on the definition in the contract
  - clause providing that the sub-contractor is deemed to have full knowledge of the contract. If this is the case the sub-contractor is best advised to ensure that it has obtained a copy of the contract (clause 3(1) CECA)
  - clause requiring the sub-contractor to carry out the works in such a way as not to cause the contractor to breach the contract (clause 3(2) CECA)

- sub-contractor to indemnify the contractor against every liability the contractor may incur to any other person (which although not explicitly stated in the CECA Sub-contract could include the employer) by reason of any breach by the sub-contractor of the sub-contract (clause 3(3) CECA)
- sub-contractor acknowledging that any breach by him of the sub-contract may result in the contractor committing a breach and becoming liable for damages under the contract and other contracts in connection with the works. All such losses and damages are agreed by the sub-contractor to be within the contemplation of the parties as being probable results of any such breach by the sub-contractor (clause 3(4) CECA).

Retention of title

Insolvency risk management is an area of great concern to suppliers and to sub-contractors. Given the often tight profit margins in which they work and also given that cash flow is often described as the lifeblood of the engineering industry, the insolvency of the employer, contractor or a sub-contractor can cause particular hardship. For this reason, and as part of the overall insolvency risk management strategy adopted by many suppliers, retention of title clauses are critical.

Retention of title clauses act to ensure that if goods are supplied to, for example, a contractor and that contractor becomes insolvent, then if the goods have not been paid for then title to those goods is made conditional on payment. In other words in all circumstances title to the goods does not pass until payment is made. This position must be explicitly stated in the contract, failing which the provisions of s17 of the Sale of Goods Act 1979 (as amended by the Sale and Supply of Goods Act 1994) will provide that title will pass on delivery of the goods. It follows that if the statutory position prevails the supplier who delivers goods to the contractor will transfer title on delivery, rather than on payment. The risk of insolvency of the contractor is then borne by the supplier until such time as payment is received.

The provisions of s17 can be circumvented in the manner described above through the operation of s19 of the Sale of Goods Act 1979 which allows the owner of the goods to retain ownership following delivery of the goods subject to transfer of title being conditional.

Despite the operation of ss17 and 19, enforcement of the retention of title clause is fraught with difficulties, some of which are briefly set out below:

- **Identification** – if relying on a retention of title clause the supplier will need to be able to accurately identify the goods which he has supplied. Identifying one batch of roof tiles from another from potentially another supplier may be difficult unless the tiles are each given serial numbers, which is unlikely. Best practice therefore suggests that suppliers should in each case find a unique way of ensuring that their goods can be identified from the goods supplied by others.
- **Section 25(1) Sale of Goods Act 1979** – if a third party buys goods originally supplied by the supplier to the contractor, and does so in good

faith having no notice of the existence of any retention of title clause in the original supply sub-contract then the retention of title is of no effect. In practice then if the supplier supplies the contractor with tiles under a sub-contract with a retention of title clause and the contract is paid by the employer for, amongst other things, the tiles (and the employer is not aware of the terms of the supplier's sub-contract) then the supplier could not rely on the retention of title clause to reclaim its tiles.

- **Incorporated into the structure** – in Scots law the title of fixtures will, in the absence of bad faith on the part of the land owner, pass to the party who owns the land onto which the fixtures have been incorporated.[8] It follows that the retention of title clause will not operate in circumstances where the goods which have been supplied have been incorporated into the structure which is the subject of the works.

Materials

The Sale of Goods Act 1979 implied into contracts a clause to the effect that, unless it could be shown otherwise,[9] materials supplied under the contract were of merchantable quality, and would be reasonably fit for the purpose for which they were used.

The Sale and Supply of Goods Act 1994 amended the Sale of Goods Act 1979 and introduced an implied term that if property in goods is transferred under a contract, and the transfer is in the course of a business, then the goods supplied under the contract should be of satisfactory quality. The question of what constitutes 'satisfactory quality' is also addressed by the Sale and Supply of Goods Act 1994 – goods are said to be of satisfactory quality if they meet the standard that a reasonable person would regard as satisfactory, taking account of any description of the goods, the price (if relevant) and all other relevant circumstances.

These statutory implied terms will be implied into contracts for the supply of materials. The implied term will not be effective if it should have been evident from a sample supplied that the goods supplied would be unsatisfactory. If the party selling the materials informs the seller what the purpose of the materials is, a term is also implied into the contract that the materials will be reasonably fit for that purpose. The terms implied by the Sale of Goods Act 1979 and the Sale and Supply of Goods Act 1994 cannot be contracted out of.

Notes

[1] *Tweddle* v. *Atkinson* [1861] 1 B&S 393.
[2] *British Workmans's and General Assurance Co.* v. *Wilkinson* [1900].
[3] *Bickerton* v. North West Metropolitan Regional Hospital Board [1970] 1 WLR 607.
[4] *Gloucestershire County Council* v. *Richardson* [1969] 1 AC 480.
[5] *Geary, Walker & Co. Ltd* v. *W. Lawrence & Son* [1906]; *Scottish Power plc* v. *Kvaerner Construction (Regions) Ltd* [1998].
[6] *Babcock Rosyth Defence Ltd* v. *Grootcon (UK) Ltd* [1998].

[7] 1988 SLT 605; also referred to in *Watson Building Services Limited*, petition for Judicial Review, Outer House, Court of Session, March 2001.

[8] *Brand's Trustees* v. *Brand's Trustees* [1876] 3R HL 16.

[9] *Young & Martin Ltd* v. *McManus Childs Ltd* [1968].

13. Professional services contracts

Introduction

Many engineering projects will require input from, and the services of, professional consultants working with the client and the contractor. Which parties form the professional team will depend on the scope of the project and the breadth of experience and expertise offered by the contractor.

As a rule of thumb, professionals undertaking design will be appointed by the party that has responsibility for design under the engineering contract.

Contracts between a client and/or contractor and the professional party are often known as professional services contracts – the terms 'appointment' and 'professional services contract' are used interchangeably throughout this chapter.

For the purposes of this chapter we will focus for reference purposes on the appointment of a consultant engineer. While this party may be the same party as performs the functions of the engineer under the engineering contract, it need not necessarily be.[1]

Forms of professional services contract

Formality and timing

While it is not unknown for professional services contracts to be based on oral contracts or an exchange of correspondence, it is advisable for clients to enter into formal written contracts with their professional consultants. An engineer may carry a lot of responsibility on a project and the fees paid to the engineer may be substantial. It is better for both the client and the engineer if they fully set out their respective rights and obligations before they proceed.

Commonly, parties enter into formal written professional services contracts after the engineer has begun providing the required services. For this reason professional services contracts will usually deem the provisions of the professional services contract to take effect from the date the engineer began to provide his services on the project.

Standard forms

There are a number of standard form professional services contracts published for different professions within the construction industry. For the engineering profession by far the best known set of standard forms is that produced by the Association of Consulting Engineers (ACE) whose latest suite of 'Conditions of Engagement' was issued as a second edition in 1998. There are a number of forms published in the suite as follows:

A.   for use where an engineer is engaged as lead consultant
B.   for use where an engineer is engaged directly by the client, but not as lead consultant
C.   for use where an engineer is engaged to provide design services for a design and construct contractor
D.   for use where an engineer is engaged to provide report and advisory services
E.   for use where engineer is engaged as a project manager
F.   for use where an engineer is engaged to act as planning supervisor.

Forms A, B and C have variants depending on whether the engineer is being appointed to provide civil and structural or mechanical and electrical engineering services.

After the ACE forms, perhaps the next best known standard form for the appointment of an engineer is the professional services contract (June 1998), which forms one part of the NEC/ECC suite of contracts. It is published as a form that can be used for appointing design consultants as well as for the appointment of such parties as the project manager. It shares a common philosophy and approach with the other contracts forming part of the NEC suite.

As these standard forms are drafted to be used in different projects as required, the user must take the form, complete any blanks where information is required and make any amendments appropriate to the project. All too often parties refer to a particular standard form being used without detailing how the forms are to be completed, which can often lead to confusion.

Bespoke forms

Many client organisations, and their advisers, are of the opinion that standard forms of professional services contracts, such as the ACE suite, have been drafted by engineers for the benefit of engineers. While ACE would likely take issue with that, it is fair to say that the defences available to an engineer under such a contract are stated in wider terms than would often be negotiated in the market place.

Most large law practices and many large client/developer organisations will have their own bespoke forms of professional services contracts for professional consultants which are in forms known to be acceptable to institutional developers, purchasers and financiers. There is a myriad of such forms and a small industry exists in advising upon and negotiating such forms.

Notwithstanding the selection of bespoke professional services contracts forms, it is possible to detect common themes that repeatedly appear and arguments concerning the drafting of such clauses are well rehearsed and refined.

Set out below are a number of the principal clauses that should be included in a professional services contract whether a bespoke or standard form, together with a note of a number of clauses of secondary importance that often appear.

Principal clauses of the professional services contract

Obligation to carry out the services

The professional services contract should explicitly state what the engineer is being appointed to carry out. In other words, the professional services contract should define the services of the engineer. It is usual to refer to a schedule of the professional services contract where a list of agreed services to be carried out can be set out.

As with the professional services contract itself, those drafting the services can create bespoke lists or seek to take advantage of the various standard forms which contain well known lists. Bespoke forms of professional services contract may make reference to or incorporate service schedules contained in standard forms of professional services contract.

The engineer will be obliged to carry out the services in accordance with the terms and conditions of the professional services contract.

Time of the provision of the services

Unlike engineering contracts, professional services contracts do not as a rule state a date by which the engineer must complete his services. The engineer may, however, be obliged to provide his services at a time that is consistent with the overall programme for the project or in accordance with the contract set under the engineering contract. In addition, provisions are sometimes added setting a programme by which the engineer should release design information.

Fees

The cost to the client of having the engineer carry out his services is the fee that will be charged by the engineer. That fee should be stated in the professional services contract.

To avoid the default provisions of the 1996 Act being applied, the professional services contract should set out the instalments by which the fee will be paid. Often a time period between payments will be set, for example, monthly, or the professional services contract will set out the percentage or amount of fee that will be paid on the engineer or the project achieving set milestones, for example, obtaining planning approval, completing the scheme design or suchlike.

Again as a result of the provisions of the 1996 Act, the professional services contract should detail when payments become 'due' and the 'final' date on which instalments of the fee should actually be paid. It should also mirror the terms of the 1996 Act in obliging the client to give required payment notices after the due date and another notice before the final date if it intends to withhold all or part of a payment that would otherwise be due.

One would expect the payment provisions to set out the procedure by which the client will make payment, whether interest will be paid by the client on late payment, and any necessary provisions concerning payment of VAT.

Quality of services

As fundamental to the client as the issue of time and cost, is the question of the quality of service that it can expect from the engineer. At common law a party appointing a professional person can expect them to perform their services using reasonable skill and taking reasonable care.[2]

It is standard practice to include a clause in a professional services contract confirming this standard and often supplementing it. Clauses will often require the engineer to use the reasonable skill, care and diligence of a qualified, experienced and competent member of its profession who has had experience in carrying out services similar to those being asked of the engineer on a project of a similar nature to that of the project in question.

A professional services contract may impose further quality requirements such as obliging the engineer to take account of contracts the client has entered into with third parties relative to the project, specific documents the client has produced or particular requirements the client may have. It may also oblige the engineer to take account of more general matters such as any applicable standards or codes of practice and/or all applicable statutory requirements.

Secondary clauses of the professional services contract

Professional indemnity insurance

Clients like to have the comfort that the obligations being undertaken by the engineer are insurance-backed. The engineer will be obliged to maintain a set amount of professional indemnity insurance for a set period. The amount of insurance required will be driven by how much insurance the engineer maintains (or is willing to disclose he maintains, which is not always one and the same thing) and what is the value of the construction works being undertaken.

The period for which the insurance must be maintained is usually stated as a set number of years following completion of the works under the construction contract. In English contracts that period can vary between six to 12 years following the English law rules on limitation of actions. In Scotland, based on a misunderstanding of the Scottish law rules of prescription, the period chosen used to be five or ten years. It is fast becoming standard for the period of 12 years to be used in both Scotland and England.

The professional services contract should reflect the nature of the professional indemnity insurance held by the engineer. Most professionals maintain insurance which will respond on an 'each and every claim' basis although, for some, certain claims such as in relation to pollution and contamination matters may be covered by an aggregate figure in any one period of insurance. This should be detailed in the relevant clause.

Clients are well advised to include obligations in the professional services contract allowing them to ask for evidence from the engineer that it is maintaining insurance and obliging the engineer to advise the client if the engineer ceases to maintain the insurance.

Whether or not the engineer is only obliged to maintain professional indemnity insurance when it is available on commercially reasonable rates and terms can be a matter for negotiation between the parties, but is becoming commonplace.

Key personnel

It may matter to the client not only which organisation he has selected to carry out the services in question but also that those services are performed or led by a particular individual. If so, the professional services contract will seek to name such individual(s). It may also give the client a role in consenting to such key personnel being removed and who they may be replaced with.

Clients on occasions seek the right to require removal of members of the engineer's staff who they consider are not adequately performing their services.

Prohibited materials

Related to the issue of the overall quality of the client's project it is standard to see provisions in design professional services contracts obliging the engineer not to specify certain materials. These will be materials that the client or its advisers consider are potentially detrimental to the project.

It used to be the case that lists of such 'deleterious materials' or 'prohibited materials' would be included in the professional services contract. It is becoming more common now for more general wording to be used referring to generally available standards or reference works which detail how, when and where to use or not to use certain materials.[3]

Assignation of the professional services contract

Assignation is a method of transferring the rights and obligations of one party to another.

Unless a contract specifically provides that it cannot be assigned then, at common law, it can be assigned, unless the identity of the party by whom performance is owed is of importance,[4] in other words if there is an element of *delectus personae*. The question of *delectus personae* will arise if, for example, a client has entered into a contract with the engineer on the basis that the engineer has a particular quality or skill. If that is the case then if the contract cannot be performed by another engineer, the engineer could not assign its interest without the consent of the client. Although outside the scope of this book, it should be noted that the position in relation to assignment is very different under the laws of England and Wales.

Commonly a professional services contract will prevent an engineer from assigning its duties under the contract but the client may seek some element of freedom to assign its interest under the professional services contract. Whether this is allowed without the consent of the engineer is a matter for commercial negotiation.

Novation

Allied to the question of assignation is the question of novation. Rather than transfer its interest by way of assignation a client may wish to effect a novation by which the contract between the original client and the engineer is substituted for one between the engineer and a successor client.

This mechanism has been used a great deal in design and build property development projects where the initial design has been worked up by consultants under contract to the client before, at some point, control of the consultants is passed to the design and build contractor by way of novation.

If a novation mechanism is to be used it is normal to attach an agreed form of novation agreement as an appendix to the professional services contract.

The case of *Blyth & Blyth* v. *Carillion*,[5] currently working its way through the courts, highlights that novation is not without its legal difficulties. In this case the Court of Session in Scotland has called into question the practice within the construction industry of 'novating' an employer's design team to a contractor.

It is common for the client in design and construct engineering contracts to seek to place the entire responsibility for design of the works onto the contractor, regardless of when or by whom the design was prepared. It is also common for clients to prefer to retain an element of control over the design of the works in their early stage. To achieve both these ends, clients often initially appoint the design team then 'novate' or transfer control of the design team to the contractor once selected. Short 'novation agreements' have commonly been used in this situation. The effect of these agreements was understood to be that the contractor was substituted for the client as the employer of the design team under each of their respective appointments, as if the contractor had always been the employer to the exclusion of the initial client.

The Blyth & Blyth case has cast doubt on the value to the contractor of this practice.

Blyth & Blyth Limited (BB) were appointed by a client and then novated to Carillion Construction Limited (C). BB sued C for payment of fees and C counterclaimed, alleging it had incurred costs as a result of inaccuracies or insufficiencies in the information provided by BB for the Employer's Requirements, a document forming part of the construction contract. BB challenged the counterclaim and the debate came before Lord Eassie in the Outer House of the Court of Session.

C's initial pleadings focused on the argument that the effect of the novation agreement was to rewrite the appointment of BB so that it should be read as if C were to be referred to in each situation where the initial client had been named. Counsel for the defenders did not maintain this argument. The Court indicated that there were 'evident and inescapable' problems with this approach. Such a substitution of the contractor for the client introduced textual difficulties with the drafting of the appointment and opened up BB to difficulties with conflict of interest.

Instead the argument of both parties focused on the idea that the novation agreement did not alter the duties owed by BB but did alter to whom the duties were owed. The central question became a matter of deciding whether it was the employer's loss or the contractor's loss that should be considered in the event of BB breaching the terms of their appointment.

The Court decided that in respect of a breach of a duty owed to the employer prior to novation what was in effect achieved by the 'novation' was the assignation of a claim that otherwise would have been enforceable by the employer. On this basis only the employer's loss was recoverable as opposed to the loss suffered by the contractor. It was accepted by the Court that from the point of novation the services were performed for the contractor as the 'true client'. Whilst it is not clear in terms of the judgment, it is assumed that loss arising from a post-novation breach would be the loss of the contractor.

The decision creates a major difficulty for contractors because the employer in this situation would not suffer any loss from the fact that BB had included inaccurate information in the employer's requirements. The party suffering the loss was the contractor who had to bear any increase in the cost of designing and constructing the works. Nonetheless, the contractor would have no recourse against the consultant.

The Court did examine the fact that the employer had potential recourse against the contractor and the consultant of the contractor while the contractor had no recourse against anyone, but this argument was not sufficient to persuade the Court to change its decision on the effect of the novation agreement.

At the time of preparation of this book the case had been appealed and the results of any such appeal will need to be monitored and assessed in due course.

The case has obvious implications for the whole industry. The decision is bound to make contractors nervous about accepting novation agreements in what was previously considered to be an acceptable form. To protect their positions, at least in the interim, contractors will require either to rewrite their novation agreements to circumvent the effects of the Blyth & Blyth case or to enter into direct appointments with design teams. Any increased focus by the contractor on the scale of its design liability may have the knock-on effect of slowing agreement being reached on the construction documentation in any particular project.

Whilst the decision is a decision of the Scottish Courts, the practice of novation is UK-wide. It is yet to be seen whether an English Court would follow the reasoning adopted by the Court of Session.

Sub-contracting by the engineer

The professional services contract should contain provisions specifying if the engineer is entitled to sub-contract the performance of its services and, if so, on what terms.

Collateral warranties

The project of which the engineering contract and the professional services contract form part may conceivably involve a variety of parties who have a financial interest in the outcome. Some or all of those parties may wish to have the comfort that the engineer, along with other professional team members and the contractor, have properly carried out their obligations. These parties will be obliged to enter into contracts collateral to the contract they have with the client under which they warrant to the third party that they have carried out their services to the required standard.

Such ancillary contracts, which are usually referred to as 'collateral warranty' agreements or 'duty of care' agreements, give the third parties a right of recourse against the engineer that they would probably not have without such an agreement being in place (though see discussion on *jus quaesitum tertio* in Chapter 2).

If collateral warranty agreements are required from the engineer then the professional services contract should specify the parties to whom the engineer must grant these warranties, when and in what form. It is standard practice to attach an agreed style of collateral warranty to the professional services contract which are then completed as and when required.

A detailed analysis of the contents of a collateral warranty agreement is beyond the scope of this work. However, it is true to say that the provisions will usually mirror many of the terms of the professional services contract itself. Clauses dealing with duty of care, professional indemnity insurance, prohibited materials, copyright and assignation will all normally be included as will, where the beneficiary of the warranty is a financier, a 'step-in' clause. Such clauses typically allow the beneficiary of the warranty to use the mechanism in the collateral warranty to effectively replace the employer of the consultant under the relevant professional services contract. The grounds on which the beneficiary can exercise this right will be strictly defined and will generally arise on the occurrence of an insolvency event. In this way the beneficiary will seek to protect its interest in the project by preventing the consultant from terminating the professional services contract, and thus allowing the beneficiary to 'build out' the project and realise its investment.

Copyright

The author of an original document will retain the copyright in that document. In a construction forum this is a matter that has to be regulated by contract as other parties involved in the project need to use documents created by other parties to the project. The professional services contract will usually contain a provision whereby the engineer will grant a licence, normally free of charge, to the client in order that the client is empowered to use the engineer's documents generally in connection with the project or for certain specified purposes.

The client may wish to insert additional provisions to ensure that the engineer has not breached the copyright of some other party in the process of creating its own copyright documents.

Suspension

The client may wish to give itself the right to suspend the provision by the engineer of all or part of the services the engineer is obliged to provide. This gives the client flexibility to make changes to the professional services contract as necessary as the project proceeds. Provision should be made for which payments become due to the engineer at that time and which payments may become due during any period of suspension.

It is conventional to provide that, if suspension continues for longer than a given period, often six or twelve months, the parties will have the right to terminate the professional services contract.

One would only expect the engineer to have a right to suspend the performance of his services in the situation where the client has failed to pay sums properly due to the engineer. This right arises from the provisions of the Act.

Termination

Often the professional services contract will specify the situations in which the parties will have the right to bring the professional services contract to an end. The client will often seek the right to terminate without the need to give reasons on giving a specified period of notice. Otherwise, parties may be given the right to terminate if the other party becomes insolvent or is in material breach of its obligations under the professional services contract.

As with suspension, provision will often be made for what payments will be made in the event of termination.

Dispute resolution

Since the majority of professional services contracts will fall within the ambit of the 1996 Act, professional services contracts normally provide a mechanism for how adjudication is to be dealt with should that become an issue. The provisions of the professional services contract will need at least to cover the basic minimum position required by the 1996 Act.

While the professional services contract could provide for arbitration to follow on from adjudication, most do not. Accordingly, any dispute not resolved by adjudication will be referred to the courts.

Limitations on liability

Engineers may seek to manage their exposure to liability by including provisions in their professional services contracts setting limits on their liability. It is a matter for commercial negotiation whether such clauses are included.

(a) **Time** – the law of prescription in Scotland can theoretically mean that an engineer could remain liable for a breach of the professional services contract for a period of up to 20 years. As mentioned above, the period for which the engineer must maintain his professional indemnity insurance is often set at 12 years. There is no rationale for the 12-year period which is probably simply carried on from the English law provision relating to limitation of action for a document executed as a deed. The 12-year period has, however, become market practice in Scotland. It is common for a clause to be inserted providing that the engineer's liability under the professional services contract will only extend to claims raised within a period that is consistent with the professional indemnity insurance time period.

(b)   **Money** – an engineer may wish to know that even if things do go badly under the professional services contract and he incurs liability, that that liability will not be such as would destroy his business. For that reason he may seek to place an upper limit on the amount of money that could be recovered from it under the professional services contract. That cap on liability would not normally be set at less than the level of the professional indemnity insurance to be maintained by the engineer, however, that is merely a rule of thumb and there should not be seen to be any causal or interpretative link between the two.

(c)   **Net contribution** – there are situations where one member of a professional team can be held jointly and severally liable with other members of the professional team for a defect arising, i.e. one consultant may be held liable for the whole of any loss despite the loss having been caused or contributed by other consultants or contractors involved in the project. For that reason an engineer may seek to include clauses having the effect of excluding joint and several liability. These are often known as net contribution clauses. The drafting of such clauses usually reflects, to a degree, s3 of the Law Reform (Miscellaneous Provisions) (Scotland) Act 1940 which allows the court to apportion damage among parties. Clauses of this nature are untested in the courts, are controversial and are normally resisted by the client or by the beneficiary of any collateral warranty in which the engineer is seeking to include the clause.

Notes

[1] For the role of the engineer under the construction contract see Chapter 3.

[2] *Hunter* v. *Hanley* 1955 SC 200.

[3] See e.g. *Good practice in the selection of construction materials*, Ove Arup & Partners, 1997.

[4] This is the issue of *delectus personnae*, see e.g. *Cole* v. *Handasyde* 1910 SC 68.

[5] Outer House 18 April 2001.

14. Environmental issues

Introduction

The engineering and construction industry can have a significant impact on the environment. With environmental issues constantly growing in prominence, it has become imperative that those issues are managed properly. While construction of any description has the potential to affect the wider environment, this chapter focuses on the impact which it can have in the key areas of waste, water, noise and contaminated land. An assessment is also made of the impact of the landfill tax on the construction industry. The Scottish Parliament has its own power to legislate and so while Scotland's environmental legislation is currently very similar to legislation south of the border, there is scope for this to change in the future.

The regulators

SEPA

The principal environmental regulator in Scotland is the Scottish Environment Protection Agency (SEPA) which was created on 1 April 1996[1] to provide an integrated environmental protection system, pollution control having previously been dealt with by a number of different bodies.[2] SEPA's headquarters, which deal with policy coordination, are in Stirling with a number of local offices throughout Scotland dealing with operational activities.

Key responsibilities of SEPA are as follows:

- air and water pollution control
- waste regulation
- integrated pollution control[3]
- radioactive substances control
- remediation of historically contaminated land (in conjunction with local authorities).

SEPA has been criticised for the low level of fines imposed on polluters in Scotland. In 2001/2002, for example, the average fines imposed in water and waste cases were, respectively, just £2780 and £1550.[4] Fine levels in Scotland have typically lagged behind those south of the border. One reason for this is that while SEPA recommends prosecutions for environmental offences, the decision whether to actually prosecute rests with the Procurator Fiscal. There have been suggestions that the Fiscal has been unwilling to take forward environmental cases as specialist knowledge is required. No action has been taken in as many as one-third of the cases submitted by SEPA.[5] SEPA has refuted criticism of its failure to achieve prosecutions by emphasising that its focus is on working in partnership with industry to prevent the need for more drastic enforcement action. SEPA's Policy Statement on Enforcement commits SEPA to observing the key principles of proportionality, consistency, openness and targeting, and notes that prosecution is only part of a number of enforcement tools including discussions, meetings, warning letters, formal enforcement notices and the granting, amendment, review, variation or revocation of licences.[6]

Local authorities

Scotland's 32 local authorities are currently responsible for enforcing the law of statutory nuisance which encompasses nuisance from, for example, noise, smoke and fumes. Local authorities will also be primarily responsible for enforcing the new contaminated land regime.

Water authorities

With effect from 1 April 2002, Scottish Water was created replacing the three water authorities which had been created in 1996.[7] Scottish Water is required for discharge of trade effluent into public sewers.

Construction law and waste

Waste management legislation

Waste management legislation has a significant impact on the construction industry, which, according to SEPA's National Waste Strategy of December 1999, is 'the largest single source of controlled waste'.[8] Waste management legislation is becoming increasingly stringent, influenced by developments at EU level which favour options for dealing with waste such as reducing, reusing and recycling in preference to traditional disposal methods of landfilling and, to a lesser extent, incineration. SEPA's National Waste Strategy identifies for the construction industry an aspirational goal of 'setting targets' by 2002 for the recovery and recycling of construction and demolition waste. SEPA has no power to enforce this target, but wishes to send a strong signal to the industry that enhanced recovery and recycling rates are now urgently required.[9]

Waste on land is currently regulated by Part II of the Environmental Protection Act 1990 (EPA) which regulates the deposit, treatment, keeping and disposal of waste by requiring waste management licences to be obtained (except where certain specific exemptions apply) and making it a criminal offence not to obtain a licence in these circumstances.[10] Waste transfer sites, civic amenity sites and landfill sites all require to be licensed.

Waste Management law is highly complicated, Part II of EPA being supplemented by a multitude of detailed regulations, guidance and codes of practice.[11] Space does not permit any more than a brief review of some of the key waste issues for the construction industry.

What is waste?

The definition of waste is complex. Waste is defined as any substance or object falling within certain specified categories which the holder discards, or intends or is required to discard.[12] Part II of EPA applies to the disposal of all 'controlled waste' which includes household, industrial and commercial waste.[13] Special, more stringent rules apply to the most hazardous forms of waste, known as special waste (see below).

Who is responsible for waste? – the duty of care

The party which is actually involved in waste removal may be considered as a producer of waste. In the case of *Gotech Industrial and Environmental Services Limited and Another* v. *Friel*[14] it was held that an asbestos-stripping sub-contractor was the producer of waste, rather than the employer or main contractor, because it was the sub-contractor who had broken up the asbestos to produce waste. This is further borne out by Circular 19/91,[15] which states

> The client for works, although he may make decisions as a result of which something becomes waste, is not himself producing waste created by the works. Where there are several contractors and sub-contractors on site, the producer of a particular waste is the particular contractor or sub-contractor who (or whose employee) takes an action which creates waste, or who begins to treat something as if it were waste.

Part II of EPA introduced a duty of care with respect to waste aimed at improving waste management practices and preventing illegal waste disposal. Producers, carriers, keepers and disposers of waste are required to take reasonable measures to ensure that:

- other parties do not dispose of waste without a licence, in contravention of a licence or in a way that causes pollution or harm
- waste is transferred only to correctly authorised persons such as waste management licence holders or registered waste carriers[16]
- when waste is transferred it is accompanied by a suitable written description of waste which will prevent others contravening Part II EPA and will prevent the waste escaping
- waste is securely contained so as to avoid it escaping to the environment.

A code of practice has been issued providing guidance on discharging the duty of care.[17] While breach of the code is not a criminal offence, adherence to it is likely to assist in establishing that reasonable steps have been taken to comply with the duty of care. Breach of the duty of care is a criminal offence[18] with the maximum penalties being a fine not exceeding the statutory maximum (£5000) on summary conviction and, on conviction on indictment, an unlimited fine.

Contractors must be alert to these provisions. If a waste carrier were to deposit a contractor's waste on an unauthorised landfill site or to 'fly tip', the contractor would be liable. When using a waste carrier (in addition to checking that the waste carrier is properly registered and that the waste is being transferred to a suitably licensed landfill site) contractors should enter into an agreement with the carrier setting out who is to be responsible for compliance with environmental issues.

Special waste

The Special Waste Regulations 1996 regulate the movement of particularly hazardous wastes and impose more stringent duty of care procedures for special waste. Special waste is controlled waste which is dangerous or difficult to treat, keep or dispose of.[19] Special waste includes waste on the EC's list of hazardous waste[20] displaying one or more hazardous properties and waste not on the EC list displaying certain hazardous properties. For example, construction waste containing no asbestos would generally not be special waste. Construction waste containing asbestos greater than 0.01 per cent by weight of amphibole would, however, be regarded as special.

The Special Waste Regulations 1996 provide for a 'consignment note' system allowing SEPA to monitor movements of special wastes. Pre-notification of movement of special waste by producers is required between one month and three days before the waste is transported to its destination. On receipt of the waste, the consignee must notify SEPA using the same unique code as the pre-notification. Producers, carriers and disposers must also keep a register of consignment notes.

Waste management licences

SEPA is the regulatory authority to whom applications for licences must be made. Licences must be granted to the occupier of the land and will typically be quite lengthy documents including detailed conditions in relation to the types and amounts of waste permitted by the licence, how these are to be treated, record keeping, operating hours, cleaning of vehicles, noise limits and the standards to be achieved to ensure there is no pollution to the wider environment.[21]

Licences will be granted only when:

(a)   planning permission exists for the proposed site use
(b)   SEPA is satisfied that pollution of the environment or harm to human health will not result from the activity subject to the licence
(c)   the operator is a 'fit and proper' person to hold a licence.[22]

SEPA has the power to take legal action to enforce compliance with licence conditions or alternatively to modify, suspend or revoke licences. Licences can only be surrendered by agreement with SEPA and, for landfills accepting biodegradable waste, it is unlikely that certificates of completion will be issued for some years after filling has ceased. The transfer of licences is permitted with the consent of SEPA, following a joint application by transferor and transferee.[23]

SEPA has powers to require occupiers of land to remove any illegally deposited waste and also has power to clean up the waste itself and recover costs if the occupier of land or the perpetrator cannot be identified.[24]

Exemptions

Various exemptions from the requirement to obtain a waste management licence are available.[25] Generally these exemptions apply to relatively small operations, or where controlled waste recovery and associated storage are being carried out. In some cases registration of the exempt activities is required with SEPA.[26] No fees are payable to SEPA for registration and SEPA will not issue registration certificates.[27] Registration will not be for any fixed period although applications for registration must be site-specific.[28]

Registration of an activity as exempt does not absolve the registered party from potential penal responsibility under Part II EPA as the activity remains exempt only for so long as it is carried out in conformity with the exemption. Additionally, the application of section 33(1)(c) of Part II EPA to exempt activities means that the treating, keeping or disposing of waste in a manner likely to cause pollution of the environment or human health is an offence.

Key exemptions for construction operations

- Spreading on land of construction/demolition industry waste, dredging or waste soil, rock, ash or sludge:
  - can be exempt if spreading is in connection with reclamation or improvement of land and land is incapable of beneficial use without such treatment
  - spreading must be in accordance with the planning permission for the reclamation or improvement of the land
  - must benefit agricultural or lead to ecological improvement
  - maximum amount of waste which can be spread: 20 000m^3 per acre.[29]
- Waste stored at the site of production awaiting collection for reuse:
  - can include construction wastes[30]
  - waste from demolition and construction work, materials from tunnelling and excavation or waste which consists of ash, slag, clinker, rock, wood or gypsum can be stored 'on a site' for construction work before work starts[31]
  - exemptions available where such wastes are used for the purposes of construction work; waste must be suitable for its intended purpose and must be for a designated construction project[32]
  - no limit on the quantity of material which may be stored.
- Reclamation and reuse of construction waste:
  - production of timber products, straw board, plasterboard, bricks, blocks, roadstone or aggregate from construction and demolition wastes is exempt[33]
  - manufacture of soil or soil substitutes is exempt provided the soil arises from demolition, construction, excavations or tunnelling work.[34]

Landfill tax

Background

Landfill tax came into force in the UK on 1 October 1996[35] with two key objectives:

- To ensure that landfill waste disposal is properly priced, thus promoting greater efficiency in the waste management market.
- To apply the 'polluter pays' principle, promoting a more sustainable approach to waste management in which production of waste is diminished and reuse or recovery of waste is encouraged.[36]

The tax is relevant to contractors who send their waste to landfill sites or operate their own landfill sites. It is essential for these contractors to understand when the tax is payable, at what rate and whether exemptions are available, as without this information there is a risk that: (a) contractors operating their own sites could be liable for penalties by failing to pay tax; and (b) contractors may pay tax to operators in circumstances where tax does not fall to be paid, is payable at a lower rate or where there is an exemption available.

Scope of tax

Tax is administered by HM Customs & Excise and applies to all waste disposed of by way of landfill at a licensed landfill site on or after 1 October 1996, unless the waste is specifically exempt.

The tax is chargeable on registered landfill site operators who are obliged to submit a Landfill Tax Return and to pay tax due for that return period on a quarterly basis. Liability for the tax extends to in-house sites where waste producers dispose of their own waste. HM Customs & Excise also publish a Landfill Tax Register.

The tax rates and calculation of the tax

The rates

- Calculated on basis of weight of waste disposed of.
- Two tax rates:
    (i)   lower rate of £2 per tonne (for 2001–2002) for inert or inactive wastes (qualifying material)
    (ii) higher rate of £2 per tonne for 2001–2002 (increasing to £13 for 2002–2003 and £14 for 2003–2004) for other wastes.
- Qualifying materials are listed in the Landfill Tax (Qualifying Material) Order 1996 and include construction stone and stone from demolition of buildings or structures.

Calculation of tax

- Tax is calculated on the basis of the weight of waste disposed of.
- A weighbridge is normally used.
- If no weighbridge is available, Customs & Excise permit alternative methods, such as recording the maximum weight a lorry or other vehicle is permitted to carry and applying the appropriate rate of tax.

What is waste?

The legislation provides that a disposal is a disposal of waste if the person disposing of the material does so with the intention of discarding the material. It is irrelevant that it would be possible for the disposer or any other person to make use of the material.[37] In practice it is often difficult to determine in any objective way whether waste has been discarded by its producer.

Mixed loads

Loads from construction sites may contain both inert and active wastes. The legislation provides that in these circumstances tax is due on the full load at the standard rate.[38] Customs & Excise have however indicated that the presence of an incidental amount of active waste in a mainly inactive load will justify an operator in treating the whole load as taxable at the lower rate. While Customs & Excise stress that it is for the operator to decide what is a reasonably incidental amount of waste and whether there is potential for that waste to pollute, they also provide examples of what they would accept as being eligible for lower rate tax. For example, lower-rate tax will be applied to a load of bricks, stone and concrete from demolition of a building that has small pieces of wood in it, and small quantities of plaster attached to bricks, as it would not have been feasible for a contractor to separate these items. Moreover, Customs & Excise also have power to direct that a mixed load may be taxed as if it were a wholly inert load.[39]

The contaminated land exemption

Various exemptions from liability to pay landfill tax are available.[40] From the perspective of the construction industry, the most important of these exemptions is the Contaminated Land Exemption.

The Contaminated Land Exemption was introduced to ensure that landfill tax would not act as a disincentive to brownfield redevelopment.

A landowner, developer or contractor intending to reclaim contaminated land and dispose of the material removed at a landfill site may apply to Customs & Excise for a Contaminated Land Exemption Certificate. The certificate must be obtained before the removal of waste – if the certificate is not so obtained landfill tax is payable. Applications require to be made at least 30 days before the commencement of the removal of waste[41] although Customs & Excise may accept late applications in certain circumstances (e.g. if pollutants are unexpectedly encountered on a site which must be cleared by a certain date).

Reclamation or construction?   Customs & Excise have made it clear that the exemption does not apply to waste from construction activity. There are cases, however, where it is not clear whether an activity giving rise to waste equates to reclamation prior to construction, or to construction activity itself. In these circumstances Customs & Excise have indicated that they will take the following factors into account:

- whether the developers' plans identify a clear intention to remediate prior to the commencement of construction
- whether the amount of material being removed amounts to that necessary to deal with any pollutants or only to that which needs to be removed for other reasons (for example, reducing site levels or instability of made ground)
- whether material is to be removed only from the construction area itself, leaving similar pollutants below or alongside, or from an area sufficient to remove any potential for harm.

Customs & Excise also indicate that in many projects or reclamations spoil is removed in order to remove pollutants which would have to be excavated in any event in order to level land or to dig foundations or service trenches.

If Customs & Excise are satisfied that reclamation is taking place then the waste arising from that work would all be exempt, even if it would have been removed in any case as part of subsequent construction operations.

Qualifications for exemption

- Reclamation must involve clearing land of pollutants that are causing harm or that have the potential to cause harm. Reclamation of derelict but non-polluted land will not qualify for exemption.
- The cause of the pollution must have ceased. The only exception to this is where the pollution is being caused by someone or something outwith the applicant's control.
- The land must not be subject to a works or remediation notice unless reclamation is being undertaken by specified statutory bodies such as local authorities, the Environment Agency and SEPA.
- If it is necessary to remove 'clean' or any slightly polluted land to get to the pollutants Customs & Excise have indicated that further wastes will be exempt.
- The applicant must be able to demonstrate that without the removal of pollutants the land could not be prevented from being put to its intended use.

The certificate   If the waste qualifies for exemption, Customs & Excise will issue a certificate to the landowner or developer specifying the land from which the qualifying waste comes and the weight of waste which may be exempted. In addition, the certificate will confirm the landfill sites nominated by the applicant to receive the waste. The certificate is divided into two parts – Part A being issued to the applicant and a separate part B being issued to the landfill site operator who is then obliged to keep records showing the amount of waste received which has been exempted on the certificate. Once the quantity shown on the certificate is reached, a landfill site operator cannot exempt further loads of waste.

Landfill tax: impact on the construction industry

A study by Environ UK for the Scottish Executive,[42] covering a study period of 1997 and 1998, indicated:

(a)   a reduction in the amount of inactive waste disposed of to landfill by between 16 per cent and 21 per cent

(b)   an increase in the number of Waste Management Licensing Exemptions since introduction of the tax, from 197 in 1996 to 821 in 1997 and 826 in 1998, with uptake of exemptions for reuse and reprocessing of construction materials increasing by 14 per cent and 64 per cent respectively

(c)   considerable uptake in the exemption for contaminated soil from redeveloped contaminated sites, with 1.2 million tonnes exempted to 13 October 1998.

While the study concluded that it is difficult to be certain about the extent of the link between the tax and exemptions, it does seem likely that a link exists, with the construction industry generally striving to avoid the impact of the tax.[43]

Construction and the aquatic environment

Background

Construction operations may have an impact on the quality of Scotland's inland, coastal and ground waters. While contractors may not handle particularly hazardous wastes in their day to day operations, the aquatic environment is particularly sensitive and relatively inert construction wastes and run-off have the potential to pollute or contribute to existing pollution. This was illustrated in the mid-1990s with a series of successful prosecutions of construction companies in connection with water pollution incidents.[44]

Discharge consents

The principal mechanism regulating discharge of potentially polluting matter into inland coastal and ground waters is a system of discharge consents by which an intending discharger must apply for a consent to SEPA.[45] SEPA have power to grant consent with or without conditions (being such reasonable conditions as SEPA thinks fit).[46] Consent must not be refused unreasonably.[47] There is a right of appeal to the Scottish Ministers on the grounds that SEPA has unreasonably withheld consent or has sought to impose unreasonable conditions.[48] If SEPA has not determined an application for consent within four months the applicant may regard the application as refused.[49] SEPA has powers to periodically review or modify any conditions attached to and ultimately revoke consents.[50] Discharge consents are not personal to the applicant and run with the property allowing any person to carry out discharges described in the consent.[51] Possession of a discharge consent and compliance with its terms forms a defence to proceedings taken against a party for causing or knowingly permitting pollution of controlled waters (see offences and penalties below).[52]

SEPA's new powers – enforcement and works notices

Until recently SEPA's regulatory powers under the Control of Pollution Act 1974 ('COPA') were limited to the use of warning letters, review or revocation of discharge consents and recommending prosecution for a serious breach of conditions. New powers for SEPA to serve enforcement notices came into force on 1 January 2001[53] which will allow SEPA to take a more proactive regulatory approach by requiring action by a consent holder in advance of a breach taking place or pollution occurring. These powers have been exercised to a great degree, with 31 notices being served in 2001 for the west of Scotland alone.

Enforcement notices cannot be reviewed or revoked, but may be appealed.[54] The bringing of an appeal notice does not suspend the operation of the enforcement notice.[55] The time limit for appealing an enforcement notice is 21 days.[56]

The Scottish Executive has also issued proposals for SEPA to be given powers to serve works notices which would allow it to reduce risk to water by requiring polluters or potential polluters to carry out works or prevent or clean up water pollution. At present SEPA's powers are limited to carrying out anti-pollution works itself and then recovering the cost of doing so from the person responsible. Given SEPA's budgetary constraints, this is not an attractive option.[57] Like enforcement notices, it is envisaged that works notices will be appealable but that an appeal will not suspend the operation of a notice.

Offences and penalties

Key offences

- Causing or knowingly permitting pollution of controlled waters (section 30F COPA).
- Failure to comply with an enforcement or works notice (section 49A (3) COPA).

Penalties

- Imprisonment for up to three months and/or a maximum fine of £20 000 on summary conviction.
- On indictment, imprisonment for up to two years and/or an unlimited fine.[58]

Managing environmental impact to water

In recognition of the difficulties experienced by the construction industry with respect to water pollution, the Construction Industry Research and Information

Centre (CIRIA)[59] has, following detailed consultation with the industry, published a useful practice guide entitled 'Control of water pollution from construction sites – guidance for consultants and contractors'. The Report covers benefits and obligations in pollution prevention, pollution sources, common types of incident, using construction contracts to implement good practice and guidance on managing water pollution in construction.[60]

Construction noise, vibration and dust

Background

The open, varied and intermittent nature of construction has considerable potential to generate nuisance to site workers and neighbouring premises through noise, vibration and dust.[61] There were at least 732 complaints received and reported by local authorities in Scotland 1997/8 and 561 in 1998/9.[62] Construction noise, vibration and dust are regulated by the following:

- specific legislation on construction noise and vibration, as provided by sections 60 and 61 of the COPA
- general statutory nuisance provisions under EPA
- the common law of delict and nuisance.

Sections 60 and 61 of COPA

Sections 60 and 61 of COPA apply specifically to the control of noise (which is defined by COPA to include vibration)[63] on construction sites in Scotland, England and Wales.

Section 60 COPA   Local authorities have power to serve notices imposing requirements as to the way in which construction works (including construction of buildings or breaking open of roads) are carried out,[64] including specification of the type of plant or machinery which is or is not to be used,[65] or limitations on the hours during which the works may be carried out.[66]

In addition such notices may specify the level of noise which may be emitted from the premises during specified hours.[67] Time limits for compliance may be specified in the notice.[68]

Section 60 notices may be served on the person carrying out, or about to carry out the works, or on persons responsible for or who will have control over the carrying out of the works 'as the local authority thinks fit'.[69] A main contractor could therefore find itself the recipient of a notice in respect of works being carried out by its sub-contractor.

Before serving a section 60 notice, the local authority must have regard to a number of factors[70] in addition to the needs of persons living in the surrounding area, these being:

- **Codes of practice** – of key relevance here is British Standard 5228 ('BS5228') entitled Noise and Vibration Control on Construction and Open Sites.[71] Compliance with BS5228 does not ensure that a section 60 notice will not be served, but should considerably reduce the prospects of this happening. BS5228 has been judicially recognised as the acknowledged code of practice for noise control.[72]

- **Best practical means** – the local authority must have regard to the best practical means for ensuring reduction of noise pollution,[73] the expression 'practical' in this context meaning 'reasonably practicable having regard among other things to local conditions and circumstances, to the current state of technical knowledge and to the financial implications'.[74]
- **Suitability of other methods having same effect** – the local authority must consider specifying other methods of plant or machinery which would be substantially as effective in minimising noise and more acceptable to the recipients of the notice.[75]

Appeal   A recipient of a section 60 notice has a right of appeal to a Sheriff Court. Appeals must be lodged within 21 days from the date of service of the notice.[76] Various grounds of appeal are set out in accompanying regulations – the grounds include the following:

(a)   the notice is not justified by the terms of section 60
(b)   the local authority have refused unreasonably to accept compliance with alternative requirements or that the requirements of the notice are otherwise unreasonable in character or extent or are unnecessary
(c)   the local authority have not had regard to some or all of the factors detailed above.[77]

Failure to comply with a section 60 notice is a criminal offence. The penalties are a fine of up to £200 for a first offence and a fine of up to £400 for a second or subsequent offence. Provision is made for a further fine not exceeding £50 for each day in which the offence continues after conviction.[78]

Section 61 COPA – prior consent   In anticipation of the possible adverse effects of noise from a construction site, a person who intends to carry out works subject to section 60 may apply to the local authority for prior consent for the work on the construction site.[79] A prudent operator will apply for such consent as existence of the consent will form a defence to any action brought by the local authority under section 60.[80] Consents may be subject to conditions or be time-limited.[81]

The local authority is bound to inform the applicant of its decision within 28 days of receipt of the application for consent.[82] If no consent is granted within the 28-day period or if the local authority qualifies the consent or attaches conditions within the 28-day period, then the applicant may appeal to the Sheriff Court within 21 days from the end of that period.[83]

General statutory nuisance

General   Noise is also generally regulated as a statutory nuisance by Part III of EPA which defines statutory nuisance as including 'noise emitted from premises as to be prejudicial to health or a nuisance'.[84] As in COPA, noise is defined as including vibration.[85]

The definition of 'premises' is less clear. General statutory nuisance in Scotland was originally regulated by sections 58 and 59 of COPA. In a case decided under those sections, the word 'premises' was held not to cover noise made in streets or public places.[86] The definition of premises under section 79(7) of EPA, however, includes land. It might also be arguable whether noise made by a person or group of persons at large in a public place could be said to be 'emitted from land'.[87] It has been held that noise which affects premises, though emanating elsewhere, can make the premises affected themselves a statutory nuisance under section 79(1)(a) if the noise is such as to be injurious to health.[88]

Local authorities have a duty to make inspections in their areas to detect statutory nuisances and to investigate complaints of statutory nuisances made by persons living in their areas.[89]

Individuals also have power to raise proceedings directly before a Sheriff in Scotland on the grounds that the individual is aggrieved by the existence of a statutory nuisance.

Abatement notices – section 80 EPA   Local authorities have powers to serve abatement notices if they are satisfied that statutory nuisances exist or are likely to occur or recur in their area. These notices may require abatement of the nuisance, prohibit or restrict its occurrence or require carrying out works or other steps.[90]

The abatement notice must specify a time limit for compliance,[91] and must be served on the person responsible for nuisance, unless:

(a)   the person responsible cannot be found, or nuisance has not yet occurred. In this case, notice is to be served on owner or occupier of premises; or

(b)   nuisance arises from any defect of a structural character.

In this case the notice must be served on the owner of the premises.

Appeal   The person served with the abatement notice may appeal against the notice in Scotland to the Sheriff Court within 21 days from the date on which he was served with the notice.[92] Grounds of appeal are set out in accompanying regulations and are similar to the grounds for appealing section 60 notices.[93]

Enforcement   Failure to comply with an abatement notice, without reasonable excuse, is an offence[94] and for offences committed on industrial, trade or business premises, the maximum fine on summary conviction is £20 000.[95]

Defence to a section 80 offence   The legislation provides for a general defence that the best practical means were used to prevent or to counteract the effects of the nuisance.[96] This defence is available only in cases of statutory noise nuisances where the noise arises on industrial, trade or business premises.[97] There is also a defence where a section 60 consent has been obtained.

Section 82 – summary proceedings   As stated above, the EPA also gives individuals the power to raise proceedings directly before a Sheriff in Scotland on the grounds that the individual is aggrieved by the existence of a statutory nuisance.[98] This provision could be invoked by an aggrieved individual to restrict or limit construction noise.

Such an action must again be raised against the person responsible for the nuisance except where the nuisance arises from any defect of a structural character, or where the person responsible for the nuisance cannot be found, in which case the action must be raised against the owner of the premises or against the owner or occupier of the premises.[99] The aggrieved person must give notice in writing to the person who he intends to institute the proceedings against and in the case of noise nuisances, the notice period is a minimum of three days.[100]

The Sheriff has power to: (i) require the defender to abate the nuisance within a specified time and to execute any works necessary for that purpose; or (ii) prohibit a recurrence of the nuisance, and require the defender, within a specified time, to execute any works necessary to prevent the recurrence.

Again, a statutory defence of best practicable means is only available in the case of noise nuisance arising on industrial, trade or business premises.[101]

Common law

General

While it is now more common for individuals affected by noise to seek redress by invoking the above statutory remedies, the common law of nuisance and delict remains relevant.[102]

Nuisance

Noise and dust fall into the category of a 'nuisance', a general term used for a type of delict which arises from the interests involved in the ownership or occupation of property. In essence, nuisance aims to protect the enjoyment of land from unlawful interference, including noise emanating from outwith the relevant premises. The law will intervene only if the state of affairs complained of is unreasonable.

In deciding what is 'reasonable' the courts take into account such factors as the type and extent of the harm, the social value of the type of use or enjoyment invaded, the suitability of the particular use or enjoyment invaded, the character of the locality, the sensitivity to harm of the persons or property affected, and the burden on the complainer of taking protective measures.

Construction noise was discussed in the case of *Webster* v. *HMA*[103] where a Mrs Webster, who lived in the vicinity of Edinburgh Castle, was successful in establishing that noise in erecting scaffolding in relation to the Edinburgh Tattoo (but not the Tattoo itself) was a nuisance, notwithstanding that she moved to her property in the knowledge the Tattoo had taken place regularly for some years. The interim interdict granted was then suspended to allow consideration of a new system of scaffolding and to allow the Tattoo to proceed.

Who can bring an action?

Under common law, an owner, tenant or landlord in occupation can raise a competent court action along with an owner not in actual occupation.

Remedies

The options open to an aggrieved person as a result of noise nuisance under Scots Law are interdict, declarator and damages. The most frequently sought remedy is interdict, which is particularly apt given the recurring intermittent nature of noise nuisance.[104] Interdict prohibits reasonably apprehended future breaches of a duty owed to the complaining party.

Interdict is also competent to restrain an anticipated nuisance which has not yet begun.[105]

Regulation of noise from construction plant and machinery

Standards regulating permissible noise levels from construction plant and machinery are detailed in the 'Noise Emission in the Environment by Equipment for use Outdoors' Regulations 2001'. The bulk of their provisions came into force on 3 July 2001.[106]

The Regulations apply to equipment for use outdoors which are listed and defined. A range of construction equipment is covered including construction winches, concrete or mortar mixers and dozers.[107] The Regulations do not apply to equipment placed on the market before 3 July 2001.

The Regulations make it an offence for a manufacturer to place equipment into service unless

(a)   the equipment satisfies requirements on sound power levels detailed in a Schedule[108]

(b)   a conformity assessment procedure has been carried out

(c)   a 'CE' marking and indication of guaranteed sound power level has been affixed; or

(d)   an EC declaration of conformity accompanies the equipment.

Further general developments

Noise nuisance has been identified as a growing area of environmental concern. The National Society for Clean Air (NSCA) is urging the government to develop a national noise strategy to improve the general noise climate.[109] The European Commission estimates that noise annoyance is damaging the health and quality of life of around one quarter of Europe's population and that noise pollution causes around 13 to 38 billion euros of damage annually.[110] A draft Directive[111] on environmental noise is currently in its final stages of being progressed through the European Institutions. In its current form the Directive will require preparation of noise maps for urban centres and action plans to control noise.[112] These general developments are likely to have a trickle-down effect with local authorities being put under pressure to exercise existing controls more vigilantly.

Contaminated land

There is a considerable amount of derelict land in Scotland (particularly in the central belt). A significant proportion of this area is thought to be contaminated. It has been estimated that between 5000 and 10 000 hectares of land might be contaminated.[113] Part II of EPA, which aims to secure the clean-up of historically contaminated land, came into force in Scotland on 14 July 2000 and has the potential to affect contractors and developers companies either in their capacity as causers/knowing permitters of contamination or through their ownership and occupation of sites.[114]

The key features of identifying and remediating contaminated land are as follows:

- Local authorities were obliged to inspect their areas to identify contaminated land in accordance with written strategies to be drawn up by them by 14 October 2001.[115]
- Contaminated land will be identified on the basis of risk assessment – for land to be contaminated there needs to be a significant possibility of significant harm or it must be demonstrated that pollution of controlled waters is being or is likely to be caused.[116]
- Once land is identified as being contaminated, local authorities are obliged to secure clean-up through the service of remediation notices.[117] Liability is retrospective.
- In the case of special sites (the most seriously contaminated sites, which will include military land and land used for oil refining) responsibility for ensuring clean-up rests with the Scottish Environment Protection Agency.
- If land is identified as being contaminated there will be (except in emergencies) a period of at least three months for consultation and negotiation[118] to encourage voluntary remediation.
- Remediation notices must be served in the first instance on polluters or knowing permitters of contamination.[119] If none of these can be found, responsibility will pass to the current owner or occupier of the site.
- Remediation must be designed to make the land suitable for its current use. The regime will only deal with sites where the land is actually unsuitable for its current use. In cases where land is suitable for its current use but an application for planning permission is being made for a change of use, the planning permission will contain appropriate clean-up conditions.
- Failure to comply with remediation notices is a criminal offence and the enforcing authority can carry out the works itself and recover costs.[120]

Contractors could accordingly be liable under the new legislation for pollution incidents even if these took place some considerable time ago. In addition, there is scope for liability as 'innocent' owners/occupiers.

Of equal concern to the industry will be the liability exclusion tests which allow a polluter, or knowing permitter, to pass on their share of liability in certain circumstances.[121] From the construction industry's viewpoint, exclusion test 6 is likely to be of particular concern as it affords a means of liability escape for polluters in cases where other parties subsequently introduce new pathways allowing a pollutant to reach a receptor. It is expressly recognised in the exclusion test that building or engineering operations could result in the creation of such a new pathway. Contractors will therefore require to be aware of these new provisions. Notwithstanding this, the new regime is, however, intended to deal not with all polluted sites but only the most pressing cases. A sense of perspective must therefore be retained about the significance of the new regime.

Notes

[1] SEPA was created by section 20 of the Environment Act 1995 and is given the status of a body corporate.

[2] SEPA inherited its functions from the seven former River Purification Authorities, Her Majesty's Industrial Pollution Inspectorate and the former District and Islands Councils (section 21 of the Environment Act 1995). SEPA has no statutory primary aim (unlike the Environment Agency) however government guidance in the form of SEPA Management Statement para 2.5 of November 1996 does state SEPA's aim as being 'to deliver well-managed integrated environment protection, not only as an end in itself but as a contribution to the Government's goal of sustainable development'.

[3] The Integrated Pollution Control regime was introduced by Part I of the Environmental Protection Act 1990 – for details on the Integrated Pollution Prevention and Control Regime see Pollution Prevention and Control Act 1999 and accompanying Pollution Prevention and Control (Scotland) Regulations 2000.

[4] See SEPA website for prosecution statistics.

[5] See ENDS Report 310 'Scottish prosecutors refuse to act in over one-third of environmental cases'.

[6] See SEPA Policy Statement on Enforcement, at www.sepa.org.uk

[7] North, West and East of Scotland Water were created by section 62 of the Local Government Etc. (Scotland) Act 1994 and replaced with Scottish Water by virtue of the Water Industry (Scotland) Act 2002. In terms of the Water Services Bill it is proposed that the three water authorities will be replaced with a single new body to be known as Scottish Water.

[8] Section 44B(1) of the Environmental Protection Act 1990 required SEPA 'as soon as possible to prepare a statement ("the strategy") containing its policies in relation to the recovery and disposal of waste in Scotland'. The strategy was unveiled by SEPA in December 1999 – see National Waste Strategy: Scotland – www.sepa.org.uk/nws/pdf/nws/national_waste_strategy.pdf. The Strategy reiterates the importance of following the waste hierarchy, for example, page 22 of the Strategy states, 'The designers and those who specify the materials to be used should think carefully about incorporating recycling material in their products and also of how waste production can be minimised. This may mean re-examining specifications and changing traditional practices. Construction companies need to be sure that surplus new material is not simply to be put in a disposal skip for

convenience. Demolition contractors should adopt demolition methods which ensure the maximum amount of reusable material is recovered'.

[9] Ibid, page 42. Central to SEPA's approach to Waste Management are the requirements of the Landfill Directive (EC/31/99 – OJ L182 16.7.99) which aims to secure reduced dependence on landfilling. The UK is obliged to reduce landfill to 75% by 2010, 50% by 2013 and 35% by 2020 (based on 1995 levels).

[10] Section 33(1)(a) and (b) of EPA. The maximum penalties which may be imposed are a £20 000 fine and/or six months' imprisonment on summary conviction; and an unlimited fine or two years' imprisonment (or both) on conviction on indictment.

[11] The most important of these are the Waste Management Licensing Regulations 1994 (SI 1994/1056) and the Special Waste Regulations 1996 (SI 1996/972) as amended. The Scottish Office Environment Department Circular 10/94 explains the waste management licensing regime and in particular contains a full discussion on the complex problem of defining waste.

[12] Section 75(2) EPA. The categories of waste referred to above are detailed in Schedule 2B to the Environmental Protection Act 1990. Included within these categories is a general sweep-up category of 'any materials, substances or products which are not contained in the above categories'.

[13] Section 75(4) EPA.

[14] 1995 SCCR22.

[15] Entitled Environmental Protection Act 1990 section 34 the Duty of Care (para 17).

[16] The Control of Pollution (Amendment) Act 1989 requires registration of waste carriers and brokers and creates at section 1 a criminal offence for failure to so register where transporting controlled waste in the course of any business or otherwise with a view to profit. Application for registration requires to be made to SEPA who will issue a certificate which is valid for three years and applicable nationally.

[17] For a brief summary see DEFRA Leaflet 'Duty of Care' at www. defra.gov.uk/environment/waste/management/doc/index .htm For fuller details see *Waste management, the duty of care, a code of practice*, HMSO, March 1996.

[18] Section 34(6) EPA.

[19] Section 62 EPA.

[20] See Council Decision of 22 December 1994 establishing a list of Hazardous Waste pursuant to Article 1(4) of Council Directive 91/689/EEC on Hazardous Waste 94/904/EC (OJL356/14 31.12.94).

[21] Section 36 EPA requires an application to be made on a SEPA application form to be accompanied by: (i) such information as SEPA may reasonably require; and (ii) a fee, the level of which is dependent on the type and quantity of waste.

[22] See section 74 EPA. A person is not to be treated as fit and proper if: (i) they have inadequate financial resources to manage the site (and cannot meet restoration liabilities); (ii) they have been convicted of offences under certain environmental legislation including EPA; (iii) they are not technically competent, evidence of which can be presented by the holding of a certificate

of competence from the Waste Management Industry Training Board (WAMITAB). The determination of who constitutes a fit and proper person is at the discretion of SEPA though the applicant does have a right of appeal to the Scottish Minister for the Environment and Rural Development.

[23] See section 40 EPA.

[24] Section 59 EPA.

[25] These are set out in Schedule 3 to the Waste Management Licensing Legislations 1994.

[26] These are applications for registration, not exemption, and SEPA does not have power to refuse registration.

[27] Except in the case of applications for exemption of metal recycling sites.

[28] A registration form will require to be completed giving contact details and an address for the party requiring registration along with an indication of the location of the proposed activity, whether the applicant is a site owner/ occupier and the precise provision under which exemption is claimed. It will not be possible therefore for a business to obtain one registration covering all its various sites (as is the case with waste carrier registration).

[29] Failure to register an exemption will subject the business concerned to a fine of £10 on Summary Conviction. SI 1994/1056 Schedule 3, para 9.

[30] SI 1994/1056 Schedule 3, para 41.

[31] SI 1994/1056 Schedule 3.

[32] Circular 11/94, Annex 5, para 5.154.

[33] SI 1994/1056 Schedule 3, para 13.

[34] SI 1994/1056 Schedule 3, para 13(2). The soil or soil substitute must be applied to the land and the total amount manufactured must not exceed 500 tonnes per day.

[35] The tax was introduced by the Finance Act 1996 (Sections 39 to 71 and Schedule 5), which Act has since been amended/supplemented by: (i) the Landfill Tax Regulations 1996 (SI 1996/1527); (ii) the Landfill Tax (Qualifying Material) Order 1996 (SI 1996/1528); (iii) the Landfill Tax (Contaminated Land) Order 1996 (SI 1996/1529); (iv) the Landfill Tax (Site Restoration and Quarries) Order 1999 (SI 1999 No. 2075); The Pollution Prevention and Control (Scotland) Regulations 2000 (SI 2000 No. 323); (vi) The Pollution Prevention and Control (England and Wales) Regulations 2000 (SI 2000 No. 1973); (vii) The Non-automatic Weighing Instruments Regulations 2000 (SI 2000 No. 3236).

[36] See 'Landfill Tax: A Consultation Paper': HM Customs & Excise, 1995. To view the landfill tax in its wider context see footnote 9 above.

[37] Section 64 of Finance Act 1996.

[38] Section 42(2) of Finance Act 1996.

[39] Section 63 Finance Act 1996.

[40] These are set out at sections 43 to 45 of the Finance Act 1996.

[41] Section 43B(1)(c) Finance Act 1996.

[42] See Scottish Executive Environmental Group Research Programme Research Findings No. 10, 'Review of the Environmental Effects of the Landfill Tax in Scotland' www.Scotland.gov.uk/cru/resfinds/erf10-00.asp See also ENDS Report 312, page 17.

[43] Customs & Excise have produced guidance which interprets the legislation. See LFT1 of February 2000 – 'A general guide to landfill tax' and also

LFT2 of May 2001 – 'Reclamation of contaminated land'. See `www.hmce.gov.uk/forms/notices/ift2-htm`

[44] For example ENDS 250 P45. Italian-owned construction company, Castelli Ginola were fined £15 000 for a discharge containing suspended solids at a concentration many times higher than that capable of damaging fish gills and salmon spawning areas. For an indication of the impact the industry is having in England see 'Construction and chemicals sectors shamed by pollution report' ENDS 314 p. 17.

[45] Issued under Section 34 COPA.

[46] Section 34(4) COPA. Section 34(4) goes on to give an exhaustive list of types of permissible conditions. These include conditions as to the origin, composition, temperature, volume, rate and period of the discharges. A discharge consent is normally quite a short document, running to one to two pages in length.

[47] Section 34(2)(b) COPA.

[48] Section 39 COPA.

[49] Section 34 COPA.

[50] Section 37 and 38 COPA.

[51] Section 36(7) COPA.

[52] Section 30I(a) COPA.

[53] Sections 49A and 49B were inserted into COPA by Schedule 22 of the Environment Act 1995. These provisions were brought into force by SS1 No 433 The Environment Act 1995 (Commencement No. 19) (Scotland) Order 2000. It was felt that compliance could be improved by the use of enforcement notices in cases where a potential polluter has failed to respond to less formal approaches. Enforcement notices could require for example the use of back-up systems, improved inlet/outlet sampling arrangements and provision of flow measurement devices. Environmental Minister Sam Galbraith has highlighted the potential of the new powers for dealing with pollution from sewage effluent; for example a notice could be served where maintenance programmes at sewage works were not complied with.

[54] Section 49B COPA.

[55] Section 49B(6) COPA.

[56] SSI No. 432 The Control of Pollution (Registers) and (Consent for Discharges) (Secretary of State Functions) Amendment Regulations 2000.

[57] See Consultation Paper by the Scottish Executive Rural Affairs Department entitled 'Water Pollution, Anti-Pollution Works Regulations, 27 January 2000, Paper No. 1/2000 – `www.scotland.gov.uk/consultations/apw-00.asp` Similar regulations have already been introduced in England – see The Anti-Pollution Works Regulations Year (SI 1006).

[58] In Scotland there were twenty-five convictions for breach of discharge consents in 2001/2002. These resulted in one admonishment and twenty-three fines and one deferral with the average fine being £3833.

[59] CIRIA is a UK-based research association concerned with improving the performance of all involved with construction and the environment. CIRIA works with industry to develop and implement best practice, leading to better performance. Contractors, clients, designers, regulators, financiers and government are all regularly involved in CIRIA's programme of activities. In conjunction with other parties CIRIA manages the Construction Industry

Environmental Forum (CIEF) which aims to improve the environmental performance of those involved in the construction industry.

[60] See *CIRIA News*, Issue 1, 2001. Also www.ciria.org.uk

[61] F. McManus, *Scottish planning and environmental law*, No. 51 at page 90.

[62] Figures obtained from Royal Environmental Health Institute of Scotland (REHIS). Note however that the number of complaints for both years may in fact have been higher as not all local authorities reported on their figures.

[63] Section 73(1) COPA.

[64] Section 60(2) COPA – The works to which section 60(2) applies are:

> (a) the erection, construction, alteration, repair or maintenance of buildings, structures or roads
>
> (b) breaking up, opening or boring under any road or adjacent land in connection with the construction, inspection, maintenance or removal of works
>
> (c) demolition or dredging work
>
> (d) (whether or not also comprised in paragraph (a), (b) or (c) above) any work of engineering construction (section 60(1) COPA).

[65] Section 60(3)(a).

[66] Section 60(3) COPA. See, for example, *Wiltshier Construction (London) Limited* v. *Westminster City Council* [1997] Env LR 321 at 321 where the notice required that 'All works and ancillary operations which are audible at the site boundary, or all such other places as may be agreed with the Council, shall be carried out only between certain specified hours and at no time on Sunday and Bank Holidays'.

[67] Section 60(3) COPA.

[68] Section 60(6) COPA.

[69] Section 60(5) COPA.

[70] Section 60(4) COPA.

[71] BS5228 consists of five parts but Parts 1, 2 and 4 have the greatest application to the construction industry: Part 1 is a Code of Practice for basic information and procedures for noise and vibration control; Part 2 is a guide to noise and vibration control legislation for construction and demolition, including road construction and maintenance; and Part 4 is a Code of Practice for noise and vibration control applicable to piling operations.

Part 1 provides guidance on protection against noise and vibration of persons living and working in the vicinity of, and those working on, construction sites. Recommendations are made for basic methods of noise and vibration control relating to construction and open sites where work activities/operations generate significant noise and vibration levels. The basis of this standard is the principle that effective noise control at source is to be regarded as the prime means of affording proper protection to employees from risk to hearing. The standard also suggests such noise reduction methods as modifications of existing plant and equipment, altering the siting of equipment and/or enclosing equipment. Detailed appendices with tables set out: (i) noise sources, remedies and their effectiveness (Annex B); (ii) typical sound levels for specific equipment and activities (Annex C); and (iii) guidance on estimating noise from sites (Annex D). Annex E provides guidance on noise monitoring.

Part 2 suggests that all reasonably practicable means should be employed to ensure the protection of local communities. The means employed should be determined by local circumstances and include noise reduction measures for individual items of plant and machinery, the use of plant and machinery with low noise output, the provision of protective shields, barriers or enclosures, the fixing of hours of work, the setting of noise vibration and any other appropriate measures.

[72] *Adam (Scotland) Limited* v. *Bearsden and Milngavie* DC SLT (Sh Ct) [1996] 21 at 22.

[73] Section 60(4)(b) COPA.

[74] Section 72 COPA.

[75] Section 60(4)(c) COPA.

[76] Section 60(7) COPA.

[77] The Control of Noise (Appeals) (Scotland) Regulations 1983 (SI 1983 No. 1455).

[78] Section 74 COPA.

[79] Section 61(1) COPA. Such an application will contain particulars of works and the methods by which they will be carried out and the steps to be taken to minimise noise resulting from the works.

[80] Section 61(8) COPA.

[81] Section 61(5) COPA.

[82] Section 61(6) COPA.

[83] Section 61(7) COPA.

[84] Section 79(1)(g) EPA.

[85] Section 79(7) EPA.

[86] *Tower Hamlets, London Borough Council* v. *Manzoni & Walder* [1984] GP 123.

[87] Tromans, S., *The Environmental Protection Act 1990 – text and commentary,* 2nd edition, Sweet & Maxwell, page 79.

[88] *London Borough Council* v. *Ince* [1989] 153 JP 597.

[89] Section 79(1) EPA.

[90] Section 80(1) EPA.

[91] Ibid.

[92] Section 80(3) EPA.

[93] See The Statutory Nuisance (Appeals) (Scotland) Regulations 1996 SI 1076.

[94] Section 80(4) EPA.

[95] Section 80(6) EPA. For offences not committed on industrial, trade or business premises, the maximum fine is at level 5 of the standard scale currently (£5000) together with a maximum daily fine at one-tenth of that level for each day upon which the offence continues (s 80(5)).

[96] Section 80(7) EPA. Section 79(a) EPA stipulates that 'best practicable means' is to be interpreted by reference to the following provisions:

    (a)   'practicable' means reasonably practicable having regard among other things to local conditions and circumstances, to the current state of technical knowledge and to the financial implications

    (b)   the means to be employed include the design, installation, maintenance and manner and periods of operation of plant and machinery and the design, construction and maintenance of buildings and structures

(c)   the test is to apply only so far as compatible with any duty imposed by law

(d)   the test is to apply only so far as compatible with safety and safe working conditions, and with the exigencies of any emergency or unforeseeable circumstances.

[97] Sections 80(2)(a) EPA and S80(8)(a) EPA.

[98] Section 82(1) EPA.

[99] Section 82(4) EPA.

[100] Section 82(7) EPA.

[101] Section 82(10) EPA.

[102] For a detailed discussion on the role of nuisance law in relation to noise see *Scottish Planning & Environmental Law (SPEL)*, No. 49 at page 48, 'Noise: Common Law Controls' by Francis McManus.

[103] 1984 SLT 13.

[104] *Murdoch* v. *Murdoch* 1973 SLT (Notes) 13, per Lord President Enslie, applied in *Webster* v. *Lord Advocate* [1985] 361 quoted in 'The Laws of Scotland' *Stair Memorial Encyclopaedia*, volume 14, para 2148. The terms of the interdict must be no wider than is necessary to curb the illegal acting complained of, and so precise and clear that the person interdicted is left in no doubt what he is forbidden to do.

[105] *Gavin* v. *Ayrshire County Council* 1950 SC197 at 207, 1950 SLT 146 at 155, per Lord President Cooper quoted in 'The Laws of Scotland' *Stair Memorial Encyclopaedia*, volume 14, 1988, para 2146.

[106] SI 2000 No. 1701. This implements the European Parliament and Council Directive 2000/14/EC on the approximation of the laws of the Member States relating to noise emission in the environment by equipment for use outdoors. The Regulations revoked The Construction Plant and Equipment (Harmonisation of Noise Emission Standards) Regulations 1985 (SI 1985 No. 1968 and the Construction Plant and Equipment (Harmonisation of Noise Emission Standards) Regulations 1988 (SI 1988 No. 361).

[107] See Schedules 1, 2 and 4 of the Regulations.

[108] See Schedules 3 and 6 of the Regulations.

[109] National Society for Clean Air Annual Review 1999–2000 Policy and Practice. The NSCA was founded in 1898 as an anti-smog campaigning group and today is comprised of organisations from the private, public and voluntary sectors, have been promoting an annual Noise Action Day which aims to raise awareness of noise issues.

[110] Ends Report No. 307, pages 38 to 39 and COM (2000) 468, final pages 3–4.

[111] See Proposal for a Directive of The European Parliament and the Council relating to the Assessment and Management of Environmental Noise COM (2000) 468 final – www/europarl.eu.int/oeil/oeil.Res

[112] ENDS Report 312, page 49.

[113] See the Scottish Parliament Information Centre Research Note of 18 April 2000 commenting on SEPA's 1996 State of the Environment Report and the 1994 Scottish Vacant and Derelict Land Survey.

[114] Part IIA of the Environmental Protection Act 1990 is supplemented by detailed regulations and guidance (referred to in the above text as 'the Regulations' and 'the Guidance') – see The Contaminated Land (Scotland) Regulations 2000 (SI 2000/178) and also Scottish Executive Statutory Guidance on Contaminated Land (forming Annex 3 of the Scottish Executive Circular 1/2000). The Guidance is extremely detailed and is broken down into five parts. Parts I to III cover the definition, identification and remediation of contaminated land. Parts IV and V cover exclusion from the apportionment of liability for circumstances where more than one person is potentially liable. Recovery of costs of remediation is dealt with in Part V. The Regulations are more restricted in scope than the Guidance and deal with the definition of special sites, the form and content of remediation notices, compensation for rights of entry, appeals and the form and content of registers of contaminated land.

[115] Section 78B(1) EPA.

[116] Section 78A(1) EPA.

[117] Section 78E(1) EPA.

[118] Section 78H EPA.

[119] Section 78F EPA. In complex cases where several parties are implicated, reference must be had to detailed guidance which sets out how liability is to be apportioned.

[120] Section 78M EPA.

[121] Where the contaminated land is on industrial, trade or business premises the maximum fine on summary conviction is £20 000 and there is provision for a further daily fine of £2000 in the event of continuing non-compliance.

Appendix 1: The Housing Grants, Construction and Regeneration Act 1996

Part II: Construction contracts

Introductory provisions

Construction contracts
104

(1) In this Part, a 'construction contract' means an agreement with a person for any of the following:

- (a)   the carrying out of construction operations
- (b)   arranging for the carrying out of construction operations by others, whether under sub-contract to him or otherwise
- (c)   providing his own labour, or the labour of others, for the carrying out of construction operations.

(2) References in this Part to a construction contract include an agreement:

- (a)   to do architectural, design, or surveying work; or
- (b)   to provide advice on building, engineering, interior or exterior decoration or on the laying-out of landscape

in relation to construction operations.

(3) References in this Part to a construction contract do not include a contract of employment (within the meaning of the Employment Rights Act 1996).

(4) The Secretary of State may by order add to, amend or repeal any of the provisions of subsection (1), (2) or (3) as to the agreements which are construction contracts for the purposes of this Part or are to be taken or not to be taken as included in references to such contracts.

No such order shall be made unless a draft of it has been laid before and approved by a resolution of each House of Parliament.

(5) Where an agreement relates to construction operations and other matters, this Part applies to it only so far as it relates to construction operations.

An agreement relates to construction operations so far as it makes provision of any kind within subsection (1) or (2).

(6) This Part applies only to construction contracts which:

- (a)   are entered into after the commencement of this Part,

    (b)   relate to the carrying out of construction operations in England, Wales or Scotland.

(7) This Part applies whether or not the law of England and Wales or Scotland is otherwise the applicable law in relation to the contract.

Meaning of 'construction operations'
105

(1) In this Part 'construction operations' means, subject as follows, operations of any of the following descriptions:

    (a)   construction, alteration, repair, maintenance, extension, demolition or dismantling of buildings, or structures forming, or to form, part of the land (whether permanent or not)

    (b)   construction, alteration, repair, maintenance, extension, demolition or dismantling of any works forming, or to form, part of the land, including (without prejudice to the foregoing) walls, roadworks, power-lines, telecommunication apparatus, aircraft runways, docks and harbours, railways, inland waterways, pipe-lines, reservoirs, water-mains, wells, sewers, industrial plant and installations for purposes of land drainage, coast protection or defence

    (c)   installation in any building or structure of fittings forming part of the land, including (without prejudice to the foregoing) systems of heating, lighting, air-conditioning, ventilation, power supply, drainage, sanitation, water supply or fire protection, or security or communications systems

    (d)   external or internal cleaning of buildings and structures, so far as carried out in the course of their construction, alteration, repair, extension or restoration

    (e)   operations which form an integral part of, or are preparatory to, or are for rendering complete, such operations as are previously described in this subsection, including site clearance, earth-moving, excavation, tunnelling and boring, laying of foundations, erection, maintenance or dismantling of scaffolding, site restoration, landscaping and the provision of roadways and other access works

    (f)   painting or decorating the internal or external surfaces of any building or structure.

(2) The following operations are not construction operations within the meaning of this Part:

    (a)   drilling for, or extraction of, oil or natural gas

    (b)   extraction (whether by underground or surface working) of minerals; tunnelling or boring, or construction of underground works, for this purpose

    (c)   assembly, installation or demolition of plant or machinery, or erection or demolition of steelwork for the purposes of supporting or providing access to plant or machinery, on a site where the primary activity is:

        (i)   nuclear processing, power generation, or water or effluent treatment; or

      (ii)   the production, transmission, processing or bulk storage (other than warehousing) of chemicals, pharmaceuticals, oil, gas, steel or food and drink;

  (d)   manufacture or delivery to site of:

      (i)   building or engineering components or equipment

      (ii)   materials, plant or machinery; or

      (iii) components for systems of heating, lighting, air-conditioning, ventilation, power supply, drainage, sanitation, water supply or fire protection, or for security or communications systems,

except under a contract which also provides for their installation;

  (e)   the making, installation and repair of artistic works, being sculptures, murals and other works which are wholly artistic in nature.

(3) The Secretary of State may by order add to, amend or repeal any of the provisions of subsection (1) or (2) as to the operations and work to be treated as construction operations for the purposes of this Part.

(4) No such order shall be made unless a draft of it has been laid before and approved by a resolution of each House of Parliament.

Provisions not applicable to contract with residential occupier
106

(1) This Part does not apply:

  (a)   to a construction contract with a residential occupier (see below); or

  (b)   to any other description of construction contract excluded from the operation of this Part by order of the Secretary of State.

(2) A construction contract with a residential occupier means a construction contract which principally relates to operations on a dwelling which one of the parties to the contract occupies, or intends to occupy, as his residence.

  In this subsection 'dwelling' means a dwelling-house or a flat; and for this purpose:

     'dwelling-house' does not include a building containing a flat

     'flat' means separate and self-contained premises constructed or adapted for use for residential purposes and forming part of a building from some other part of which the premises are divided horizontally.

(3) The Secretary of State may by order amend subsection (2).

(4) No order under this section shall be made unless a draft of it has been laid before and approved by a resolution of each House of Parliament.

Provisions applicable only to agreements in writing
107

(1) The provisions of this Part apply only where the construction contract is in writing, and any other agreement between the parties as to any matter is effective for the purposes of this Part only if in writing.

  The expressions 'agreement', 'agree' and 'agreed' shall be construed accordingly.

(2) There is an agreement in writing:

(a)   if the agreement is made in writing (whether or not it is signed by the parties)

(b)   if the agreement is made by exchange of communications in writing; or

(c)   if the agreement is evidenced in writing.

(3) Where parties agree otherwise than in writing by reference to terms which are in writing, they make an agreement in writing.

(4) An agreement is evidenced in writing if an agreement made otherwise than in writing is recorded by one of the parties, or by a third party, with the authority of the parties to the agreement.

(5) An exchange of written submissions in adjudication proceedings, or in arbitral or legal proceedings in which the existence of an agreement otherwise than in writing is alleged by one party against another party and not denied by the other party in his response constitutes as between those parties an agreement in writing to the effect alleged.

(6) References in this Part to anything being written or in writing include its being recorded by any means.

Adjudication

Right to refer disputes to adjudication
108

(1) A party to a construction contract has the right to refer a dispute arising under the contract for adjudication under a procedure complying with this section.

For this purpose 'dispute' includes any difference.

(2) The contract shall:

(a)   enable a party to give notice at any time of his intention to refer a dispute to adjudication

(b)   provide a timetable with the object of securing the appointment of the adjudicator and referral of the dispute to him within seven days of such notice

(c)   require the adjudicator to reach a decision within 28 days of referral or such longer period as is agreed by the parties after the dispute has been referred

(d)   allow the adjudicator to extend the period of 28 days by up to 14 days, with the consent of the party by whom the dispute was referred

(e)   impose a duty on the adjudicator to act impartially

(f)   enable the adjudicator to take the initiative in ascertaining the facts and the law.

(3) The contract shall provide that the decision of the adjudicator is binding until the dispute is finally determined by legal proceedings, by arbitration (if the contract provides for arbitration or the parties otherwise agree to arbitration) or by agreement.

The parties may agree to accept the decision of the adjudicator as finally determining the dispute.

(4) The contract shall also provide that the adjudicator is not liable for anything done or omitted in the discharge or purported discharge of his functions as adjudicator unless the act or omission is in bad faith, and that any employee or agent of the adjudicator is similarly protected from liability.

(5) If the contract does not comply with the requirements of subsections (1) to (4), the adjudication provisions of the Scheme for Construction Contracts apply.

(6) For England and Wales, the Scheme may apply the provisions of the Arbitration Act 1996 with such adaptations and modifications as appear to the Minister making the scheme to be appropriate.

For Scotland, the Scheme may include provision conferring powers on courts in relation to adjudication and provision relating to the enforcement of the adjudicator's decision.

Payment

Entitlement to stage payments
109

(1) A party to a construction contract is entitled to payment by instalments, stage payments or other periodic payments for any work under the contract unless:

   (a)   it is specified in the contract that the duration of the work is to be less than 45 days; or
   (b)   it is agreed between the parties that the duration of the work is estimated to be less than 45 days.

(2) The parties are free to agree the amounts of the payments and the intervals at which, or circumstances in which, they become due.

(3) In the absence of such agreement, the relevant provisions of the Scheme for Construction Contracts apply.

(4) References in the following sections to a payment under the contract include a payment by virtue of this section.

Dates for payment
110

(1) Every construction contract shall:

   (a)   provide an adequate mechanism for determining what payments become due under the contract, and when;
   (b)   provide for a final date for payment in relation to any sum which becomes due.

The parties are free to agree how long the period is to be between the date on which a sum becomes due and the final date for payment.

(2) Every construction contract shall provide for the giving of notice by a party not later than five days after the date on which a payment becomes due from him under the contract, or would have become due if:

   (a)   the other party had carried out his obligations under the contract

(b)   no set-off or abatement was permitted by reference to any sum claimed to be due under one or more other contracts,

specifying the amount (if any) of the payment made or proposed to be made, and the basis on which that amount was calculated.

(3) If or to the extent that a contract does not contain such provision as is mentioned in subsection (1) or (2), the relevant provisions of the Scheme for Construction Contracts apply.

Notice of intention to withhold payment
111

(1) A party to a construction contract may not withhold payment after the final date for payment of a sum due under the contract unless he has given an effective notice of intention to withhold payment.

The notice mentioned in section 110(2) may suffice as a notice of intention to withhold payment if it complies with the requirements of this section.

(2) To be effective such a notice must specify:

(a)   the amount proposed to be withheld and the ground for withholding payment; or
(b)   if there is more than one ground, each ground and the amount attributable to it, and must be given not later than the prescribed period before the final date for payment.

(3) The parties are free to agree what that prescribed period is to be.

In the absence of such agreement, the period shall be that provided by the Scheme for Construction Contracts.

(4) Where an effective notice of intention to withhold payment is given, but on the matter being referred to adjudication it is decided that the whole or part of the amount should be paid, the decision shall be construed as requiring payment not later than:

(a)   seven days from the date of the decision; or
(b)   the date which apart from the notice would have been the final date for payment,

whichever is the later.

Right to suspend performance for non-payment
112

(1) Where a sum due under a construction contract is not paid in full by the final date for payment and no effective notice to withhold payment has been given, the person to whom the sum is due has the right (without prejudice to any other right or remedy) to suspend performance of his obligations under the contract to the party by whom payment ought to have been made ('the party in default').

(2) The right may not be exercised without first giving to the party in default at least seven days' notice of intention to suspend performance, stating the ground or grounds on which it is intended to suspend performance.

(3) The right to suspend performance ceases when the party in default makes payment in full of the amount due.

(4) Any period during which performance is suspended in pursuance of the right conferred by this section shall be disregarded in computing for the purposes of any contractual time limit the time taken, by the party exercising the right or by a third party, to complete any work directly or indirectly affected by the exercise of the right.

Where the contractual time limit is set by reference to a date rather than a period, the date shall be adjusted accordingly.

Prohibition of conditional payment provisions
113

(1) A provision making payment under a construction contract conditional on the payer receiving payment from a third person is ineffective, unless that third person, or any other person payment by whom is under the contract (directly or indirectly) a condition of payment by that third person, is insolvent.

(2) For the purposes of this section a company becomes insolvent:

  (a)   on the making of an administration order against it under Part II of the Insolvency Act 1986
  (b)   on the appointment of an administrative receiver or a receiver or manager of its property under Chapter I of Part III of that Act, or the appointment of a receiver under Chapter II of that Part
  (c)   on the passing of a resolution for voluntary winding-up without a declaration of solvency under section 89 of that Act; or
  (d)   on the making of a winding-up order under Part IV or V of that Act.

(3) For the purposes of this section a partnership becomes insolvent:

  (a)   on the making of a winding-up order against it under any provision of the Insolvency Act 1986 as applied by an order under section 420 of that Act; or
  (b)   when sequestration is awarded on the estate of the partnership under section 12 of the Bankruptcy (Scotland) Act 1985 or the partnership grants a trust deed for its creditors.

(4) For the purposes of this section an individual becomes insolvent:

  (a)   on the making of a bankruptcy order against him under Part IX of the Insolvency Act 1986; or
  (b)   on the sequestration of his estate under the Bankruptcy (Scotland) Act 1985 or when he grants a trust deed for his creditors.

(5) A company, partnership or individual shall also be treated as insolvent on the occurrence of any event corresponding to those specified in subsection (2), (3) or (4) under the law of Northern Ireland or of a country outside the United Kingdom.

(6) Where a provision is rendered ineffective by subsection (1), the parties are free to agree other terms for payment.

In the absence of such agreement, the relevant provisions of the Scheme for Construction Contracts apply.

Supplementary provisions

The Sceme for Construction Contracts
114

(1) The Minister shall by regulations make a scheme ('the Scheme for Construction Contracts') containing provision about the matters referred to in the preceding provisions of this Part.

(2) Before making any regulations under this section the Minister shall consult such persons as he thinks fit.

(3) In this section 'the Minister' means:

    (a)   for England and Wales, the Secretary of State

    (b)   for Scotland, the Lord Advocate.

(4) Where any provisions of the Scheme for Construction Contracts apply by virtue of this Part in default of contractual provision agreed by the parties, they have effect as implied terms of the contract concerned.

(5) Regulations under this section shall not be made unless a draft of them has been approved by resolution of each House of Parliament.

Service of notices, etc.
115

(1) The parties are free to agree on the manner of service of any notice or other document required or authorised to be served in pursuance of the construction contract or for any of the purposes of this Part.

(2) If or to the extent that there is no such agreement the following provisions apply.

(3) A notice or other document may be served on a person by any effective means.

(4) If a notice or other document is addressed, pre-paid and delivered by post:

    (a)   to the addressee's last known principal residence or, if he is or has been carrying on a trade, profession or business, his last known principal business address; or

    (b)   where the addressee is a body corporate, to the body's registered or principal office,

it shall be treated as effectively served.

(5) This section does not apply to the service of documents for the purposes of legal proceedings, for which provision is made by rules of court.

(6) References in this Part to a notice or other document include any form of communication in writing and references to service shall be construed accordingly.

Reckoning periods of time
116

(1) For the purposes of this Part periods of time shall be reckone as follows.

(2) Where an act is required to be done within a specified period after or from a specified date, the period begins immediately after that date.

(3) Where the period would include Christmas Day, Good Friday or a day which under the Banking and Financial Dealings Act 1971 is a bank holiday in

England and Wales or, as the case may be, in Scotland, that day shall be excluded.

Crown application

117

(1) This Part applies to a construction contract entered into by or on behalf of the Crown otherwise than by or on behalf of Her Majesty in her private capacity.

(2) This Part applies to a construction contract entered into on behalf of the Duchy of Cornwall notwithstanding any Crown interest.

(3) Where a construction contract is entered into by or on behalf of Her Majesty in right of the Duchy of Lancaster, Her Majesty shall be represented, for the purposes of any adjudication or other proceedings arising out of the contract by virtue of this Part, by the Chancellor of the Duchy or such person as he may appoint.

(4) Where a construction contract is entered into on behalf of the Duchy of Cornwall, the Duke of Cornwall or the possessor for the time being of the Duchy shall be represented, for the purposes of any adjudication or other proceedings arising out of the contract by virtue of this Part, by such person as he may appoint.

Source: www.hmso.gov.uk/act/acts1996
© Crown Copyright 1996.

Appendix 2: The Scheme for Construction Contracts (Scotland) Regulations 1998

Made	*6th March 1998*
Coming into force	*1st May 1998*

The Lord Advocate, in exercise of the powers conferred on him by sections 108(6), 114 and 146 of the Housing Grants, Construction and Regeneration Act 1996[1] and of all other powers enabling him in that behalf, having consulted such persons as he thinks fit, hereby makes the following Regulations, a draft of which has been laid before and has been approved by resolution of each House of Parliament:

Citation, commencement and extent

1. (1) These Regulations may be cited as the Scheme for Construction Contracts (Scotland) Regulations 1998 and shall come into force at the end of the period of eight weeks beginning with the day on which they are made.

    (2) These Regulations extend to Scotland only.

Interpretation

2. In these Regulations, 'the Act' means the Housing Grants, Construction and Regeneration Act 1996.

The Scheme for Construction Contracts (Scotland)

3. Where a construction contract does not comply with the requirements of subsections (1) to (4) of section 108 of the Act, the adjudication provisions in Part I of the Schedule to these Regulations shall apply.

4. Where:

    (a) the parties to a construction contract are unable to reach agreement for the purposes mentioned respectively in sections 109, 111 and 113 of the Act; or

    (b) a construction contract does not make provision as required by section 110 of the Act,

    the relevant provisions in Part II of the Schedule to these Regulations shall apply.

5.   The provisions in the Schedule to these Regulations shall be the Scheme for Construction Contracts (Scotland) for the purposes of section 114 of the Act.

Hardie
Lord Advocate

Edinburgh
6th March 1998

SCHEDULE

Regulations 3 to 5

THE SCHEME FOR CONSTRUCTION CONTRACTS (SCOTLAND)

Part I: Adjudication

Notice of intention to seek adjudication

1.   (1)   Any party to a construction contract ('the referring party') may give written notice ('the notice of adjudication') of his intention to refer any dispute arising under the contract to adjudication.

(2)   The notice of adjudication shall be given to every other party to the contract.

(3)   The notice of adjudication shall set out briefly:

(a)   the nature and a brief description of the dispute and of the parties involved

(b)   details of where and when the dispute has arisen

(c)   the nature of the redress which is sought

(d)   the names and addresses of the parties to the contract (including, where appropriate, the addresses which the parties have specified for the giving of notices).

2.   (1)   Following the giving of a notice of adjudication and subject to any agreement between the parties to the dispute as to who shall act as adjudicator:

(a)   the referring party shall request the person (if any) specified in the contract to act as adjudicator

(b)   if no person is named in the contract or the person named has already indicated that he is unwilling or unable to act, and the contract provides for a specified nominating body to select a person, the referring party shall request the nominating body named in the contract to select a person to act as adjudicator; or

(c)   where neither head (a) nor (b) above applies, or where the person referred to in (a) has already indicated that he is unwilling or unable to act and (b) does not apply, the referring party shall request an adjudicator nominating body to select a person to act as adjudicator.

(2)   A person requested to act as adjudicator in accordance with the provisions of sub-paragraph (1) shall indicate whether or not he is willing to act within two days of receiving the request.

(3)   In this paragraph, and in paragraphs 5 and 6 below, 'an adjudicator nominating body' shall mean a body (not being a natural person and not being a party to the dispute) which holds itself out publicly as a body which will select an adjudicator when requested to do so by a referring party.

3.   The request referred to in paragraphs 2, 5 and 6 shall be accompanied by a copy of the notice of adjudication.

4.   Any person requested or selected to act as adjudicator in accordance with paragraphs 2, 5 or 6 shall be a natural person acting in his personal capacity. A person requested or selected to act as an adjudicator shall not be an employee of any of the parties to the dispute and shall declare any interest, financial or otherwise, in any matter relating to the dispute.

5.   (1)   The nominating body referred to in paragraphs 2(1)(b) and 6(1)(b) or the adjudicator nominating body referred to in paragraphs 2(1)(c), 5(2)(b) and 6(1)(c) must communicate the selection of an adjudicator to the referring party within five days of receiving a request to do so.

(2)   Where the nominating body or the adjudicator nominating body fails to comply with sub-paragraph (1), the referring party may:

(a)   agree with the other party to the dispute to request a specified person to act as adjudicator; or

(b)   request any other adjudicator nominating body to select a person to act as adjudicator.

(3)   The person requested to act as adjudicator in accordance with the provisions of sub-paragraph (1) or (2) shall indicate whether or not he is willing to act within two days of receiving the request.

6.   (1)   Where an adjudicator who is named in the contract indicates to the parties that he is unable or unwilling to act, or where he fails to respond in accordance with paragraph 2(2), the referring party may:

(a)   request another person (if any) specified in the contract to act as adjudicator

(b)   request the nominating body (if any) referred to in the contract to select a person to act as adjudicator; or

(c)   request any other adjudicator nominating body to select a person to act as adjudicator.

(2)   The person requested to act in accordance with the provisions of sub-paragraph (1) shall indicate whether or not he is willing to act within two days of receiving the request.

7. (1) Where an adjudicator has been selected in accordance with paragraphs 2, 5 or 6, the referring party shall, not later than seven days from the date of the notice of adjudication, refer the dispute in writing ('the referral notice') to the adjudicator.

(2) A referral notice shall be accompanied by copies of, or relevant extracts from, the construction contract and such other documents as the referring party intends to rely upon.

(3) The referring party shall, at the same time as he sends to the adjudicator the documents referred to in sub-paragraphs (1) and (2), send copies of those documents to every other party to the dispute.

8. (1) The adjudicator may, with the consent of all the parties to those disputes, adjudicate at the same time on more than one dispute under the same contract.

(2) The adjudicator may, with the consent of all the parties to those disputes, adjudicate at the same time on related disputes under different contracts, whether or not one or more of those parties is a party to those disputes.

(3) All the parties in sub-paragraphs (1) and (2) respectively may agree to extend the period within which the adjudicator may reach a decision in relation to all or any of these disputes.

(4) Where an adjudicator ceases to act because a dispute is to be adjudicated on by another person in terms of this paragraph, that adjudicator's fees and expenses shall be determined and payable in accordance with paragraph 25.

9. (1) An adjudicator may resign at any time on giving notice in writing to the parties to the dispute.

(2) An adjudicator must resign where the dispute is the same or substantially the same as one which has previously been referred to adjudication, and a decision has been taken in that adjudication.

(3) Where an adjudicator ceases to act under sub-paragraph (1):

(a) the referring party may serve a fresh notice under paragraph 1 and shall request an adjudicator to act in accordance with paragraphs 2 to 7; and

(b) if requested by the new adjudicator and insofar as it is reasonably practicable, the parties shall supply him with copies of all documents which they had made available to the previous adjudicator.

(4) Where an adjudicator resigns in the circumstances mentioned in sub-paragraph (2), or where a dispute varies significantly from the dispute referred to him and for that reason he is not competent to decide it, that adjudicator's fees and expenses shall be determined and payable in accordance with paragraph 25.

10. Where any party to the dispute objects to the appointment of a particular person as adjudicator, that objection shall not invalidate the adjudicator's appointment nor any decision he may reach in accordance with paragraph 20.

11. (1) The parties to a dispute may at any time agree to revoke the appointment of the adjudicator and in such circumstances the fees and expenses of that adjudicator shall, subject to sub-paragraph (2), be determined and payable in accordance with paragraph 25.

   (2) Where the revocation of the appointment of the adjudicator is due to the default or misconduct of the adjudicator, the parties shall not be liable to pay the adjudicator's fees and expenses.

Powers of the adjudicator

12. The adjudicator shall:

   (a) act impartially in carrying out his duties and shall do so in accordance with any relevant terms of the contract and shall reach his decision in accordance with the applicable law in relation to the contract; and

   (b) avoid incurring unnecessary expense.

13. The adjudicator may take the initiative in ascertaining the facts and the law necessary to determine the dispute, and shall decide on the procedure to be followed in the adjudication. In particular, he may:

   (a) request any party to the contract to supply him with such documents as he may reasonably require including, if he so directs, any written statement from any party to the contract supporting or supplementing the referral notice and any other documents given under paragraph 7(2)

   (b) decide the language or languages to be used in the adjudication and whether a translation of any document is to be provided and, if so, by whom

   (c) meet and question any of the parties to the contract and their representatives

   (d) subject to obtaining any necessary consent from a third party or parties, make such site visits and inspections as he considers appropriate, whether accompanied by the parties or not

   (e) subject to obtaining any necessary consent from a third party or parties, carry out any tests or experiments

   (f) obtain and consider such representations and submissions as he requires, and, provided he has notified the parties of his intention, appoint experts, assessors or legal advisers

   (g) give directions as to the timetable for the adjudication, any deadlines, or limits as to the length of written documents or oral representations to be complied with

   (h) issue other directions relating to the conduct of the adjudication.

14. The parties shall comply with any request or direction of the adjudicator in relation to the adjudication.

15. If, without showing sufficient cause, a party fails to comply with any request, direction or timetable of the adjudicator made in accordance with his powers, fails to produce any document or written statement requested by the adjudicator, or in any other way fails to comply with a requirement under these provisions relating to the adjudication, the adjudicator may:

    (a)   continue the adjudication in the absence of that party or of the document or written statement requested

    (b)   draw such inferences from that failure to comply as may, in the adjudicator's opinion, be justified in the circumstances

    (c)   make a decision on the basis of the information before him, attaching such weight as he thinks fit to any evidence submitted to him outside any period he may have requested or directed.

16.   (1)   Subject to any agreement between the parties to the contrary and to the terms of sub-paragraph (2), any party to the dispute may be assisted by, or represented by, such advisers or representatives (whether legally qualified or not) as he considers appropriate.

    (2)   Where the adjudicator is considering oral evidence or representations, a party to the dispute may not be represented by more than one person, unless the adjudicator gives directions to the contrary.

17.   The adjudicator shall consider any relevant information submitted to him by any of the parties to the dispute and shall make available to them any information to be taken into account in reaching his decision.

18.   The adjudicator and any party to the dispute shall not disclose to any other person any information or document provided to him in connection with the adjudication which the party supplying it has indicated is to be treated as confidential, except to the extent that it is necessary for the purposes of, or in connection with, the adjudication.

19.   (1)   The adjudicator shall reach his decision not later than:

    (a)   28 days after the date of the referral notice mentioned in paragraph 7(1)

    (b)   42 days after the date of the referral notice if the referring party so consents; or

    (c)   such period exceeding 28 days after the referral notice as the parties to the dispute may, after the giving of that notice, agree.

    (2)   Where the adjudicator fails, for any reason, to reach his decision in accordance with sub-paragraph (1):

    (a)   any of the parties to the dispute may serve a fresh notice under paragraph 1 and shall request an adjudicator to act in accordance with paragraphs 2 to 7

    (b)   if requested by the new adjudicator and insofar as it is reasonably practicable, the parties shall supply him with copies of all documents which they had made available to the previous adjudicator.

(3) As soon as possible after he has reached a decision, the adjudicator shall deliver a copy of that decision to each of the parties to the contract.

Adjudicator's decision

20. (1) The adjudicator shall decide the matters in dispute and may make a decision on different aspects of the dispute at different times.

(2) The adjudicator may take into account any other matters which the parties to the dispute agree should be within the scope of the adjudication or which are matters under the contract which he considers are necessarily connected with the dispute and, in particular, he may:

(a) open up, review and revise any decision taken or any certificate given by any person referred to in the contract, unless the contract states that the decision or certificate is final and conclusive

(b) decide that any of the parties to the dispute is liable to make a payment under the contract (whether in sterling or some other currency) and, subject to section 111(4) of the Act, when that payment is due and the final date for payment

(c) having regard to any term of the contract relating to the payment of interest, decide the circumstances in which, the rates at which, and the periods for which simple or compound rates of interest shall be paid.

21. In the absence of any directions by the adjudicator relating to the time for performance of his decision, the parties shall be required to comply with any decision of the adjudicator immediately on delivery of the decision to the parties in accordance with paragraph 19(3).

22. If requested by one of the parties to the dispute, the adjudicator shall provide reasons for his decision.

Effects of the decision

23. (1) In his decision, the adjudicator may, if he thinks fit, order any of the parties to comply peremptorily with his decision or any part of it.

(2) The decision of the adjudicator shall be binding on the parties, and they shall comply with it, until the dispute is finally determined by legal proceedings, by arbitration (if the contract provides for arbitration or the parties otherwise agree to arbitration) or by agreement between the parties.

24. Where a party or the adjudicator wishes to register the decision for execution in the Books of Council and Session, any other party shall, on being requested to do so, forthwith consent to such registration by subscribing the decision before a witness.

25. (1) The adjudicator shall be entitled to the payment of such reasonable amount as he may determine by way of fees and expenses incurred by him and the parties shall be jointly and severally liable to pay that amount to the adjudicator.

(2) Without prejudice to the right of the adjudicator to effect recovery from any party in accordance with sub-paragraph (1), the adjudicator may by direction determine the apportionment between the parties of liability for his fees and expenses.

26. The adjudicator shall not be liable for anything done or omitted in the discharge or purported discharge of his functions as adjudicator unless the act or omission is in bad faith, and any employee or agent of the adjudicator shall be similarly protected from liability.

Part II: Payment

Entitlement to and amount of stage payments

1. Where the parties to a relevant construction contract fail to agree:

(a) the amount of any instalment or stage or periodic payment for any work under the contract

(b) the intervals at which, or circumstances in which, such payments become due under that contract; or

(c) both of the matters mentioned in sub-paragraphs (a) and (b),

the relevant provisions of paragraphs 2 to 4 shall apply.

2. (1) The amount of any payment by way of instalments or stage or periodic payments in respect of a relevant period shall be the difference between the amount determined in accordance with sub-paragraph (2) and the amount determined in accordance with sub-paragraph (3).

(2) The aggregate of the following amounts:

(a) an amount equal to the value of any work performed in accordance with the relevant construction contract during the period from the commencement of the contract to the end of the relevant period (excluding any amount calculated in accordance with head (b))

(b) where the contract provides for payment for materials, an amount equal to the value of any materials manufactured on site or brought onto site for the purposes of the works during the period from the commencement of the contract to the end of the relevant period

(c) any other amount or sum which the contract specifies shall be payable during or in respect of the period from the commencement of the contract to the end of the relevant period.

(3) The aggregate of any sums which have been paid or are due for payment by way of instalments, stage or periodic payments during

the period from the commencement of the contract to the end of the relevant period.

(4) An amount calculated in accordance with this paragraph shall not exceed the difference between:

    (a)   the contract price

    (b)   the aggregate of the instalments or stage or periodic payments which have become due.

Dates for payment

3. Where the parties to a construction contract fail to provide an adequate mechanism for determining either what payments become due under the contract, or when they become due for payment, or both, the relevant provisions of paragraphs 4 to 7 shall apply.

4. Any payment of a kind mentioned in paragraph 2 above shall become due on whichever of the following dates occurs later:

    (a)   the expiry of seven days following the relevant period mentioned in paragraph 2(1); or

    (b)   the making of a claim by the payee.

5. The final payment payable under a relevant construction contract, namely the payment of an amount equal to the difference (if any) between:

    (a)   the contract price

    (b)   the aggregate of any instalment or stage or periodic payments which have become due under the contract,

shall become due on:

        (i)   the expiry of 30 days following completion of the work; or

        (ii)   the making of a claim by the payee,

whichever is the later.

6. Payment of the contract price under a construction contract (not being a relevant construction contract) shall become due on:

    (a)   the expiry of 30 days following the completion of the work; or

    (b)   the making of a claim by the payee,

whichever is the later.

7. Any other payment under a construction contract shall become due on:

    (a)   the expiry of seven days following the completion of the work to which the payment relates; or

    (b)   the making of a claim by the payee,

whichever is the later.

Final date for payment

8. (1) Where the parties to a construction contract fail to provide a final date for payment in relation to any sum which becomes due under a construction contract, the provisions of this paragraph shall apply.

(2) The final date for the making of any payment of a kind mentioned in paragraph 2, 5, 6 or 7 shall be 17 days from the date that payment becomes due.

Notice specifying amount of payment

9. A party to a construction contract shall, not later than five days after the date on which any payment:

(a) becomes due from him; or

(b) would have become due, if:

(i) the other party had carried out his obligations under the contract

(ii) no set-off or abatement was permitted by reference to any sum claimed to be due under one or more other contracts,

give notice to the other party to the contract specifying the amount (if any) of the payment he has made or proposes to make, specifying to what the payment relates and the basis on which that amount is calculated.

Notice of intention to withhold payment

10. Any notice of intention to withhold payment mentioned in section 111 of the Act shall be given not later than the prescribed period, which is to say not later than seven days before the final date for payment determined either in accordance with the construction contract or, where no such provision is made in the contract, in accordance with paragraph 8.

Prohibition of conditional payment provisions

11. Where a provision making payment under a construction contract conditional on the payer receiving payment from a third person is ineffective as mentioned in section 113 of the Act and the parties have not agreed other terms for payment, the relevant provisions of:

(a) paragraphs 2, 4, 5, and 7 to 10 shall apply in the case of a relevant construction contract

(b) paragraphs 6 to 10 shall apply in the case of any other construction contract.

Interpretation

12.   In this Part:

'claim by the payee' means a written notice given by the party carrying out work under a construction contract to the other party specifying the amount of any payment or payments which he considers to be due, specifying to what the payment relates (or payments relate) and the basis on which it is, or they are, calculated

'contract price' means the entire sum payable under the construction contract in respect of the work

'relevant construction contract' means any construction contract other than one:

(a)   which specifies that the duration of the work is to be less than 45 days; or

(b)   in respect of which the parties agree that the duration of the work is estimated to be less than 45 days

'relevant period' means a period which is specified in, or is calculated by reference to, the construction contract or, where no such period is so specified or is so calculable, a period of 28 days

'value of work' means an amount determined in accordance with the construction contract under which the work is performed or, where the contract contains no such provision, the cost of any work performed in accordance with that contract together with an amount equal to any overhead or profit included in the contract price

'work' means any of the work or services mentioned in section 104 of the Act.

Explanatory note

(This note is not part of the Regulations)

Part II of the Housing Grants, Construction and Regeneration Act 1996 makes provision in relation to construction contracts. Section 114 empowers the Lord Advocate to make the Scheme for Construction Contracts (as regards Scotland). Where a construction contract does not comply with the requirements of sections 108 to 111 (adjudication of disputes and payment provisions), and section 113 (prohibition of conditional payment provisions), the relevant provisions of the Scheme for Construction Contracts have effect.

The Scheme which is contained in the Schedule to these Regulations is in two parts. Part I provides for the selection and appointment of an adjudicator, gives powers to the adjudicator to gather and consider information, and makes provisions in respect of his decisions. Part II makes provision with respect to payments under a construction contract where either the contract fails to make provision or the parties fail to agree:

(a)   the method for calculating the amount of any instalment, stage or periodic payment

(b)   the due date and the final date for payments to be made

(c)   the prescribed period within which a notice of intention to withhold payment must be given.

Source: www.hmso.gov.uk/si/si1998
© Crown Copyright 1998.

Appendix 3: Useful addresses and websites

NB: Where ANB appears, this denotes that the relevant organisation is an Adjudicator Nominating Body (see Chapter 10 on Dispute resolution).

Association of Building Engineers

Postal address:	Association of Building Engineers
	Lutyens House
	Billing Brook Road
	Northampton
	NN3 8NW
Telephone no.:	+44 (0)1604 404121
Fax no.:	+44 (0)1604 784220
Website address:	www.abe.org.uk

Association of Consulting Engineers

Postal address:	Association of Consulting Engineers
	Alliance House
	12 Caxton Street
	London
	SW1H 0QL
Telephone no.:	+44 (0)20 7222 6557
Fax no.:	+44 (0)20 7222 0750
Website address:	www.acenet.co.uk

The Association of Cost Engineers

Postal address:	The Association of Cost Engineers
	Lea House
	5 Middlewich Road
	Sandbach
	Cheshire
	CW11 1XL

Telephone no.:	+44 (0)1270 764798
Fax no.:	+44 (0)1270 766180
Website address:	www.acoste.org.uk

British Cement Association

Postal address:	British Cement Association
	Century House
	Telford Avenue
	Crowthorne
	Berkshire
	RG45 6YS
Telephone no.:	+44 (0)1344 762676
Fax no.:	+44 (0)1344 761214
Website address:	www.bca.org.uk

British Plastics Federation

Postal address:	British Plastics Federation
	6 Bath Place
	Rivington Street
	London
	EC2A 3JE
Telephone no.:	+44 (0)20 7457 5000
Fax no.:	+44 (0)20 7457 5045
Website address:	www.bpf.com

British Precast Concrete Federation

Postal address:	British Precast Concrete Federation
	60 Charles Street
	Leicester
	LE1 1FB
Telephone no.:	+44 (0)116 253 6161
Fax no.:	+44 (0)116 251 4568
Website address:	www.britishprecast.org

British Standards Institution

Postal address:	British Standards Institution
	389 Chiswick High Road
	London
	W4 4AL

Telephone no.:	+44 (0)20 8996 9000
Fax no.:	+44 (0)20 8996 7001
Website address:	www.bsi-global.com

The Chartered Institute of Arbitrators (Scottish Branch) (ANB)

Postal address:	The Chartered Institute of Arbitrators (Scottish Branch)
	Whittinghame House
	1099 Great Western Road
	Glasgow
	G12 0AA
Telephone no.:	+44 (0)141 334 7222
Website address:	www.scottish-arbitrators.org

Civil Engineering Contractors' Association

Postal address:	Civil Engineering Contractors' Association
	Construction House
	56–64 Leonard Street
	London
	EC2A 4JX
Telephone no.:	+44 (0)20 7608 5060
Fax no.:	+44 (0)20 7608 5061
Website address:	www.ceca.co.uk

The Concrete Society

Postal address:	The Concrete Society
	Century House
	Telford Avenue
	Crowthorne
	Berkshire
	RG45 6YS
Telephone no.:	+44 (0)1344 466007
Fax no.:	+44 (0)1344 466008
Website address:	www.concrete.org.uk

Confederation of Construction Specialists (ANB)

Postal address:	Confederation of Construction Specialists
	75/79 High Street
	Aldershot
	Hampshire
	GU11 1BY

Telephone no.:   +44 (0)125 2312 122
Fax no.:   +44 (0)125 2343 081

Construction Confederation (ANB)

Postal address: Construction Confederation
                        Construction House
                        56–64 Leonard Street
                        London
                        EC2A 4JX
Telephone no.:   +44 (0)20 7608 5000
Fax no.:   +44 (0)20 7608 5001
Website address: www.constructionconfederation.co.uk

Construction Industry Council (ANB)

Postal address: Construction Industry Council
                        26 Store Street
                        London
                        WC1E 7BT
Telephone no.:   +44 (0)20 7637 8692
Fax no.:   +44 (0)20 7580 6140
Website address: www.cic.org.uk

Department for Transport

Postal address: Department for Transport
                        Great Minster House
                        76 Marsham Street
                        London
                        SW1P 4DR
Telephone no.:   +44 (0)20 7944 8300
Website address: www.dft.gov.uk

Department of Trade and Industry

Postal address: Department of Trade and Industry
                        DTI Enquiry Unit
                        1 Victoria Street
                        London
                        SW1H 0ET
Telephone & Fax no.:   +44 (0)20 7215 5000
Website address: www.dti.gov.uk

Engineering Council

Postal address:	Engineering Council (UK) 10 Maltravers Street London WC2R 3ER
Telephone no.:	+44 (0)20 7240 7891
Fax no.:	+44 (0)20 7240 7517
Website address:	www.engc.org.uk

FIDIC (International Federation of Consulting Engineers)

Postal address:	FIDIC World Trade Centre 12 Box 311 CH-1215 Geneva 15 Switzerland
Telephone no.:	+41 212 799 4900
Fax no.:	+41 212 799 4901
Website address:	www.fidic.org

Health and Safety Executive

Postal address:	Belford House 59 Belford Road Edinburgh EH4 3UE
Telephone no.:	+44 (0)131 247 2000
Fax no.:	+44 (0)131 247 2121
Website address:	www.hse.gov.uk

Institution of Chemical Engineers (ANB)

Postal address:	Institution of Chemical Engineers Davis Building 165–189 Railway Terrace Rugby CV21 3HQ
Telephone no.:	+44 (0)1788 578214
Fax no.:	+44 (0)1788 560833
Website address:	www.icheme.org

Institution of Civil Engineering Surveyors

Postal address:	Institution of Civil Engineering Surveyors Dominion House Sibson Road Sale Cheshire M33 7PP

Telephone no.:   +44 (0)161 972 3100
Fax no.:   +44 (0)161 972 3118
Website address: www.ices.org.uk

The Institution of Civil Engineers (ANB)

Postal address: The Institution of Civil Engineers
                          One Great George Street
                          Westminster
                          London
                          SW1P 3AA

Telephone no.:   +44 (0)20 7222 7722
Fax no.:   +44 (0)20 7222 7500
Website address: www.ice.org.uk

The Institution of Electrical Engineers (ANB)

Postal address: The IEE
                          Savoy Place
                          London
                          WC2R 0BL

Telephone no.:   +44 (0)20 7240 1871
Fax no.:   +44 (0)20 7240 7735
Website address: www.iee.org

The Institution of Mechanical Engineers (ANB)

Postal address: The Institution of Mechanical Engineers
                          1 Birdcage Walk
                          London
                          SW1H 9JJ

Telephone no.:   +44 (0)20 7222 7899
Fax no.:   +44 (0)20 7222 4557
Website address: www.imeche.org.uk

The Institution of Structural Engineers

Postal address: The Institution of Structural Engineers
                          11 Upper Belgrave Street
                          London
                          SW1X 8BH

Telephone no.:   +44 (0)20 7235 4535
Fax no.:   +44 (0)20 7235 4294
Website address: www.istructe.org.uk

The Law Society of Scotland (ANB)

Postal address:	The Law Society of Scotland
	26 Drumsheugh Gardens
	Edinburgh
	EH3 7YR
Telephone no.:	+44 (0)131 476 8137
Fax no.:	+44 (0)131 225 2934
Website address:	www.lawscot.org.uk

Royal Institution of Chartered Surveyors in Scotland (ANB)

Postal address:	Royal Institution of Chartered Surveyors in Scotland
	9 Manor Place
	Edinburgh
	EH3 7DN
Telephone no.:	+44 (0)131 225 7078
Fax no.:	+44 (0)131 240 0830
Website address:	www.rics-scotland.org.uk

Scottish Building (ANB)

Postal address:	Scottish Building
	Carron Grange
	Carrongrange Avenue
	Falkirk
	FK5 3BQ
Website address:	www.scottish-building.co.uk

The Technology and Construction Solicitors Association (ANB)

Postal address:	The Technology and Construction Solicitors Association
	353 Strand
	London
	WC2R 0HS
Telephone no.:	+44 (0)207 1956 9354
Fax no.:	+44 (0)207 1956 9355
Website address:	www.tecsa.org.uk

UK Steel Association

Postal address:	UK Steel Association
	Broadway House
	Tothill Street
	London
	SW1P 9HQ
Telephone no.:	+44 (0)20 7343 3150
Fax no.:	+44 (0)20 7343 3190
Website address:	www.uksteel.org.uk

Miscellaneous website addresses

Case law

Court Service	www.courtservice.gov.uk
Crown Office and Procurator Fiscal Service	www.procuratorfiscal.gov.uk
House of Lords Judgments	www.scottishcourts.gov.uk
Case Track	www.casetrack.com

Environmental

Department for Environment, Food & Rural Affairs	www.defra.gov.uk
Environmental Data Services	www.ends.co.uk
Environment Agency of England and Wales	www.environment-agency.gov.uk
European Environmental Law	www.eel.nl
Scottish Environment Protection Agency	www.sepa.org.uk

Legislation

Acts of the UK Parliament	www.hmso.gov.uk/acts.htm
Acts of the Scottish Parliament	www.scotland-legislation.hmso.gov.uk
Bills of the UK Parliament	www.parliament.the-stationery-office.co.uk/pa/pabills.htm
Bills of the Scottish Parliament	www.scottish.parliament.uk/parl_bus/legis.html

Professional organisations

Adjudication Society	www.adjudication.org and www.adjudication.co.uk
Society of Construction Law	www.scl.org.uk

Appendix 4: Procurement routes

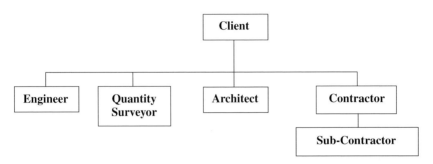

1. Traditional procurement route.

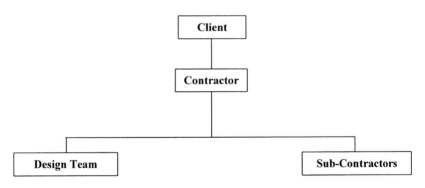

2. Design and build procurement route.

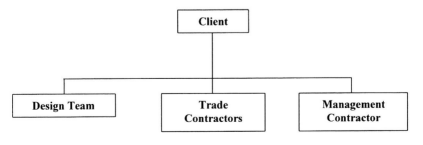

3. Management contracting procurement route.

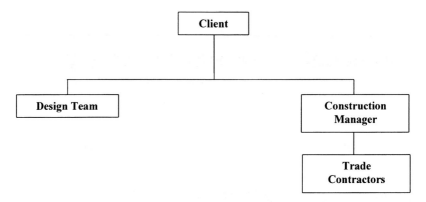

4.   Construction management procurement route.

Appendix 5: Health and safety

This Appendix sets out briefly the essential duties set out under each of the following pieces of legislation.

Health and Safety at Work etc. Act 1974

- Ensure so far as reasonably practicable the health and safety and welfare of employees.
- Ensure provision of maintenance and plant and systems of work that are so far as reasonably practicable safe and without risk to health.
- Provide a safe system for the use storage and transport of articles and substances so far as reasonably practicable.
- Provide such information instruction training and supervision as is necessary to ensure the health and safety at work of employees.
- Maintenance of a safe place of work and provision of access to and egress from that place of work so far as reasonably practicable.
- Provide and maintain a working environment that is so far as is reasonably practicable safe without risks to health and adequate as regards facilities and arrangements for employees' welfare at work.

Management of Health and Safety at Work Regulations 1992

- Carry out risk assessments covering hazard identification, the type and severity of injury which may result from those hazards and likelihood of such an injury arising.
- Develop preventative and protective measures and keep records of such measures.
- Provide employees with health surveillance.
- Appoint a competent person to facilitate implementation of appropriate procedures in relation to health and safety.
- Keep employees informed of heath and safety requirements and issues
- In relation to common workplaces to co-operate and co-ordinate on health and safety issues.
- When allocating tasks take into account the abilities of particular employees.

Appendix 6: Formal requirements for executing documents under Scots Law

The Requirements of Writing (Scotland) Act 1995 provides for two standards in the signing of documents, the standard required for a document to be formally valid, and the standard required for the document to benefit from the presumption that it has been validly executed. The following is a check list of requirements for satisfying the latter (higher) standard.

The following deals only with execution by individuals, companies incorporated under the Companies Acts (and Unregistered Companies) and partnerships. Other specific rules will apply to, for example, execution by corporations outside the Companies Acts, by foreign corporations, by limited partnerships, by limited liability partnerships, local authorities, Ministers of the Crown, etc.

Execution by individuals

- Individuals to sign with their full name as set out in the body of the document or testing clause, or with their full first name or initial followed by full surname.
- Signature to be at the end of the last page of the main body of the document (excluding any annexation or schedule, whether or not it is incorporated into the document).
- If there is more than one individual, at least one should sign at the end of the last page which has some of the text of the document on it.
- The document should be subscribed by a single witness.

Execution by companies incorporated under the Companies Acts (and unregistered companies as provided in section 718 of the Companies Act 1985)

- Execution to be in accordance with the constitution of the relevant corporation.
- Subscription required by two directors; or
- By a director and the company secretary; or
- By two authorised signatories; or

- By one director and one witness; or
- By the company secretary and one witness; or
- By one authorised signatory and a witness.

Execution by corporations outside the Companies Act

These provisions apply to such bodies as friendly societies, trade unions, and universities.

- Subscription by a member of the governing body, or the secretary or an authorised signatory; and
- By a witness or the common seal of the body.

Execution by partnerships

- Subscription to be on behalf of the partnership by a partner or by a person authorised to sign the document on behalf of the partnership using either their own name or the firm name; and
- By one witness.

Appendix 7: Court procedure terminology – a brief guide

Following the progress of a court action in Scotland can often be complicated by unfamiliar terms. Some of the more commonly encountered terms and labels are described below. Many of these terms are also often used in arbitrations.

Written pleadings

The Scottish system of written 'pleadings' is quite distinct from that employed in England and requires far greater detail or a party's case to be recorded in writing or 'plead'. The ultimate stage of any action is a proof (see below), which is basically a trial of the controversial factual and legal issues set out in the parties' pleadings. A party will not be allowed to lead evidence at a proof to establish a fact he has not referred to in his pleadings. The aim of written pleadings is to provide a coherent written case for a claim, or a defence to a claim, which, if proved when evidence is lead on that written case, will allow the court to make an award in favour of a Pursuer or reject the Pursuer's claim.

Pursuer and Defender

In Scottish Court proceedings the person, firm, association or company making a claim is known as the Pursuer, while the person, firm, association or company defending the claim is known as the Defender.

Writ and Summons

This is the document which is prepared to commence an action. In the Sheriff Court it is known as an Initial Writ, and in the Court of Session a Summons. The Writ or Summons should describe the parties to the action, the legal relationship between the parties (for example, the terms upon which the parties contracted), the remedy sought by the Pursuer (for example, payment, damages or interdict) and the basis in law for that remedy.

If the action is one for payment of a sum said to be due to a Pursuer for damages (following a breach of contract or duty of care), it should also provide a basis for proving how the sum sued for has been calculated.

The written statements of fact and law asserted in a Writ or Summons (commonly known as 'averments') will be answered in Defences lodged by the Defender.

Productions

Productions most commonly comprise originals or copies of documentation that a party wishes to rely upon to prove its case or rebut the other party's case. Witnesses will frequently be referred to productions and asked to answer questions on them. Expert witnesses reports are often lodged as productions. Productions are not limited to documentary evidence – for instance, test samples, examples of defective building materials and photographs could all be lodged as productions.

Adjustment and Amendment

Both parties to an action will be afforded an opportunity to adjust, expand and alter their written pleadings for a period of time after Defences are lodged. The aim of this process is to focus the factual and legal issues in dispute between the parties. The end of the adjustment period is followed by the 'closing of the Record' – the Record is simply the term for the document containing the complete written pleadings of the parties.

If further alternations are required to a party's pleadings after the Record has closed this can be done by way of 'amendment'. While amendment of pleadings is not uncommon, it is more difficult to carry out than adjustment and will often trigger an award of expenses against the amending party.

Debate and Procedure Roll

A Debate (which is known as a Procedure Roll Hearing in the Court of Session) is held when one party (or both) believes that the other party's written pleadings are irrelevant in a legal sense, or do not provide adequate specification of an important factual issue. Two simple examples illustrate the type of matters which could be addressed at Debate.

(a) **Relevancy** – the Pursuer asserts the Defender is in breach of contract and that he has suffered loss as a result of this. The Pursuer's written pleadings do not disclose, however, which term of the contact the Defender is said to have breached. Even if, therefore, the Pursuer was able to prove everything he had asserted in his written pleadings, he would still not have pleaded enough to establish a breach of contract and an entitlement to damages as he would have not (in the absence of reference to it in his pleadings) been able to prove **which** term of the contract had been breached. For the purposes of a Debate parties' pleadings are taken at face value and assumed as being provable by the party concerned.

No evidence is required during a Debate. Submissions are made by agents or Counsel to the presiding Sheriff or Judge.

(b) **Specification** – a Defender asserts an agreement was reached between it and the Pursuer whereby a full and final settlement of a dispute arising under a contract was reached, and that the Pursuer accordingly agreed not to seek any further payment pursuant to a contract. The Defender does not, however, provide the Pursuer with adequate notice in his pleadings as to how and when the alleged agreement was reached and precisely who is said to have made the agreement.

Such lack of notice of an important component of the Defender's case may persuade a court to 'delete' the averment asserting that there was an agreement and thus prevent evidence being lead at proof on this matter.

Adverse Debate decisions are not always fatal to a party's case. Amendment of pleadings to address criticisms made of pleadings is generally possible. It is not uncommon for a party to seek permission from the court to amend his pleadings shortly before (or even during) a Debate.

Proof and Evidence

If there are no issues which parties wish to take to Debate, a Proof will generally be assigned. A Proof is commonly the final stage of a court action and involves the leading of evidence from witnesses to establish a party's written case. Unfortunately, an action often will not arrive at Proof until some considerable time after it has been commenced. Gaps of up to two years between starting an action and the first day of a Proof are not at all uncommon (albeit this process should be quicker if the action is a Commercial Action at the Court of Session or in a Sheriff Court). Evidence should be lead to prove each averment that is not admitted by the other party.

Evidence is sometimes required to determine preliminary issues in a case. A preliminary proof, which will be restricted to evidence on the preliminary issue, can be held to determine these matters. Issues which may be dealt with at a preliminary proof include questions of prescription (the time barring of claims) and the applicability of particular terms of contract.

The 'standard of proof' in civil cases in Scotland is proof on the balance of probabilities. In other words, in order for a party to prove its case it must persuade the court that the likelihood of its version of events being correct is greater than 50 per cent. The balance of probabilities is distinct from, and is a lower standard of proof, than proof beyond reasonable doubt. Proof beyond reasonable doubt is employed as the standard of proof in criminal cases.

The evidence of 'witnesses to fact', and, commonly in engineering disputes, expert witnesses (who will speak to technical matters and their opinion on these) is lead by the Pursuer to establish its case. These witnesses are then cross examined by the Defender's agent or Counsel. The aim of cross examination is to (1) weaken a witness' evidence by suggesting it is incredible or unreliable; and (2) to elicit or develop unfavourable evidence which the witness has not mentioned, or has only briefly referred to. Re-examination of a witness by the Pursuer's lawyer is then allowed.

After all the evidence for the Pursuer has been presented the Defender's witnesses will then be lead and cross examined and so on.

The Proof will conclude with oral submissions on the evidence presented to the court and on the correct application of the law to that evidence. The Sheriff or Judge will almost always then reserve judgment has finished and issue a written decision as soon as possible after the Proof ('avizandum').

Table of cases

Table of statutes

Table of statutory instruments

References to ICE 7th Conditions of Contract

References to CECA Form of Sub-contract

Bibliography

Anderson, A. J., Bichford-Smith, S., Palmer, N. E. and Cooper, R., *Emden's construction law*, 2000.

Arrowsmith, S., *The law of public and utilities procurement*, Sweet & Maxwell, London, 1996.

Carnell, N. J., *Causation and delay in construction disputes*, Blackwell Science, 2000.

Chitty, J., *Chitty on contracts*, 28th edition, Sweet & Maxwell, 1999.

CIRIA, '*Control of water pollution from construction sites – guidance for consultants and contractors*', CIRIA News, Issue 1, 2002.

Cottam, G., *Adjudication under the scheme for construction contracts*, Thomas Telford, 1998.

Department for Environment, Food and Rural Affairs, '*Waste management, the duty of care, a code of practice*', HMSO, 1996.

DETR Consultation Paper, '*Improving adjudication in the construction industry*', HMSO, 2001.

Egan, J., Sir, '*Rethinking construction*', DETR, 1998.

Egglestone, B., *Liquidated damages and extensions of time*, 2nd edition, Blackwell Science, 1997.

Egglestone, B., *The new engineering contract – a commentary*, Blackwell Science, 1996.

Environmental Data Services Limited (ENDS) Reports Numbers 250, 304, 307, 310, 312 and 314.

Furst, S. and Ramsey, V., *Keating on building contracts*, 7th edition, Sweet & Maxwell, 2000.

Geddes, A., *Public and utility procurements*, 1996.

Halsbury, *Laws of England*, 4th edition, Butterworths, 1993.

H M Customs & Excise, '*Landfill tax: a consultation paper*', HMSO, 1995.

Latham, M., Sir, '*Constructing the team – final report of the government/industry review of procurement and contractual arrangements in the UK construction industry*', HMSO, 1994.

Levine, M., *Construction and engineering precedents*, 4th edition, Sweet & Maxwell, 2000.

Madge, P., *A guide to the indemnity and insurance aspects of building contracts*, RIBA Publications, 1990.

Ove Arup & Partners, '*Good practice in the selection of construction materials*', 1997.

Pickavance, K., *Delay and disruption in construction contracts*, Informa Publishing Group, 1997.

Redmond, J., *Adjudication in construction contracts,* Blackwell Science, 2001.

Scottish Executive Rural Affairs Department, '*Water pollution, anti pollution works regulations*', 27 January 2000, Paper Number 1/2000.

Scottish Law Commission, *Report on penalty clauses*, May 1999.

Simmonds, K. R., *Encyclopaedia of EC Law*, Sweet & Maxwell, 1993.

Stair Memorial Encyclopaedia, volumes 12 and 15, Butterworths, 1992.

Tromans, S., *The Environmental Protection Act 1990 – text and commentary*, 2nd edition, Sweet & Maxwell.

Walker, D. M., *Prescription and limitation of actions,* 5th edition, W. Green, 1996.

Wallace, D., *Construction contracts: principles and policies in tort and contract*, 1996.

Wallace, D., *Hudson's building and civil engineering contracts*, 11th edition, Sweet & Maxwell, 1994.

Index